PHTHALOCYANINE
COMPOUNDS

PHTHALOCYANINE COMPOUNDS

FRANK H. MOSER
Director of Research

and

ARTHUR L. THOMAS
Chemical Engineer

**STANDARD ULTRAMARINE & COLOR COMPANY
HUNTINGTON, WEST VIRGINIA**

American Chemical Society
Monograph Series

REINHOLD PUBLISHING CORPORATION

NEW YORK

CHAPMAN & HALL, LTD., LONDON

Series
Chem.
no series card in Public Catalog

SD   5/9/63

To

HENRY DOURIF

President

STANDARD ULTRAMARINE & COLOR COMPANY

and

ARTHUR W. THOMAS

Pioneer American Chemist

148

GENERAL INTRODUCTION

American Chemical Society's Series of Chemical Monographs

By arrangement with the Interallied Conference of Pure and Applied Chemistry, which met in London and Brussels in July, 1919, the American Chemical Society was to undertake the production and publication of Scientific and Technologic Monographs on chemical subjects. At the same time it was agreed that the National Research Council, in cooperation with the American Chemical Society and the American Physical Society, should undertake the production and publication of Critical Tables of Chemical and Physical Constants. The American Chemical Society and the National Research Council mutually agreed to care for these two fields of chemical progress. The American Chemical Society named as Trustees, to make the necessary arrangements for the publication of the Monographs, Charles L. Parsons, secretary of the Society, Washington, D. C.; the late John E. Teeple, then treasurer of the Society, New York; and the late Professor Gellert Alleman of Swarthmore College. The Trustees arranged for the publication of the ACS Series of (a) Scientific and (b) Technological Monographs by the Chemical Catalog Company, Inc. (Reinhold Publishing Corporation, successor) of New York.

The Council of the American Chemical Society, acting through its Committee on National Policy, appointed editors (the present list of whom appears at the close of this sketch) to select authors of competent authority in their respective fields and to consider critically the manuscripts submitted.

The first Monograph of the Series appeared in 1921. After twenty-three years of experience certain modifications of general policy were indicated. In the beginning there still remained from the preceding five decades a distinct though arbitrary differentiation between so-called "pure science" publications and technologic or applied science literature. By 1944 this differentiation was fast becoming nebulous. Research in private enterprises had grown apace and not a little of it was pursued on the frontiers of knowledge. Furthermore, most workers in the sciences were coming to see the artificiality of the separation. The methods of both groups of workers are the same. They employ the same instrumentalities, and frankly recognize that their objectives are common, namely, the search for new knowledge for the service of man. The officers of the Society therefore combined the two editorial Boards in a single Board of twelve representative members.

Also in the beginning of the Series, it seemed expedient to construe rather broadly the definition of a Monograph. Needs of workers had to be recognized. Consequently among the first hundred Monographs appeared works in the form of treatises covering in some instances rather broad areas. Because such necessary works do not now want for publishers, it is considered advisable to hew more strictly to the line of the Monograph character, which means more complete and critical treatment of relatively restricted areas, and, where a broader field needs coverage, to subdivide it into logical subareas. The prodigious expansion of new knowledge makes such a change desirable.

These Monographs are intended to serve two principal purposes: first, to make available to chemists a thorough treatment of a selected area in form usable by persons working in more or less unrelated fields to the end that they may correlate their own work with a larger area of physical science discipline: second, to stimulate further research in the specific field treated. To implement this purpose the authors of Monographs are expected to give extended references to the literature. Where the literature is of such volume that a complete bibliography is impracticable, the authors are expected to append a list of references critically selected on the basis of their relative importance and significance.

AMERICAN CHEMICAL SOCIETY

BOARD OF EDITORS

PREFACE

This monograph is the result of an extensive search in the world literature of the phthalocyanine class of organic compounds. In the twenty-
five years that have elapsed since the first commercial production of
phthalocyanine pigments in the United States, phthalocyanine compounds
have become a decisive economic factor in the technology and application of pigments and dyes. Since the elucidation of the structure
of the phthalocyanines by Sir Reginald P. Linstead and his collaborators
in 1933, there has been a phenomenal burst of activity in the phthalocyanine
field. Theoretical chemists throughout the world have devoted themselves to the chemistry of the phthalocyanines: their structure, their
formation, and their properties as reactants and catalysts in a host of
situations. Also, it has been attempted to produce phthalocyanines in
the non-blue-green portion of the visible spectrum but so far without
success.

Applied chemists and chemical engineers have made serious efforts to
develop a series of phthalocyanine pigments covering a wide range of
shades in the blue-green region of the spectrum, to develop phthalocyanine dyes applicable on animal, vegetable, and synthetic fibers,
to design processes and improved processes, and to manufacture these
pigments and dyes at increasingly lower cost to the consumer.

The interest of the market place in phthalocyanines is witnessed by
the outpouring of hundreds of patents from at least fourteen countries.

It has seemed appropriate, therefore, at this time to collate and to
summarize in book form this vast new knowledge on the, as yet, only
new chromogen discovered in the twentieth century.

The authors hope this book on the phthalocyanines will prove of vital
use to chemists, engineers, and all those interested in the application of
phthalocyanines as pigments and dyes and in the future potential of
the phthalocyanines in other fields.

FRANK H. MOSER
ARTHUR L. THOMAS

Huntington, West Virginia
March, 1963

ix

ACKNOWLEDGMENT

The authors acknowledge the gracious assistance and encouragement given by the management of the Standard Ultramarine & Color Company in the preparation of this book, and to Messrs. Lyle E. Squire, Thomas Jenkins, and Norman Weichmann.

The authors are particularly indebted to Dr. Harold E. Burdick whose many hours of painstaking proofreading materially advanced the preparation of the text.

A debt of gratitude is extended to Mrs. Jean Weekly, Librarian, whose extensive labors to find and collate references materially aided in the preparation of this book. Mrs. Faye Holley's typing of the major portion of the manuscript is gratefully acknowledged. The assistance of Mrs. Jane Pigman, Mrs. Shirley Stiltner, Miss Mary F. Salmons, Miss Dorothy Stewart, and Miss Ellen L. Grimes in typing portions of the manuscript is also well and sincerely appreciated.

CONTENTS

PHTHALOCYANINE COMPOUNDS

"La pensée sans action est un vrai mirage,
l'action sans pensée un vain effort."

—Inscription over the entrance to
Moyse Hall, McGill University, Montreal.

CHAPTER 1

DISCOVERY AND DETERMINATION OF STRUCTURE

DISCOVERY

The word *phthalocyanine* is derived from the Greek terms for naphtha (rock oil) and for cyanine (dark blue). Naphtha was mentioned in ancient Greek literature. Dioscorides stated naphtha to be a clear, combustible rock oil procured from Babylonian asphalt. Cyanine was in the written vocabulary of several ancient Greek writers, including Homer.

Naphthalene was found in coal tar by Gordon in 1819. It was further examined by Professor Kidd (12) of Oxford University who gave it its name in 1821, in a paper entitled "Observations on Naphthaline, a peculiar substance resembling a concrete essential oil, which is apparently produced during the decomposition of coal tar, by exposure to a red heat." Professor Kidd's final remarks were, "It remains for me to propose a name for the white concrete substance which has been described in this paper and, unless a more appropriate term should be suggested by others, I would propose to call it naphthaline." o-Phthalic acid was obtained by Laurent (13) in 1836 by the oxidation of naphthalene and of tetrachloronaphthalene by nitric acid. "Schwache und verdünnte Säuren scheinen ohne Wirkung auf dasselbe zu seyn, und von Chlor wird es nicht angegriffen. Concentrierte Schwefelsäure löst es in der Wärme auf, verdünnt man diese Auflösung mit etwas Wasser und lässt dann erkalten, so lässt sie Krystalle von Naphthalinsäurehydrat fallen."

Professor Reginald P. Linstead (14) of the Imperial College of Science and Technology first used the term "phthalocyanine" in 1933, to describe the class of organic compounds which are the subject of this monograph.

1

Phthalocyanine itself is:

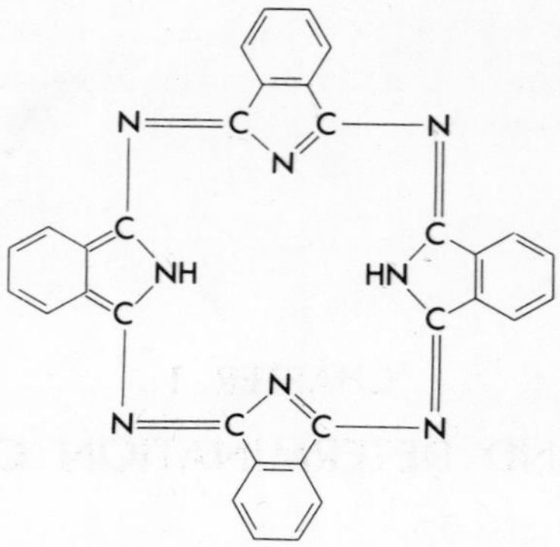

Phthalocyanine

The phthalocyanine class of compounds consists of metal derivatives of phthalocyanine. The two hydrogen atoms in the center of the molecule have been replaced by metals from every group of the Periodic Table to form the group of compounds known as the metal phthalocyanines. Also, from 1 to 16 of the peripheral hydrogen atoms in the 4 benzene rings in the phthalocyanine molecule have been replaced by halogen atoms and by numerous organic and inorganic groups.

More than 40 metal phthalocyanines have been prepared and several thousand different phthalocyanine compounds have been synthesized.

All phthalocyanine compounds absorb light on both sides of the blue-green portion of the visible spectrum. Therefore, "phthalocyanine" is an apt nomenclature for all members of the phthalocyanine class.

The phthalocyanines were discovered by accident. In 1907, Braun and Tcherniac (1), at the South Metropolitan Gas Company in London, upon examining the properties of a cyanobenzamide which they made from the reaction of phthalamide and acetic anhydride, found a trace amount of a blue substance after heating *o*-cyanobenzamide, cooling, dissolving in alcohol, and filtration. This substance undoubtedly was phthalocyanine:

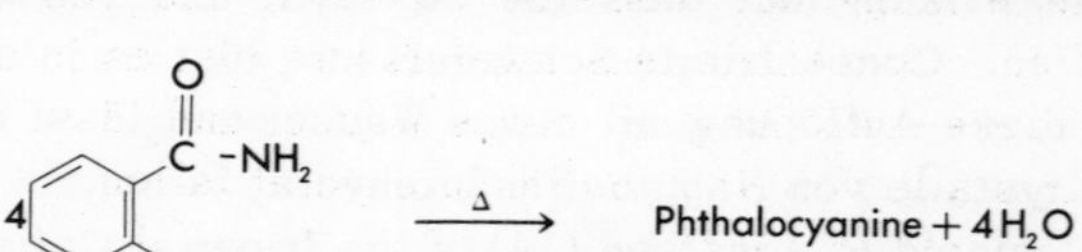

"Beim Schmelzen grösserer Mengen von *o*-Cyanbenzamid... im Rückstand lässt sich neben dem Hauptprodukt auch etwas Phthalimid nachweisen. Wird die grüne Schmelze in Alkohol gelöst und filtriert, so hinterbleibt zuweilen auf dem Filter eine geringe Menge einer blauen Substanz" (1).

In 1923, at the University of Fribourg, de Diesbach and co-workers (8) studied the preparation of acids made from dinitriles formed from bromoxylenes and cuprous cyanide in pyridine:

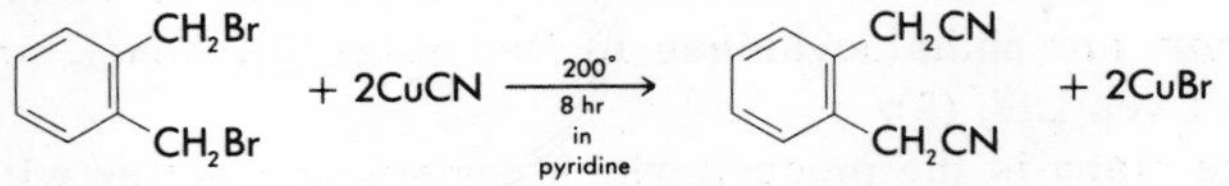

$$\underset{CH_2Br}{\overset{CH_2Br}{\bigcirc}} + 2CuCN \xrightarrow[\substack{8\ hr \\ in \\ pyridine}]{200°} \underset{CH_2CN}{\overset{CH_2CN}{\bigcirc}} + 2CuBr$$

In 1927, de Diesbach and von der Weid (9) attempted to make the corresponding nitriles of benzene:

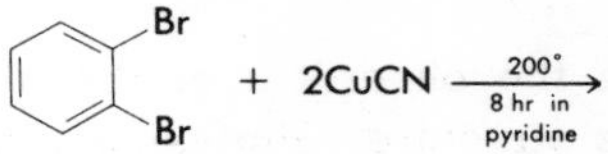

$$\underset{Br}{\overset{Br}{\bigcirc}} + 2CuCN \xrightarrow[\substack{8\ hr\ in \\ pyridine}]{200°}$$

However, instead of obtaining nitriles, a blue product was obtained in indicated yields of 23 per cent.

"Cependant lorsque nous avons soumis des produits o-bibromés à l'action de cyanure cuivreux et de la pyridine, nous n'avons pas obtenu les dinitriles attendus, mais des produits complexes contenant du cuivre et de la pyridine...

"On chauffe un mélange de 5 gr d'o-dibromobenzène, 5 gr de cyanure cuivreux et 15 gr de pyridine pendant 8 heures à 200° en tube scellé. On reprend la masse par l'acide chlorhydrique dilué et l'on filtre. En extrayant le résidu à l'éther, il entre un peu de phtalimide en solution. Le résidu, insoluble dans l'éther, est chauffé avec de l'acide azotique dilué qui décompose le cyanure cuivreux en excès. Il reste un produit bleu indigo que l'on lave à l'eau bouillante, puis à l'alcool et à l'éther."

Analysis gave the formula $C_{26}H_{18}N_6Cu$. The product undoubtedly was copper phthalocyanine. de Diesbach and von der Weid also observed the remarkable stability of their product to alkalies, concentrated sulfuric acid, and heat.

de Diesbach and von der Weid appreciated the properties of this compound and ended their study with the hope that other colleagues would address themselves to the problem of determining its structure:

"Retenus par d'autres travaux, nous serions heureux si des collègues plus spécialisés dans l'étude des sels complexes voulaient bien éclaircir la constitution et les causes de la stabilité de ces nouveaux produits."

In 1928, during the preparation of phthalimide from phthalic anhydride and ammonia in a glass-lined iron kettle at the Grangemouth works of Scottish Dyes Ltd., the formation of a blue impurity in the reaction mass was observed. This impurity, iron phthalocyanine, was formed by the reaction of phthalimide with the iron lining in a flaw of the glass lining of the vessel. Dunworth and Drescher carried out the preliminary examination of the iron compound and remarked on its crystalline form, stability, and the fact that it contained iron which was not removed by sulfuric acid.

In 1929 the first patent was issued with respect to compounds that we now know are phthalocyanines to Dandridge, Drescher, and Thomas of Scottish Dyes Ltd. (5):

"What we claim is the process which comprises reacting with ammonia or primary monoamines of the aliphatic series or of the benzene or naphthalene series on phthalic anhydride, phthalimide, or the mono or diamide of phthalic acid in the presence of iron, nickel or copper in the form of metals or compounds. . . ."

Up to 1929, none of the observers of the blue coloring matters attempted to determine its structure. Professor Linstead and his students, at the University of London, supported by grants from Imperial Chemical Industries, starting in 1929, determined and announced the structure of phthalocyanine and several metal phthalocyanines in 1933 and 1934 (2,6,7,14–17).

The discovery of the phthalocyanine class of organic compounds terminated, therefore, in 1934. Perhaps investigators had observed the blue color prior to 1907, and subsequent to the first synthesis of reactive species which condense to form phthalocyanine, in the presence of trace amounts of certain metal catalysts, at temperatures in the range 100–200°. Thus, blue coloring matters may have been formed during investigations of phthalonitrile, which was synthesized by Pinnow and Sämann (19) in 1896, and of phthalimide, which was prepared by Laurent in 1836 (13).

It is improbable that the phthalocyanines have ever been produced in nature because of the absence in nature of the principal phthalocyanine precursors.

Not only are the phthalocyanines a new class of organic compounds but also they constitute a new class of coloring matter or chromogen. Moderate cost of manufacture, good stability and tinctorial properties, in a region of the visible spectrum which had been lacking in chromogens of as good color properties, stability, and manufacturing cost, have led the phthalocyanines to become, since 1934 and continuing to the present day, the object of intensive world-wide investigations, particularly with respect to applications in the field of color. Also, numerous production facilities for the manufacture of the principal phthalocyanine coloring matter, copper phthalocyanine, have been constructed throughout the world. In 1935, the Imperial Chemical Industries began to manufacture copper phthalocyanine. In a New York Times' report it was said "BLUE

PIGMENT DISCOVERY IS THE FIRST IN 100 YEARS. London, Nov. 25—Discovery of a new blue dye possessing all the qualifications of a pigment was announced today by the Imperial Chemical Industries, Ltd. It is named Monastral fast blue and is the first discovery of a blue pigment for over a century.

"The new pigment is expected to be of especial importance to the printing ink industry. A spectrophotometric analysis shows it is the nearest approach yet produced to the ideal blue in true color printing" (18).

In 1936 I. G. Farbenindustrie began to produce copper phthalocyanine at Ludwigshafen, and in the late 1930's the du Pont Company, at Deepwater Point, New Jersey, began to produce copper phthalocyanine (4). The Standard Ultramarine & Color Company began production of this substance in 1949. Today, it is estimated not less than six million pounds of phthalocyanine coloring matters are produced annually in the United States by about twelve producers.

Concurrently with the study of phthalocyanines as chromogens, scholars throughout the world have addressed themselves to the determination of the physical as well as chemical properties of this class of compounds. As a result, uses other than in the field of color have developed (11,20,26).

The phthalocyanines are macrocyclic compounds containing four pyrrole (I) units. They are a member of one of three series of macrocyclic compounds containing four pyrrole units:

1. The porphins or porphyrins (II).
2. The tetraazaporphins or porphyrazines (III).
3. Porphins containing one, two, or three aza atoms in place of the porphin methine groups.

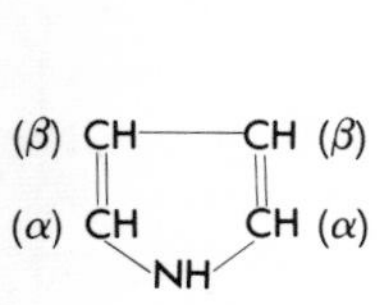

pyrrole (I)

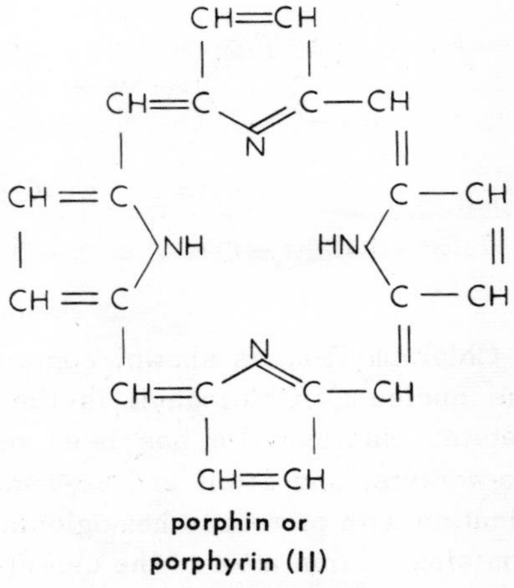

porphin or
porphyrin (II)

$$CH = CH$$

$$N = C \diagup \diagdown C - N$$

tetraazaporphin or
porphyrazine (III)

The pyrrole nuclei in the porphin series are joined together in the α-carbon position by four methine (—CH=) groups. The pyrrole nuclei in the porphyrazine series are linked in the α-carbon position by four aza (—N=) groups.

Porphin itself occurs in nature and has been synthesized. Porphyrazine has not been found in nature and has not been synthesized.

Two important classes of porphins containing substituents on the β-carbons of porphin are chlorophyll and hemin:

chlorophyll a

Chlorophyll-a, as shown, contains a magnesium atom in the center of the nucleus. Chlorophyll is the fundamental green coloring matter of nature; chlorophyll-a has been recently synthesized by Woodward and co-workers, and Strell and co-workers (3). Hemin itself, which in combination with protein is hemoglobin, i.e., the coloring matter of mammals, contains an iron atom in the center of the nucleus.

hemin

There are three main classes of symmetrically-substituted tetraaza-porphins:

1. Phthalocyanines in which the two β-carbon atoms of each pyrrole unit are part of a benzene ring.
2. Tetracyclohexeno (I) and octamethyl (II) tetraaza porphins where the pyrrole β-carbon substituents are alkyl groups.
3. Tetraazaporphins such as magnesium tetraazaporphin.

(I) tetracyclohexenotetraazaporphin

octamethyltetraazaporphin (II)

Synonyms for phthalocyanine are tetrabenzotetraazaporphin, and tetrabenzoporphyrazine.

Phthalocyanine can also be said to be the condensation product of four isoindole groups:

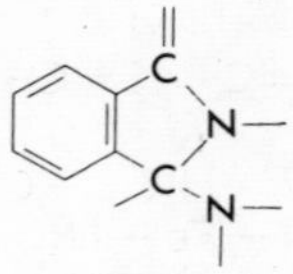

isoindole grouping

More generally, the term phthalocyanine has been defined to include tetraazaporphins in which each of the four pyrrole nuclei is fused to an aromatic nucleus, e.g., benzene (I), naphthalene (II), and anthracene (III).

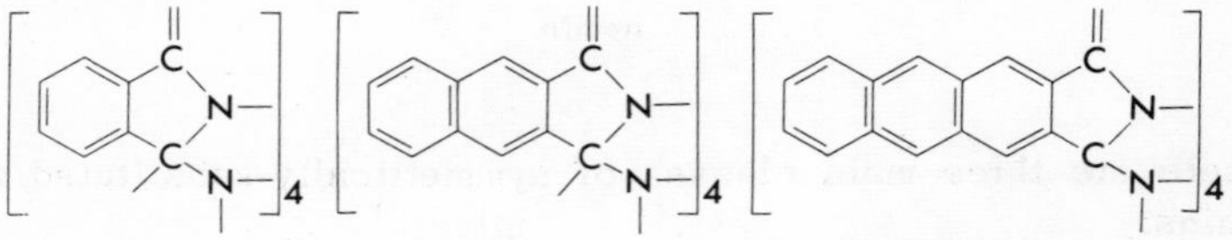

(I)   (II)   (III)

Phthalocyanines with nuclear hydrogen atoms replaced by other atoms or groups are defined according to the positions occupied by the atoms or the groups on the available reactive nuclear sites of the phthalocyanine molecule:

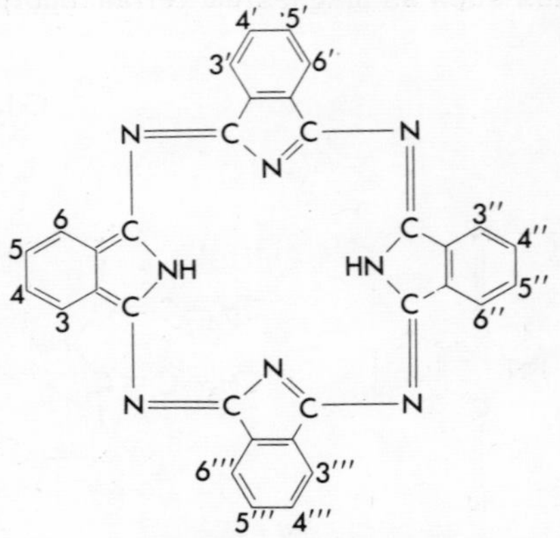

phthalocyanine reactive sites

There is a close connection between phthalocyanines and porphyrins: both are stable to alkalies, less so to acids; both are highly colored and form complex metallic compounds; both can be degraded by oxidation to the imides of dibasic acids. Also, the order of stability of the metallic derivatives of the porphyrin and phthalocyanine series is similar. Magnesium compounds of phytochlorin and phytorhodin are intermediate in stability between the potassium derivatives, which lose the metal in dilute alcoholic solution, and the copper compounds, which are of great stability (7).

DETERMINATION OF STRUCTURE

Preliminary experiments on the blue impurity formed in the iron vessels in which phthalimide was being produced by reaction of ammonia in molten phthalic anhydride showed that it contained C, 62.4; H, 2.9; N, 19.2; and Fe, 12.5 per cent, leaving a deficiency of 3 per cent. These values corresponded to an atomic ratio of 4C : 1N, indicating that two atoms of nitrogen were combined with a phthalic residue. This result indicated that the substance contained an isoindole unit capable of yielding this skeleton (15).

The reaction between o-cyanobenzamide and magnesium at 240–250° produced 40 per cent of a bright blue compound which after purification yielded a macrocrystalline magnesium phthalocyanine $C_{32}H_{20}O_2N_8Mg$ or $(C_8H_4N_2)_4 Mg \cdot 2H_2O$ (2).

$$4 \left[\begin{array}{c} \overset{O}{\overset{\|}{C}}-NH_2 \\ CN \end{array} \right] + Mg \longrightarrow (C_8H_4N_2)_4 \, Mg \cdot 2H_2O + 2H_2O$$

When its solution in cold concentrated sulfuric acid or in hot concentrated hydrochloric acid was poured on ice, a blue solid which contained no metal was obtained. The eliminated magnesium could be isolated nearly quantitatively from the solution. The product was phthalocyanine.

Analysis indicated that phthalocyanine has the formula $C_{32}H_{18}N_8$ or $(C_8H_4N_2)_4 \cdot H_2$.

The supposition that the phthalocyanine molecule contains a C_{32} unit was confirmed by determination of the molecular weight of magnesium phthalocyanine by the ebullioscopic method in naphthalene solvent. Magnesium phthalocyanine, 0.4 parts, dissolved in 100 parts naphthalene, raised the boiling point about 0.04°, giving an average molecular weight of 551 (calc. for $C_{32}H_{20}O_2N_8Mg$; 572) (17).

Reagents which readily yielded phthalocyanines with o-phthalonitrile gave no similar products with terephthalonitrile (I), homophthalonitrile (II), o-xylylene dicyanide (III), o-cyanocinnamonitrile (IV), and 2,2′-diphenonitrile (V) (7).

These facts indicated that the two nitrile groups involved in phthalocyanine formation must be linked to adjacent carbon atoms of an aromatic nucleus and cannot be separated by other atoms or groups. Oxidation of magnesium phthalocyanine with ceric sulfate solution gave oxidation

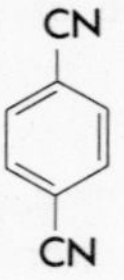

(I)

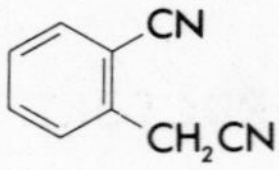

(II)

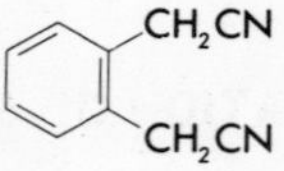

(III)

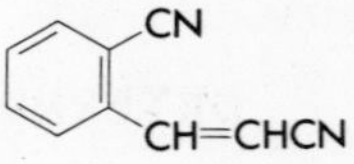

(IV)

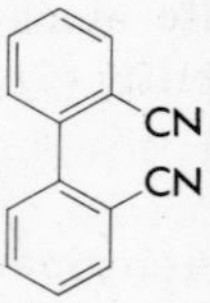

(V)

values of hydrogen and magnesium equivalent to the calculated value $(C_8H_4N_2)_4$ Mg. The solution obtained in the oxidation of magnesium phthalocyanine gave phthalimide in 90 per cent yield (7).

The evidence of synthesis and fission thus indicate the presence of the phthalonitrile group. The only units which satisfy these conditions are isoindole (VI) and phthalazine (VII):

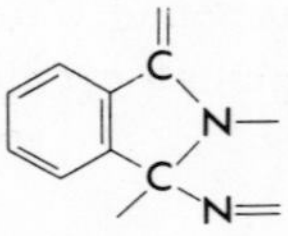

(VI)

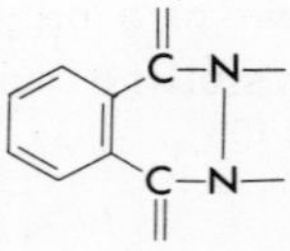

(VII)

Monoiminophthalimide (VIII), and 1,3-diiminoisoindoline (IX) which contain the isoindole unit, readily yield phthalocyanine. Phthalazone (X) and phthalazine (XI) do not yield phthalocyanine.

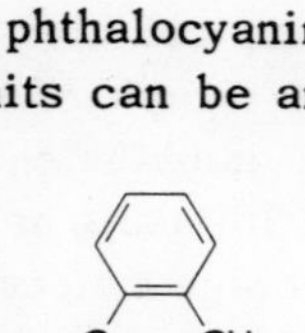

(VIII)

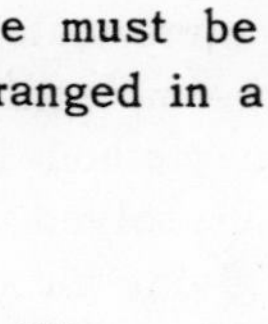

(IX)

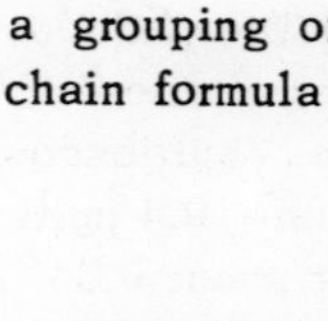

(X)

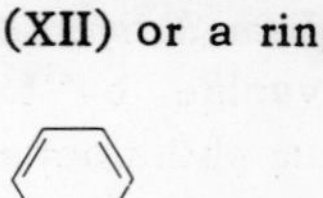

(XI)

Thus, phthalocyanine must be a grouping of four isoindole units. These units can be arranged in a chain formula (XII) or a ring formula (XIII):

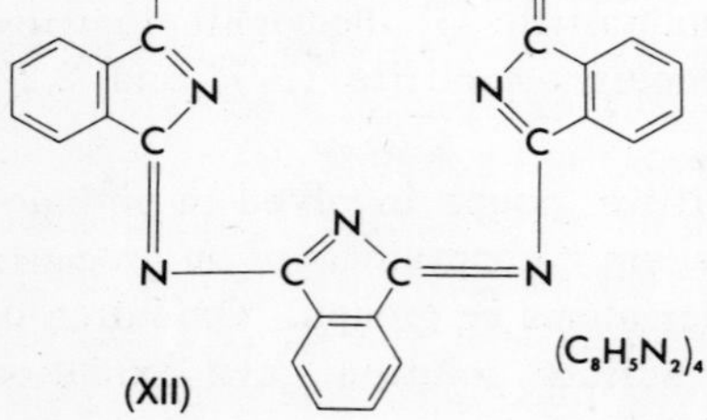

(XII) $(C_8H_5N_2)_4$

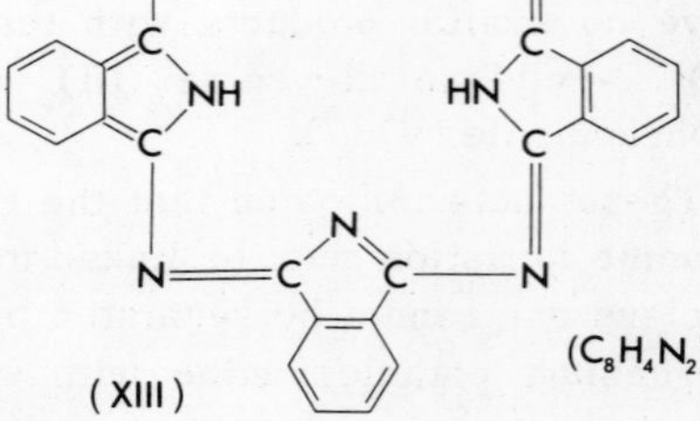

(XIII) $(C_8H_4N_2)_4H_2$

The chain formula is excluded by the results of quantitative oxidation with ceric sulfate. Formula (XII) would give 0.78 per cent H; formula (XIII) would give 0.39 per cent H. Oxidation gave 0.49, 0.56 per cent.

Formula (XIII) contains an o-quinonoid structure. A slightly different formula (XIV) which contains no imino-hydrogen atoms and in which all the aromatic rings are benzenoid, is (XIV):

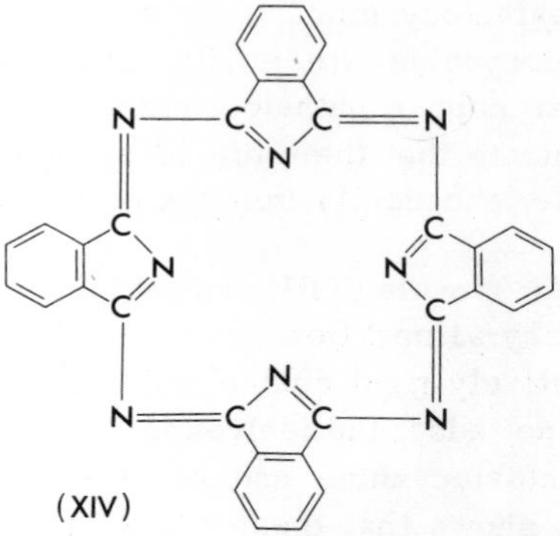

(XIV)

The corresponding formula of (XIII) for copper phthalocyanine is (XV); the corresponding formula of (XIV) for copper phthalocyanine is (XVI):

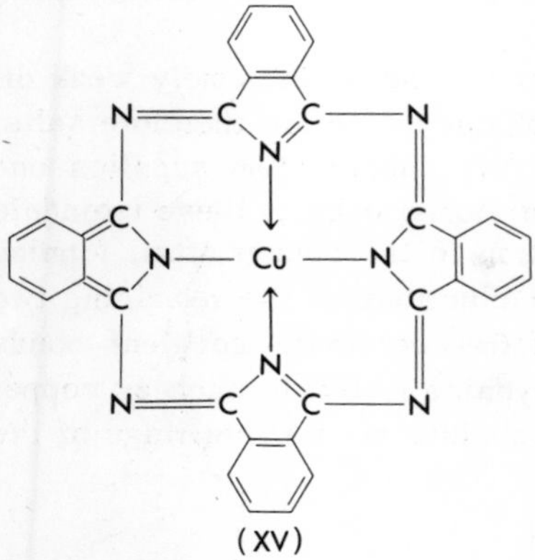

(XV) 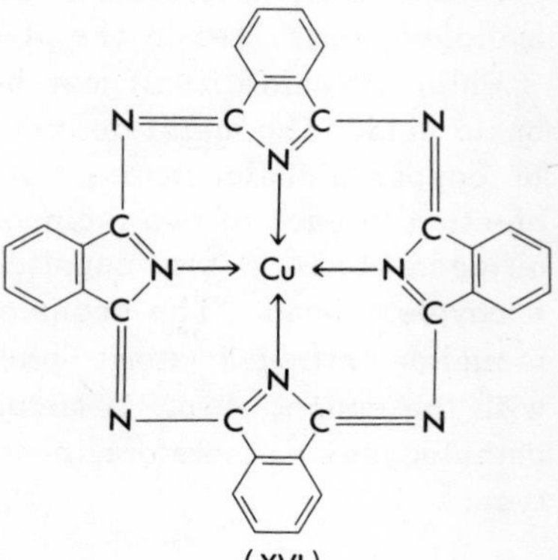   (XVI)

In formula (XV) the copper atom has replaced two hydrogen atoms, is attached by covalent bonds to two insoindole nitrogen atoms, and is co-ordinated to the other two. In formula (XVI) the copper atom is coordinated to the four nitrogen atoms. The stability of copper phthalocyanine to chemical attack and to heat indicates covalent bonding. Upon oxidation of a suspension of phthalocyanine or copper phthalocyanine in dilute sulfuric acid at room temperature by ceric sulfate, one atom of oxygen is taken up for each C_{32} unit; phthalonitrile takes up no oxygen. Therefore, it is indicated that phthalocyanines contain two hydrogen atoms and one o-quinonoid group (7):

$$(C_8H_4N_2)_4H_2 + 7\ H_2O + O \longrightarrow 4\ C_8H_5O_2N + 4\ NH_3$$

$$(C_8H_4N_2)_4 + 8\ H_2O \longrightarrow 4\ C_8H_5O_2N + 4\ NH_3$$

This logic has been confirmed recently when, in developing a synthesis of deuterio-phthalocyanine, it is shown that 2/18 of the total hydrogens in phthalocyanine are easily replaced by deuterium under conditions such that copper phthalocyanine shows no exchange (10). This is taken to indicate that there are 18 hydrogen atoms per mole and that two of them differ chemically from the others in accord with formula (XIII).

Further evidence for formula (XIII) and the o-quinonoid structure is the failure to make porphyrazines from pyrrole and furane derivatives. In these cases the relatively rigid double and single bond arrangements in these compounds do not adapt themselves to an o-quinonoid structure.

X-ray study of phthalocyanine and of nickel, copper, and platinum phthalocyanines has shown that these compounds form monoclinic crystals, space groups $P2_1/a$, with two centrosymmetrical molecules per unit cell. It is shown that the metal atom and the four surrounding isoindole nitrogen atoms all lie in one plane. The X-ray evidence also shows that the whole molecule, with the possible exception of the two central imino-hydrogen atoms, lies in one plane (21–25).

Phthalocyanine itself may be considered to be an extremely weak dibasic acid. The metal derivatives of phthalocyanine are therefore salts. In copper phthalocyanine, for example, the copper atom supplies one electron to each of two isoindole nitrogen atoms; each of these isoindole nitrogen atoms in turn supplies an electron to the copper atom, forming a covalent bond. The unshared pairs of electrons in the remaining two isoindole nitrogen atoms presumably form coordinate covalent bonds with the copper atom. A metal phthalocyanine molecule such as copper phthalocyanine, therefore, contains four chelate six member rings of the type:

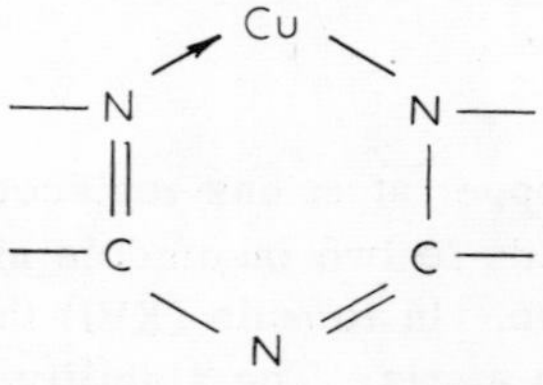

The coordination and covalent coordination of the central metal atoms explain the unusual stability of these atoms in the phthalocyanine molecule.

REFERENCES

1. Braun, A., and Tcherniac, J., *Ber.*, **40**, 2709–14 (1907).
2. Byrne, G. T., Linstead, R. P., and Lowe, A. R., *J. Chem. Soc.*, **1934**, 1017–22.
3. *Chem. Eng. News*, p. 20, July 11, 1960, and pp. 35–39, Aug. 1, 1960.
4. Dahlen, M. A., and Detrick, S. R. (to E. I. Du Pont de Nemours & Co.), U. S. Patent 2,153,300 (Apr. 4, 1939).
5. Dandridge, A. G., Drescher, H. A., and Thomas, J. (to Scottish Dyes Ltd.), British Patent 322,169 (Nov. 18, 1929).
6. Dent, C. E., and Linstead, R. P., *J. Chem. Soc.*, **1934**, 1027–31.
7. Dent, C. E., Linstead, R. P., and Lowe, A. R., *J. Chem. Soc.*, **1934**, 1033–9.
8. de Diesbach, H., Schmidt, V., and Decker, E., *Helv. Chim. Acta*, **6**, 548–9 (1923).
9. de Diesbach, H., and von der Weid, E., *Helv. Chim. Acta*, **10**, 886–8 (1927).
10. Frigerio, N. A., *J. Org. Chem.*, **26**, 2115–6 (1961).
11. Haddock, N. H., and Linstead, R. P., "Thorpe's Dictionary of Applied Chemistry," ed. by M. A. Whitely, London, Longmans, Green & Co., **9**, 617–20 (1949).
12. Kidd, J., *Phil. Trans. Roy. Soc. London*, **1821**, 209–21.
13. Laurent, A., *Ann.*, **19**, 47 (1836).
14. Linstead, R. P., Brit. Assoc. Advance. Sci., Rep., 465–6 (1933).
15. Linstead, R. P., *J. Chem. Soc.*, **1934**, 1016–7.
16. Linstead, R. P., and Lowe, A. R., *J. Chem. Soc.*, **1934**, 1022–7.
17. Linstead, R. P., and Lowe, A. R., *J. Chem. Soc.*, **1934**, 1031–3.
18. *New York Times*, page 12, November 25, 1935.
19. Pinnow, J., and Sämann, C., *Ber.*, **29**, 630 (1896).
20. Pratt, L. S., "Organic Pigments," pp. 214–25, New York, John Wiley & Sons, 1947.
21. Robertson, J. M., *J. Chem. Soc.*, **1935**, 615–21.
22. Robertson, J. M., *J. Chem. Soc.*, **1936**, 1195–1209.
23. Robertson, J. M., Linstead, R. P., and Dent, C. E., *Nature*, **135**, 506–7 (1935).
24. Robertson, J. M., and Woodward, I., *J. Chem. Soc.*, **1937**, 219–30.
25. Robertson, J. M., and Woodward, I., *J. Chem. Soc.*, **1940**, 36–48.
26. Venkataraman, K., "The Chemistry of Synthetic Dyes," pp. 1118–42, New York, Academic Press, 1952.

CHAPTER 2

PROPERTIES

The phthalocyanine molecule may be unique with respect to the number of structural and reaction properties that it exhibits and which have been investigated.

The structural properties of phthalocyanines are discussed under the headings of X-ray structure determination, polymorphism, electron microscope, absorption spectra, central metal atom-ligand bonding, magnetic properties, and field electron microscope.

The rôle of the phthalocyanines in dark reactions is discussed under the titles of oxidation, reduction, and catalysts.

Electrical and light effects are treated in the sections relating to semiconductors, photoconductivity, photochemical reactions, photosensitizers, luminescence, and fluorescence.

The effects of neutron bombardment on metal phthalocyanines and the use of the great phthalocyanine ring as a cage for the purpose of converting the central metal atom into radioactive isotopes are discussed in the section on neutron irradiation.

Finally, flocculation, solubility, molecular weights, extinction coefficient, and dielectric properties are treated under the title Other Properties.

X-RAY STRUCTURE DETERMINATION

"In his work on the phthalocyanines, Robertson accomplished the first direct X-ray analysis of an organic molecule, not even involving the assumption of the presence of discrete atoms. This was possible because of the crystallization of phthalocyanine in a molecular arrangement having centers of symmetry at which different metal atoms can be inserted by means of chemical reactions without appreciable alteration in the crystal structure. The X-ray contour diagram, showing the electron distribution in the molecule, has not merely confirmed Linstead's structure for phthalocyanine, but has also indicated the additional regularity of a complete resonance system.... In the metal phthalocyanines the dimensions of the molecule are very similar for the several compounds examined, with slight variations in the nitrogen-metal distances due to the differences in the radii of the atoms. Thus the nitrogen-metal distance in platinum phthalocyanine is 2.01 Å as compared with 1.92 Å and 1.83 Å in the metal-free and the nickel compound respectively (270)."

Robertson's X-ray studies of the phthalocyanines at the Davy Faraday Research Laboratory of the Royal Institution were published in five parts (159,214,215,217,218). In the first publication, crystals of phthalocyanine, copper, nickel, and platinum phthalocyanines were obtained in the form of long needles by low pressure sublimation in a stream of carbon dioxide at temperatures above 500° (214). The crystals were all monoclinic, the needle axis corresponding with the b axis. Samples were 0.1 × 0.3 × 1 cm with the (001), (100), (20$\bar{1}$), and (10$\bar{1}$) faces developed. X-rays of the crystals were made with copper radiation by rotation, oscillation, and moving-film photographs. Cell dimensions and other constants are given in Table 2-1 (214).

TABLE 2-1. CELL DIMENSIONS AND CONSTANTS FROM X-RAY ANALYSIS (214).

	Phthalo-cyanine	Nickel Phthalo-cyanine	Copper Phthalo-cyanine	Platinum Phthalo-cyanine
a, Å	19.85	19.9	19.6	23.9
b, Å	4.72	4.71	4.79	3.81
c, Å	14.8	14.9	14.6	16.9
β	122.25°	121.9°	120.6°	129.6°
Space Group C_2^5h	P2$_1$/a	P2$_1$/a	P2$_1$/a	P2$_1$/a
Mols. per cell	2	2	2	2
Molecular Symmetry	Center	Center	Center	Center
Vol. of unit cell, Å^3	1173	1186	1180	1186
Density (found)	1.44	1.63	1.63	1.98
Density (calc.)	1.445	1.59	1.61	1.97
Mol. Wt.	514	571	576	707
No. of electrons per unit cell, F (000)	532	584	586	684

"The observed halvings of ($h0l$) when h is odd and of (010) were obtained from long-exposure moving-film photographs. Between 100 and 200 ($h0l$) reflexions were observed from each crystal, without yielding any exception to the general halving. To establish the (010) halving, only a few reflexions are available.... Prolonged exposures were taken about the a and c axes, and this halving was established for phthalocyanine and the copper and the nickel compound up to the (050), and for the platinum compound up to the (030). The (020) and (040) reflexions are definite, but weak. These results definitely establish that the space group is $P2_1/a$ and, consequently, that the molecule has a centre of symmetry" (214).

Also, the dimensional similarity of the crystals indicates that the molecule consists of a large, rigid framework which is not altered in size or form by the entrance of the metal atom.

For phthalocyanine, and copper and nickel phthalocyanines, one molecule contains about $1/2$ abcsinβ or $9.9 \times 12.5 \times 4.7$ Å³ and about $12.0 \times 13.0 \times 3.8$ Å³ for platinum phthalocyanine, indicating large, square, and flat molecules lying in the ac plane (214). The distance between successive molecules along the b axis is about 4–5 Å.

The molecular weights can be calculated from the cell dimensions, space group, measured density, and metal content, to within 5 per cent. Also, "*The metal atom and the four surrounding isoindole nitrogen atoms must all lie strictly in one plane.* For the metal atom, being unique, must coincide with the centre of symmetry. If a straight line be drawn from the centre of one of the nitrogen atoms to the centre of the metal atom and produced an equal distance beyond, it will touch the centre of the opposite nitrogen atom, by the definition of a centre of symmetry. The metal atom and the other two nitrogen atoms must similarly lie on another straight line. Hence it is possible to describe a plane containing these two straight lines and the five atom centres situated on them."

"It would seem to follow from the stereochemistry that the two imino-hydrogen atoms in phthalocyanine must lie out of the great plane, giving rise to the possibility of a *cis*- and a *trans*- form."

Finally, "the intensities of the reflexions shows that the molecules possess at least four-fold symmetry.... By comparing corresponding reflexions from the metal-free and from the metal compounds, a direct determination of the phase constants of some of the reflexions can be made" (214).

In his second publication, Robertson determined the structure of phthalocyanine by direct X-ray Fourier analysis of the monoclinic crystal (215). The interatomic distances and bond angles were determined completely. See Figure 2-1.

To determine the structure amplitudes and phase constants, absolute intensity measurements were made from phthalocyanine and nickel phthalocyanine. Nickel phthalocyanine was most suitable because the cell measurements are practically identical with those of free phthalocyanine, it is obtained in well-formed single crystals, the absorption coefficient for copper radiation is relatively low, and the scattering power of the nickel atom for X-rays affects the intensities without obscuring the reflections. The crystals were exposed to copper radiation, and the reflections were recorded by moving film cameras.

The phase constants for the significant reflections in the ($h0l$) zones were determined by comparing measurements of absolute intensities of corresponding reflections from phthalocyanine and nickel phthalocyanine. From the data, two coordinates of each carbon and nitrogen atom were determined from a *b*-axis Fourier projection. The third coordinate was calculated from the orientation of the molecule deduced from this projection.

"The results show that the chemical structure assigned to the compound by Linstead is correct, and give further information about the type of valency bonds. The inner nucleus of the molecule, which is common to the porphyrins, consists of a closed system of 16 carbon and nitrogen atoms, which appear to be in a state of double bond-single bond resonance, the interatomic distance having the appreciably constant value of

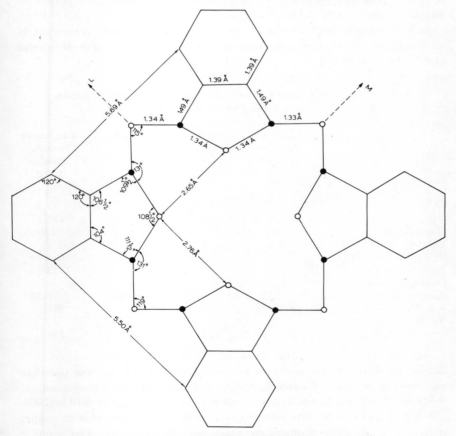

Figure 2-1. Dimensions of the phthalocyanine molecule (215).

O Nitrogen   ● Carbon

1.34 ± 0.03 Å. This inner system is connected to the four benzene rings by C—C bonds of length 1.49 ± 0.03 Å, which indicates a small percentage of double-bond character. The benzene rings are sensibly regular, such variations in their C—C distance as do occur being of small order and apparently erratic, probably owing to deficiencies in the Fourier series. The carbon links emerging from the benzene rings are strained about 15° from their normal positions. In addition, the molecule as a whole suffers a small distortion from true tetragonal symmetry, probably due to the existence of an internal hydrogen bond between the two isoindole nitrogen atoms.

"In the crystal, the planes of adjoining rows of molecules are almost at right angles, and the minimum intermolecular approach distance is 3.35 Å. The perpendicular distance between the molecular planes of parallel molecules is 3.38 Å" (215).

In Robertson's third article, X-ray data for single monoclinic crystals of beryllium, cobalt, iron and manganese phthalocyanines were developed (159). See Table 2-2.

TABLE 2-2. CELL DIMENSIONS AND CONSTANTS FROM X-RAY ANALYSIS (159).

	Beryllium Phthalo-cyanine	Cobalt Phthalo-cyanine	Iron Phthalo-cyanine	Manganese Phthalo-cyanine
a, Å	21.2	20.2	20.2	20.2
b, Å	4.84	4.77	4.77	4.75
c, Å	14.7	15.0	15.0	15.1
β	121.0°	121.3°	121.6°	121.7°
Space Group	$P2_1/a$	$P2_1/a$	$P2_1/a$	$P2_1/a$
Mols. per Cell	2	2	2	2
Molecular Symmetry	Center	Center	Center	Center
Vol. of Unit Cell, Å³	1293	1235	1231	1233
Density (found)	—	—	—	—
Density (Calc.)	1.33	1.53	1.52	1.52
Mol. Wt.	521	571	568	567
No. of electrons per unit Cell, F (000)	536	582	580	578

Single crystals of the phthalocyanines were obtained by low pressure sublimation in carbon dioxide at 550°. Samples used were long needles, 0.3 × 0.1 mm in cross section and several mm long with the (001), (100), (20$\bar{1}$), and (10$\bar{1}$) faces developed. The b axes were measured with copper radiation by rotation photographs about the needle axes. The a and c axial length and the β angles were measured from analysis of moving-film photographs of the ($h0l$) zones of reflections.

"From the standpoint of general stereochemistry, the most important fact which arises is that all the compounds have centrosymmetrical molecules. From this it follows that the metal atoms lie in the same plane as the four nitrogen atoms which carry them" (159).

In 1936, it was already known that 4-coordinate bivalent platinum and copper can exhibit planar symmetry, and that nickel often exhibits planar symmetry. However, cobalt, iron and manganese phthalocyanines were the first examples of planar symmetry for cobalt, iron and manganese metals. "The most remarkable result is provided by beryllium, for which a tetrahedral symmetry is well established by investigations of its benzoylpyruvic acid derivative and of its basic acetate.... The planar arrangement appears to be very unstable, for the anhydrous beryllium compound readily forms a dihydrate even in moist air. This behaviour is not paralleled by other phthalocyanines except the magnesium derivative" (159).

Investigation of a number of cobalt compounds by X-ray analysis has led Poraĭ-Koshits to conclude also that cobalt phthalocyanine is the only cobalt compound in which the cobalt valencies are planar (202).

The stereochemistry of the four isoindole nitrogen atoms is unique also in that their three valencies lie in one plane at 110°, 125°, and 125°. This arrangement is further evidence of the aromatic, resonant nature of the phthalocyanine molecule because if the double and single bonds were fixed, the third valency bond of the isoindole nitrogen atoms would be inclined to the general plane.

In Robertson's fourth paper, a quantitative structure determination by Fourier analysis using X-ray data of nickel phthalocyanine was made (217). The over-all dimensions, interatomic distances, and bond angles were determined. See Figure 2-2.

As in phthalocyanine, the benzene rings in nickel phthalocyanine are regular, plane hexagons. "The structure of the molecule is also closely similar to that of free phthalocyanine, but there is a definite inward shift, amounting to about 0.09 Å, of each of the four isoindole atoms towards the central nickel atom to which they are bound by covalent links. The C—N interatomic distance of the inner nucleus is 1.38 Å, slightly greater than the value found for free phthalocyanine" (217).

Finally, Robertson made a Fourier analysis of platinum phthalocyanine (218). See Figure 2-3.

The molecular structure is similar to phthalocyanine and nickel phthalocyanine. However, the crystal structure is different or polymorphic because the molecular arrangement is such that the planes are inclined at a much smaller angle to the (010) plane (26.5° instead of 44.2°).

Robertson was not aware of the possibility of the existence of polymorphic forms of crystals of various phthalocyanines. It is now known

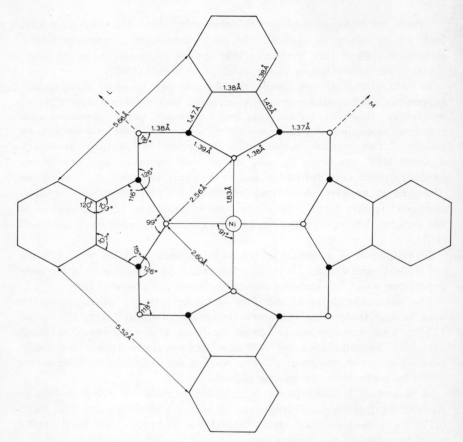

Figure 2-2. Dimensions of the nickel phthalocyanine molecule (217).

O Nitrogen   ● Carbon

that his determinations of molecular structure (159,214,215,217) were
made with crystals in the β-form. Single crystals of the β-form are
easily obtainable by sublimation; the β-polymorph has a high tendency
to crystallize. The subject of phthalocyanine polymorphs is discussed
in the next section of this chapter.

That phthalocyanines can exist in at least two polymorphic forms was
recognized initially by chemists at I. G. Farbenindustrie in the period
1935–1937 (84,195,248), who studied X-ray diffraction powder patterns of
phthalocyanine crystals. "Kupferphtalocyanin kommt in zwei poly-
morphen Formen vor, die wir als α- und β-Modifikation bezeichnet haben.
Diese besitzen verschiedene Kristallgitter, verschiedene physikalische
Eigenschaften, sie zeigen demnach völlig verchiedenes coloristisches

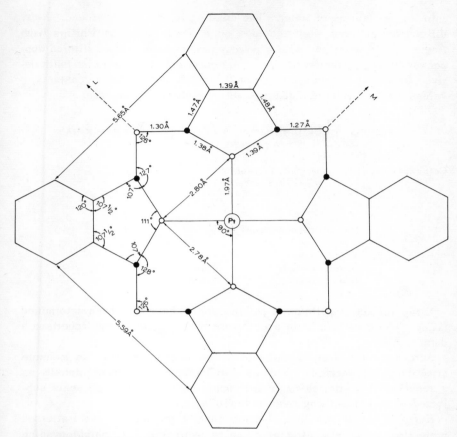

Figure 2-3. Dimensions of the platinum phthalocyanine molecule (218).

O Nitrogen   ● Carbon

Verhalten und sie werden durch Röntgendiagramm eindeutig charakter-isiert'' (195).

More recently, the fine structures of X-ray K absorption edges of cop-per phthalocyanine in the α- and β-forms have been measured using a Norelco X-ray diffraction apparatus and wide range goniometer (260).

X-ray diffraction patterns of β-copper phthalocyanine in monoclinic needle form prepared by sublimation, and of α-copper phthalocyanine in granular form prepared from solution of the α-form in 98 per cent sulfuric acid have little in common (234). Unit cell constants for α-copper phthalo-cyanine have been measured (220). α-Copper phthalocyanine was pre-pared by dissolving β-copper phthalocyanine in 98 per cent sulfuric acid and precipitating α-copper phthalocyanine by pouring the solution slowly into a large volume of water. The dried solid was finely ground. X-ray diffraction patterns were recorded on a North American Philips High Angle Spectrometer and with a powder camera using nickel filtered copper radiation. Twenty-nine lines were obtained. Unit cell constants derived from the patterns are given in Table 2-3. Using these constants, *d* values were calculated that agree with the observed values.

TABLE 2-3. CELL DIMENSIONS AND CONSTANTS FROM X-RAY
ANALYSIS (220).

Cell constants of α-copper phthalocyanine:

a, Å	17.367
c, Å	12.790
Probable space group	$C_{4h}^1 - P4/m$
Mols. per cell	6
Density (found)	1.49
Density (calc.)	1.488

X-ray diffraction patterns of phthalocyanine have also been determined (127). The β-pattern is in accord with that computed from Robertson's data.

A commercial X-ray high-angle diffractometer, adapted to measure small-range scattering has been used to determine scattering intensity as a function of scattering angle for copper phthalocyanine pigments subjected to various milling treatments (167).

Huggins has shown that electron density projections and Patterson projections of crystal structures can be synthesized for phthalocyanine molecules by the photographic addition of patterns of light and dark bands with the use of suitable masks, using 35 mm film inserted into a photographic enlarger, with exposures made through the masks. A photograph of a phthalocyanine molecule from X-ray data of Robertson is made (123). Taylor and Lipson (253) have described a method using optically derived Fourier transforms as a starting point in crystal structure analysis, with particular reference to phthalocyanine. Masks comprising holes punched in cardboard are prepared as a model of the phthalocyanine molecule. The diffraction pattern of the mask is then obtained with an X-ray diffraction spectrometer. A Difference-Patterson projection of the phthalocyanines along the *b* axis, using Robertson's data for the isomorphous crystal pair of phthalocyanine and nickel phthalocyanine has been made by Kartha and Ramachandran (128). It is suggested that this method merits more attention as a means for structure analysis.

Thermal expansion coefficients of crystals of phthalocyanine, and copper and platinum phthalocyanines have been determined in single crystals by X-ray powder photographs over the temperature range 90–600°K (261). Thermal expansion over the (010) plane and in the plane containing the *b* crystal axis are given for phthalocyanine and platinum phthalocyanine. See Table 2-4.

TABLE 2-4. AVERAGE THERMAL EXPANSION PER °K FROM
290 TO 475°K (261).

	Phthalocyanine	Platinum Phthalocyanine
(010) plane minimum expansion	0.40×10^{-4}	-0.14×10^{-4}
maximum expansion	0.75×10^{-4}	0.60×10^{-4}
plane containing *b* crystal axis:		
minimum expansion	0.18×10^{-4}	-0.10×10^{-4}
maximum expansion	0.63×10^{-4}	1.14×10^{-4}

Several reviews treat the structure of the phthalocyanines as determined by X-ray analysis (33,117,122,153,173,184). In the opinion of Huggins (122):

"The applicability of modern X-ray methods to the determination of the structural details of complex molecules has nowhere been more beautifully exemplified than in the researches by Robertson and co-workers on phthalocyanine and its salts."

POLYMORPHISM

Both phthalocyanine and copper phthalocyanine are known to exist in at least three polymorphic forms. Two of the forms are metastable.

At the time of Robertson's X-ray analyses, von Susich (84) found two polymorphs of copper phthalocyanine and three of phthalocyanine, and therefore found it necessary to differentiate between the polymorphs. von Susich named the stable polymorph studied by Robertson "β-form," and designated the two metastable forms "α-form" and "γ-form." A more recent paper gives the X-ray diffraction spectrographs of all three forms of phthalocyanine (234). The β-form is obtained as long needles or laths.

Both solvent and melt methods of manufacture of copper phthalocyanine result in the formation of the β-form. Heating the α-form to 200° also reconverts it to the β-form. When copper phthalocyanine precipitates from high boiling solvents such as quinoline or dichlorobenzene, the β-form is also obtained.

Linstead (50) found that copper phthalocyanine sublimes under vacuum at 550° with rapid sublimation at 580°. The vapor is a pure deep blue and the crystals formed therefrom have the purple luster characteristic of the β-form. Vaporization also occurs at one atmosphere pressure in an atmosphere of nitrogen or carbon dioxide. Crystals as long as 2 cm are formed, as shown in Figure 2-4. According to von Susich (248), "Die β Form ist wegen ihrer Härte und Neigung grosse Kristalle zu bilden, coloristisch kaum brauchbar, da man damit nur schwache und trübe Färbungen bekommt."

The β-form may be converted to the α-form by dissolution in concentrated sulfuric acid and drowning the solution in water. The α-form is also obtained from the β-form by the permutoid swelling process, i.e.,

1 cm

Figure 2-4. Crystals of β-form copper phthalocyanine prepared by sublimation in nitrogen at one atmosphere and 550°. (*Courtesy Standard Ultramarine & Color Company, Photograph by R. G. Schroeder.*

by adding the β-form pigment to 68 per cent sulfuric acid, forming a yellowish-green sulfate, followed by drowning in water, with hydrolysis of the sulfate and precipitation of the α-type crystal.

α-Copper phthalocyanine thus prepared has a particle size range from 0.01 to 0.5 μ, with many particles at the lower limit of particle size. These crystals tend to dissolve in aromatic, ester, and other "crystallizing" type solvents because of the greater solubility of very small particles (136). "Crystallizing" type solvents are solvents in which phthalocyanines have slightly greater solubility as compared to solubility in straight chain aliphatic solvents. After solution in the "crystallizing" type solvents phthalocyanines form much larger β-type crystals, the normal type formed from solvents, as the supersaturated solution formed from the small size particles reverts to saturation. Formation of the larger crystals by this method is a type of Ostwald ripening (32,136).

Both the α- and β-forms of copper phthalocyanine have been characterized by X-ray diffraction curves (252,280), see Figure 2-5. The abscissae are on the customary non-uniform scale of interplanar spacing as drawn by a recording spectrophotometer. Ordinate units are per cent absorption relative to the most intense absorption.

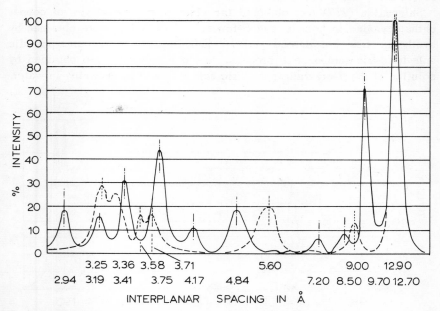

Figure 2-5. X-ray diffraction characteristics of α- and β-copper phthalocyanine (280).

α-form - - - -   β-form ———

Kendall (131) described a method for both quantitative and qualitative identification of the polymorphic forms of copper phthalocyanine by infrared spectroscopy. The samples are prepared as Nujol mulls. The extent of chlorination and the percentage of each polymorphic copper chlorophthalocyanine present may also be determined by this method.

The enthalpy difference between α- and β-copper phthalocyanine has been measured with an isothermal calorimeter (24). Transition from the α- to the β-form was complete in about 6 hours at 80° in o-chlorophenol, using a calorimeter of the Bunsen type capable of measuring such slow heat changes. The heat of transition of the α- to β-crystal is 2.57 ± 0.03 kcal/mole.

A third polymorph, γ-copper phthalocyanine, first reported by Eastes (54) in 1956, is obtained by stirring crude copper phthalocyanine with sulfuric acid of less than 60 per cent concentration. Salts of copper phthalocyanine made by slurrying copper phthalocyanine in nitrobenzene and adding a non-oxidizing strong mineral acid, followed by filtration and hydrolysis of the filtered salt by water also produce the γ-type crystal (155). An X-ray diffraction spectrograph shows maximum intensities at an interplanar spacing of about 13.5 Å with the next strongest lines at 11.95, 5.57, and 3.38 Å (54), as shown in Figure 2-6.

Shigemitsu (232) has obtained the chlorinated derivatives of copper phthalocyanine in both α- and β-forms. β-Form laths were obtained by synthesis from chlorinated phthalic anhydride using the urea-phthalic anhydride-trichlorobenzene process. α-Form crystals were obtained by solution of the β-crystals in sulfuric acid followed by drowning in water.

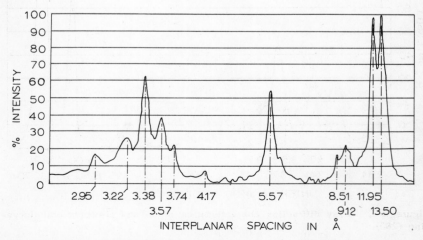

Figure 2-6. X-ray diffraction spectrograph of γ-copper phthalocyanine (54).

Two forms of the following copper chlorophthalocyanines were prepared by Shigemitsu: copper tetra-3-chlorophthalocyanine, copper tetra-4-chlorophthalocyanine, copper octa-3,6-chlorophthalocyanine, copper octa-4,5-chlorophthalocyanine, and copper hexadecachlorophthalocyanine. Heating the α-form of copper tetra-3-chlorophthalocyanine with a solvent readily converts it to the β-form. However, this is not the case when the chlorine is in the 4, 3-6, 4-5, or 3-4-5-6 positions since these pigments may be boiled in trichlorobenzene for 10 hours without visibly changing to the β-form. There is little change in shade to the yellow when copper tetra-4-chlorophthalocyanine or copper octa-4,5-chlorophthalocyanine is heated with trichlorobenzene. However, there is a slight change in shade toward the yellow with copper octa-3,6-chlorophthalocyanine and other more highly chlorinated phthalocyanines and with the fully chlorinated hexadecachloro compound.

Phthalocyanine, as mentioned above, exists in three polymorphs (84). β-Phthalocyanine is obtained when α-phthalocyanine is sublimed or recrystallized. The β-form is converted to α-phthalocyanine when it is subjected to intensive shear action for a long period of grinding in the presence of sodium chloride or sodium sulfate, or when it is slurried in 64 per cent sulfuric acid and drowned in water. It is also obtained directly by hydrolyzing sodium phthalocyanine with methanol. γ-Phthalocyanine is made by demetallizing calcium phthalocyanine with hydrochloric acid. Calcium phthalocyanine is made from phthalonitrile and calcium oxide in the presence of formamide. The γ-form is converted to α-phthalocyanine when slurried in 60 to 70 per cent sulfuric acid and poured into water. Both the α- and γ-forms are converted to β-phthalocyanine when they are heated to 300°. Commercial methods of making the α- and β-forms of copper phthalocyanine and phthalocyanine are discussed in Chapter 4.

Bradbrook and Linstead (30) characterized two types of magnesium 1,2-naphthalocyanines: the α-form does not form a hydrate, although it is unusually soluble in ether, acetone and ethyl acetate. The β-form may be isolated as the monohydrate, which loses its water of hydration at 215°. The anhydrous form will regain a molecule of water, although there is no tendency to form a dihydrate. Both α- and β-magnesium naphthalocyanines yield 1,2-naphthalamide on oxidation with ceric sulfate.

The β-form of naphthalocyanine is darker than the α-form, but does not show any marked difference in solubility. Naphthalocyanine prepared from lead naphthalocyanine appears to be identical with the α-modification.

The two magnesium 1,2-naphthalocyanines yield two different metal-free compounds on treatment with sulfuric acid. When these are heated with magnesium, they regenerate the isomeric α- and β-magnesium derivatives, indicating that there is a persistent structural difference between the two forms.

The α-, β-, γ-nomenclature of phthalocyanine polymorphs has been used since their recognition by von Susich in 1935. Nonetheless, occasional references, for example, references 54, 131, and 247 have called the stable β-form: "α" and have called the metastable α-form: "β." It is to be hoped that with the passage of time the nomenclature that has been so widely used will be universally accepted.

ELECTRON MICROSCOPE

Hamm and Van Norman have found that polymorphism of crystalline phthalocyanine can be distinguished by electron diffraction patterns (114). Electron micrographs of the α-form and of crystal needles of the β-form were made at 14,700 × magnification. Transformation of α-copper phthalocyanine to β-copper phthalocyanine was observed neatly under the electron microscope (114).

Suito and Ueda (243) have studied dimorphism and crystal habit of copper phthalocyanine by electron micrographs and diffraction patterns. These authors and Menter (29,172) have tabulated differences in the electron diffraction patterns of the dimorphs.

Suito, Ueda, and Takiyama (243,245) have developed a "raft" technique whereby information relative to β-form crystals of phthalocyanines can be obtained from electron diffraction patterns. A sample of β-form zinc or copper phthalocyanine, for example, is dispersed in a suitable organic medium. The suspension is poured over a surface of water whereby the suspension spreads over the surface without mixing with water and the crystal needles flow along the stream lines, coming together, forming "rafts" of crystal needles. The dried suspension is then studied by electron diffraction.

Menter (29,172) was the first investigator to observe lattice structure and lattice dislocations in crystals of metal phthalocyanines. The author studied β-crystals of copper and platinum phthalocyanines, prepared by sublimation, in the electron microscope. In copper and platinum phthalocyanines, the (001) planes represent the surface of thin ribbons, the (010) planes are inclined to the (001) plane, and the (20$\bar{1}$) plane is oriented parallel to the axis, making an angle of 88° in platinum phthalocyanine and of 80° in copper phthalocyanine with the (001) plane. The crystals were examined in a Siemens Elmiskop 1 at 80 kv, with 200 μ condenser aperture and 50 μ objective aperture. The images were recorded at a magnification of 77,000x. The electron micrographs appear as parallel lines with equal spacing. The spacing of the (20$\bar{1}$) planes in platinum phthalocyanine by X-ray analysis is 11.94 Å. In the electron microscope, the spacing is 12.0 Å. The spacing of the (010) planes in β-copper phthalocyanine is determined to be 10.30 Å. in the electron microscope; this value differs only slightly from the X-ray value of 9.8 Å. Imperfections and dislocations in the crystal lattices of copper and platinum phthalocyanines can be observed also. Suito and Ueda have measured the spacing of successive ($20\bar{1}$) planes to be 9.8 Å, and of the (001) planes to be 12.6 Å. in copper phthalocyanine (244).

Espagne (67,68) has also observed monoclinic crystals of copper and platinum phthalocyanines under the electron microscope, at 80 kv, with magnification of 80,000x, with condenser aperture at 200 μ and objective aperture of 50 μ. It is determined that the ($20\bar{1}$) planes are 11.9 Å apart in platinum phthalocyanine, in agreement with Menter, and 9.8 Å apart in copper phthalocyanine, in agreement with Suito and Ueda.

Labaw and Wyckoff caution that faithfulness of surface reproduction by the electron microscope and surface contamination of the specimen are limitations in the detail possible from the microscope and care must be used in judging the validity of photographs obtained (150).

Both Menter and Espagne have noted copper phthalocyanine screw deformations or crystals of copper phthalocyanine rolled into helixes (67,172). Espagne has used an evaporation technique to prepare multiple crystal samples (68). Suito, Ueda, and co-workers have observed that the β-form of copper phthalocyanine may contain a twin structure (242, 246). The electron diffraction diagram, taken with a Hitachi HU-10 electron microscope, shows that "two crystal habits are parallel and side by side, separated only with a narrow gap. The electron microdiffraction pattern of the selected area has two series of equi-distant diffraction spots that are attributable to ($20\bar{1}$) and (001) reflexions with their higher-order reflexions superimposed on the equator, which is taken in the direction perpendicular to the b axis" (246).

Hasimoto and Yotsumoto (116) have observed spacing anomalies in moiré patterns of copper, platinum, and zinc phthalocyanines. In the electron micrograph it is seen that the "spacing of the weak lines is larger than that of the strong ones, and at the maximum the relative displacement is almost a quarter of the spacing." This anomaly is attributed to dynamic effects of electron diffraction by the crystals and not to any anomaly in the crystal lattice spacing. The spacing anomaly may occur both as a result of bending and of thickness variation across the crystal face.

ABSORPTION SPECTRA

Absorption spectra in the visible and infrared regions of numerous phthalocyanines have been measured (3). Absorption spectra in the ultraviolet region, however, are sparse since the phthalocyanine dispersion media are commonly aromatic in nature.

Assuming that the π-electrons in the phthalocyanines are a one dimensional free-electron gas, resonating between two equivalent limiting structures, of the phthalocyanine ring, with constant potential energy along its length, Kuhn has calculated that the absorption maximum of phthalocyanine lies between 6000 and 7000 Å (147,148).

"In the normal state the stablest energy states of the electron gas each contain two electrons in accordance with Pauli's exclusion principle. The remaining states are empty. The existence of the first absorption band is a consequence of the jump of a π-electron from the highest energy level occupied in the normal state to the lowest empty level.

"For the wave-length of the maximum of the first absorption band of this group of dyes, the relationship obtains that $\lambda_1 = (8\ mc/h)\ (L^2/[N + 1])$ where L is the length of the polymethine zig-zag chain, N, the number of π-electrons, m, the mass of the electron, c, the velocity of light, h, Planck's universal constant. Good agreement with experimental results for λ_1 is obtained by the use of this equation" (147).

Absorption maxima and extinction coefficients in the visible region have been measured for phthalocyanine and copper phthalocyanine (79, 211). Phthalocyanine: in dioxane, 3440 Å($\varepsilon = 0.78$), 5950 (0.29), 6290 (0.44), 6360 (0.46), 6550 (1.4), 6880 (1.5); and in 95 per cent sulfuric acid, 3050 (0.55), 4400 (0.23), 6900 (0.23), 7450 (0.65), 7730 (0.83), and 8380 (1.14). Copper phthalocyanine: in dioxane 3470 (0.86), 3750 (1.0), 4360 (0.14), 6050 (0.43), 6150 (0.4), 6480 (1.4), and 6700 (2.8), and in 95 per cent sulfuric acid, 3050 (0.57), 4400 (0.27), 6980 (0.35), 7480 (0.41), and 7910 (2.02) (79).

The spectrum of phthalocyanine in the visible region is composed of at least seven bands, the main absorption occurring between 6000 and 7000 Å. The spectra of the metallic derivatives of phthalocyanine differ in some respects from that of phthalocyanine and among themselves but certain features appear in common: there are one or two intense bands in the region 5600–7000 Å and a relatively strong band near 6000 Å. The intensity of the absorption increases in general with increasing wavelength except that the band at about 6000 Å is nearly always more intense than that next to it of longer wave length.

"...all the metal-containing pigments possess frequencies common to each other and to those of the metal-free one. However, shifts of frequencies are exhibited peculiar to each metal atom, and especially conspicuous around 900 and 1500 cm⁻¹ (111,111 and 66,666 Å). The shift is systematically to the higher frequencies in the sequence of the phthalocyanines:

$$\nu\ \text{Mg} < \nu\ \text{Zn} < \nu\ \text{Cu} < \nu\ \text{Fe} < \nu\ \text{Co}$$

The spectrum of the metal-free pigment differs in some respects from that of the metal-containing ones. This shows that the introduction of a central metal atom affects the whole array of the bonds in the organic part of the molecule. The spectrum of the metal-free phthalocyanine possesses a narrow absorption maximum at 3298 cm^{-1} (30,300 Å) belonging to the NH frequency of two such bands at the N atoms of the pyrrole rings. The position of this maximum is a normal one, as is the case for an imino or amino group and does not suggest the presence of two protons shared in common by all the four nitrogen atoms of the central ring'' (257).

Measurements of absorption spectra of polycyclic aromatic compounds including phthalocyanine suspended in Nujol in the near infrared in the 50,000–150,000 Å region were made by Cannon and Sutherland (38).

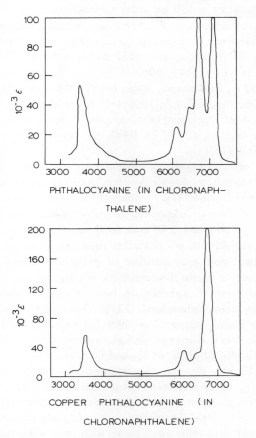

Figure 2-7. Absorption spectra of phthalocyanine and copper phthalocyanine in the visible region (85).

"The spectra described in this paper were obtained at Cambridge during 1944–45 and at that time no systematic study of the infrared spectra of aromatic compounds had been made with the exception of the single ring compounds."

Introduction of metals into the phthalocyanine molecule has a variable effect on the intensity and spacing but does not alter the general type; the weakest absorption bands of phthalocyanine no longer appear and the spectrum is shifted to higher frequencies. The extent of the displacement is proportional to the atomic number of the central atom.

Absorption spectra of phthalocyanine and copper phthalocyanine in the visible, over the range 3,000–10,000 Å, obtained by Ficken and Linstead (85), are given in Figure 2-7. The spectra were drawn with a Hilger-Nutting spectrometer using solutions of 0.5–1.0 mg pigment in 100–400 cc chloronaphthalene.

Absorption data for nickel phthalocyanine have been obtained (249).

The absorption spectrum of magnesium phthalocyanine in the visible region has four–five maxima as determined in numerous solvents: in acetone 3440, 6010, 6380, and 6650 Å; in ethanol, 2830, 3440, 6050, 6400, 6680 Å; in ether 2440, 6010, 6380, and 6660 Å; in pyridine, 3490, 6080, 6470, 6730 Å; in dioxane, 3440, 6020, 6380 and 6660 Å; in benzene, 3460, 6080, 6460, and 6720 Å; in methyl benzene, 3460, 6090, 6460, and 6720 Å; in 1,2,4-tetrahydronaphthalene, 3470, 6090, 6460, and 6720 Å; in α-bromonaphthalene, 3550, 6130, 6490, and 6780 Å; in solid film, 2900, 3350, and 6300 Å (78).

Absorption of chlorogallium phthalocyanine, chloroindium phthalocyanine, and iodoindium phthalocyanine has been measured in the visible region 4000–7000 Å also (41). Extinction coefficients are calculated from solutions of these compounds in chloronaphthalene. The principal absorption occurs between 6000 and 7000 Å.

Extinction coefficients are not often reported, however, because of the slight solubility with precipitation of phthalocyanines in the aromatic solvents in which they are dispersed for absorption measurements.

Infrared and visible spectra of bromoaluminum phthalocyanine tripyridinate have been determined (132). The infrared spectra were determined in a Nujol suspension over 30,000–150,000 Å. The visible spectrum of the bromoaluminum phthalocyanine dissolved in pyridine has maxima at 4340, 4650, 6120, 6500, and 6820 Å.

Whalley (278) has revised the absorption data of Anderson and coworkers (3) and of Evstigneev and Krasnovskiĭ (79). See Table 2-5. "Previous determinations of the electronic absorption spectra of phthalocyanines involved visual instruments (3) or unusual solvents (79). The results of recent determinations made with photoelectric instruments on carefully purified samples are now recorded. These data are considered

TABLE 2-5. VISIBLE AND ULTRAVIOLET ABSORPTIONS (278)

$\lambda_{\max}$ (Å) (and $\log_{10}\varepsilon$)

Phthalocyanines	Solvent											
Metal-free	a	3500 / 4.74				5540 / 3.57		6020 / 4.43	6380 / 4.62	6650 / 5.18		
*Cu	a	3500 / 4.76		5100 / 3.56	5260 / 3.57	5670 / 3.91	5880 / 4.06	6110 / 4.56	6480 / 4.51	6780 / 5.34	6980 / 5.21	
Ni	a	3510 / 4.57				5600 / 3.75	5800 / 3.82	6030 / 4.51	6430 / 4.47	6710 / 5.10		
Co	a	3480 / 4.65						6065 / 4.53		6720 / 5.19		
*Co	b	3300 / 4.86						5965 / 4.51		6575 / 5.07		
Fe·2py	b	3295 / 4.88	4140 / 4.29					5930 / 4.47		6540 / 5.03		
Fe	c	3300 / 4.68						5950 / 3.95		6560 / 4.84		
Zn·py	b	3475 / 4.81						6070 / 4.59	6460 / 4.56	6720 / 5.45		
*Mg·H$_2$O	b	3470 / 4.73				5680 / 3.59	5870 / 3.79	6100 / 4.45	6470 / 4.39	6745 / 4.94		
*Pd	a	3470 / 4.69				5570 / 3.98	5765 / 4.07	5955 / 4.57	6330 / 4.51	6605 / 5.32		
Sn diphthalocyanine	d	3380 / 5.11						5755 / 4.33		6260 / 5.06		7740 / 4.57
Tetrazaporphin												
*Co tetracyclohexeno	c	3515 / 4.72						5395 / 4.17		5890 / 4.95		

a, 1-Chloronaphthalene; *b*, pyridine; *c*, *o*-dichlorobenzene; *d*, chlorobenzene.
*With Dr. G. E. Ficken.

to be accurate and replace those previously published. Quantitative spectral details for palladium and cobalt phthalocyanine are given for the first time. The spectrum of metal-free phthalocyanine and those of its metal derivatives, here examined, all showed the single band at ca 350 mμ (3500 Å) which is characteristic of tetraazaporphins. The visible spectra of the phthalocyanine complexes of bivalent Cu, Ni, Co, Fe, Zn, Pd, and Mg were very similar to one another, having a single, narrow, intense band in the 650–675 mμ (6500–6750 Å) region. The spectrum of magnesium phthalocyanine is thus different from that reported earlier by Barrett *et al.* (10). The positions of the additional peaks found correspond to those of metal-free phthalocyanine which have been formed by traces of hydrochloric acid in the solvent (1-chloronaphthalene). I find that magnesium phthalocyanine which has been crystallized from pyridine, contrary to a previous report (78), is not contaminated with metal-free pigment.''

Unimolecular films of magnesium and iron phthalocyanine, and magnesium naphthalocyanine have been prepared. A unimolecular film of magnesium naphthalocyanine is green-blue in color even to the naked eye. The molecular extinction coefficient of this compound is of the same order in the unimolecular film as in bulk in alcoholic solution (124).

Absorption spectra of magnesium phthalocyanine have been measured over the range 3800–7100 Å in pyridine solution (161). The absorption spectra of the lowest triplet state were measured by a flash photolytic-flash photographic technique. The principal absorption maxima of the ground state are replaced in the triplet state by a broad absorption having a maximum on the long wavelength side of the Soret band, which decreases gradually toward the red.

Elvidge and Lever (65) have obtained spectra of chromium phthalocyanine in various solvents in the infrared, visible, and ultraviolet regions. The infrared spectra of chromium phthalocyanine in the 30,000–140,000 Å region are similar to the planar cobalt (II) and iron (II) phthalocyanines prepared in a Nujol mull. In the 2,300–10,000 Å region, with chromium phthalocyanine in methanol solvent, the most intense band in the visible portion is at 6,700–6,900 Å and the second most intense band is at 3300–3500 Å. Corresponding extinction coefficients are also reported, in chlorobenzene, methanol, propylene carbonate, and in pyridine solvents. The absorption spectra of solid pigments in layers formed by sublimation have been compared with corresponding absorption spectra obtained by solvent evaporation (266).

The advantages of the sublimation technique are that the pigment molecules are in perfect condition for spectrophotometric measurements;

the technique is applicable with pigments insoluble in readily vaporizable solvents; the pigments are subjected to additional purification by sublimation. The method is not applicable to pigments that cannot be sublimed because of decomposition at elevated temperature.

Infrared absorption spectra of phthalocyanines show differences between the α- and β-polymorphic forms (55). Infrared absorption spectra of α- and β-forms of phthalocyanine, and copper, nickel, zinc, and cobalt phthalocyanines have been determined (55). The α- and β-polymorphic forms were determined by X-ray diffraction patterns to characterize the polymorphic crystal modifications, the infrared spectra of which were measured. Infrared spectra of the five phthalocyanines suspended in Nujol were similar in the 30,000–80,000 Å range; however, there were noticeable differences at 125,000 to 145,000 Å. The transformation of α-copper phthalocyanine to β-copper phthalocyanine in cyclohexanol (55) and in Nujol (131) was followed at room temperature by the change in infrared absorption. See Figure 2-8.

Absorption at 34,000, 68,500 and 72,500 Å is due principally to Nujol absorption.

Infrared spectroscopy has been used to study the effect of electron donors on phthalocyanines (238,257). The infrared spectra of phthalo-

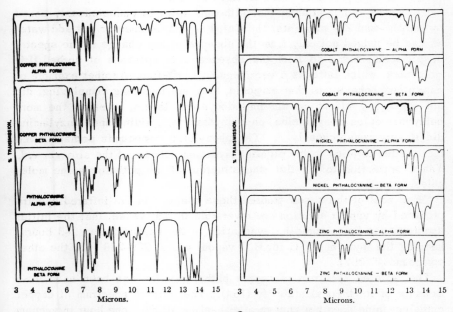

Figure 2-8. Infrared spectra of α- and β-forms of phthalocyanine, and cobalt, copper, nickel, and zinc phthalocyanines (55). From *JACS*, 74, 3806 (1952).

cyanine, and cobalt, copper, iron, magnesium, and zinc phthalocyanines were determined before and after exposure to vapors of electron donor substances: water, hydrogen sulfide, ammonia, phenylhydrazine, hydrazine, benzylamine, aniline, diphenylamine, pyridine, indole, and oxygen. Before use the phthalocyanines were subjected to purification by sublimation in vacuum (10^{-4} mm Hg). For obtaining the infrared spectra the phthalocyanines were deposited as thin films (0.01 mm) on sylvite plates after sublimation in vacuum at 400–450°. After the first plotting of the spectrum, the layer of phthalocyanine was brought into contact with the vapor of an electron donor, and after 15–20 hours the spectrum was determined again. The infrared determinations were made under vacuum conditions in a glass cuvette with sylvite windows. Spectral measurements were made in an IKS-11 infrared spectrometer with sodium chloride and lithium fluoride windows at 50,000–150,000 Å. The infrared spectrum of phthalocyanine remained unchanged, indicating a lack of interaction. The infrared spectra of cobalt and copper phthalocyanines were not altered either. However, shape and position of the bands of the infrared spectra of iron, magnesium, and zinc phthalocyanines were changed in the presence of the electron donors. In other words, iron, magnesium, and zinc atoms, after entering the phthalocyanine ring, do not completely lose their ability to react with electron donors.

"It seems rather strange that although water is conspicuously bound by the Mg- and Zn- pigments, the Cu-, Fe- and Co-ones do not add water as can be judged not only from the absence of any change in the spectra of pigments, but also from the absence of a spectrum of sorbed H_2O molecules, which latter is a very sensitive criterion. Another example of anomalous behavior is that ammonia, very apt to strong complexing, did not show any effect on the phthalocyanine layers, whereas the more bulky molecules of hydrazine, phenylhydrazine, pyridine and benzylamine did it very conspicuously... The phenylated compounds perhaps owed their better sorption in the pigment layers on account of the stronger v.d. Waals' attraction to the flat ring structure of the phthalocyanine molecules.

"For most of the cases studied these changes in the infrared spectra produced by vapour sorption are reversible in that sense, that the initial spectrum can be restored by evacuation of the vapour during 2–3 hours, keeping the layer at 20°C for H_2O vapour and at 200–250° for the other compounds" (257).

The infrared spectrum of copper phthalocyanine has been used as a measure of its thermal stability (154). The infrared spectrum of copper phthalocyanine does not change after heating at 800° one hour in vacuum at an initial pressure of 10^{-5} mm Hg. The absorption spectrum of the potassium salt of tetrasulfonated copper phthalocyanine during one-electron oxidation in phosphoric acid has been used in a kinetic study of this reaction (57). A fugitive red intermediate is considered to be a one-electron oxidation product or phthalocyanine free radical. Lyons, Walsh, and White have measured the polarized spectra of phthalocyanine crystals in the region 2860–7700 Å (165). The authors discussed the differences between theoretical and experimental absorption bands, and are sympathetic with the expectations based on molecular orbital theory, in which the thirty-eight double bond electrons in phthalocyanine are not combined in pairs to form bands but move freely from atom to atom. Basu (12) has made molecular orbital calculations for phthalocyanine. These calculations, predicting absorption at about 4760 Å and 7140 Å where the absorption at 4760 Å is due to polarization parallel and perpendicular to the b-axis of the molecule, are made use of by Lyons, Walsh, and White (165). A molecular orbital analysis of phthalocyanines has been made elsewhere (40). Using known X-ray crystal structures and extinction coefficients of solutions, Lyons has calculated characteristics of crystal spectra of phthalocyanine with the aid of first-order theory (164). "The spectra of metal phthalocyanines in general resemble the spectrum of metal-free phthalocyanine, which in solution shows a series of absorption maxima. It has been suggested (3) that two electronic transitions are present with origins at 14,290 and 15,060 cm^{-1} (6999 and 6640 Å). It is not clear that this must be the case and that a 770 cm^{-1} (129,700 Å) vibrational interval is not responsible. A further possibility arises from a consideration of the molecular symmetry. At least in the crystal the molecular symmetry is described either by C_{2h} or, if the two hydrogen atoms are ignored, by D_{2h}. The departure from D_{4h} symmetry is not great, but is quite definite. The significance of the departure from D_{4h} is hard to determine quantitatively. It is roughly estimated in cm^{-1} from the separation of the four central nitrogen atoms as of the order of a molecular vibration.

"It may be suggested tentatively that the 14,290 and 15,060 cm^{-1} (6999 and 6640 Å) bands are components of a transition which in D_{4h} would be terminated by a degenerate level."

Kuhn (149) has made theoretical suggestions relative to the relationship between the behavior of π-electrons and light absorption of the phthalocyanines.

Eigenmann and Kern (57) have observed phototropy in films of certain copper phthalocyanine compounds dispersed in suitable binders, on cellophane sheets, after a two hour exposure in a Fadeometer. Cellophane sheets were dyed with copper phthalocyanine di-3-sulfonic acid, copper phthalocyanine tetra-3,4′,4″,4‴-sodium sulfonate, copper phthalocyanine tetra-3-sodium sulfonate, copper phthalocyanine tetra-3-sulfonic acid, copper phthalocyanine tetra-4-sulfonic acid, and α-copper phthalocyanine, and were treated with precondensates of numerous resins including bis-hydroxymethyl melamine, bis-hydroxymethyl urea and bis-hydroxymethyl methyltriazone. Phototropy was measured in the spectral region 4000–7500 Å, and was observed to be a function of the degree of dispersion of the copper phthalocyanine compound as well as of the particular compound. Phototropy, therefore, in these systems, may be related to a reversible equilibrium between different physical forms of the phthalocyanine compound. It is definitely a function of the binder. Copper phthalocyanine di-3-sulfonic acid on cellophane is more phototropic in dimethylolmelamine than in dimethylolurea.

CENTRAL METAL ATOM-LIGAND BONDING

The metal phthalocyanines have elicited considerable interest concerning the nature of the chemical bonding between the central metal atom and the great organic ring structure surrounding it. In particular, attention has been given to the bonding of the central metal atom to the surrounding four nitrogen atoms which form the corners of a square.

Two types of bonding are possible: electrovalent and covalent. The electrovalent bond is characterized by its ionic character and relative weakness. For example, atoms forming an ionic bond separate readily in aqueous media into cations and anions. The covalent bond is noted for its non-ionic character and relative strength. In electrovalent bonding, the electropositive atom readily donates an electron to the electronegative atom, and in covalent bonding both electrons involved in a bond are tightly held and are shared in common by the atoms involved. An extension of the covalent bond is the coordinate covalent bond in which both electrons forming the covalent bond are donated by only one of the atoms involved. The common symbol for the electrovalent bond as such is, for example, Na—Cl. The "—" symbol is also used for the covalent bond. Pauling has suggested that the electrovalent bond be represented by + −, such as, for example, Na^+ Cl^-. The coordinate covalent bond is commonly represented by ⟶, such as in H—Ö ⟶ H—Ö.
$$\underset{H}{|} \qquad \underset{H}{|}$$

The nitrogen atom which has five electrons available for bonding, usually in covalent bonding, normally enters into covalent relationship with two or three other atoms such that two of the available electrons are not

$$H$$
$$|$$

involved in bonding, such as in ammonia, H—N: and in the diazo bond,
$$|$$
$$H$$

—N̈=N̈—. In the usual representation of the phthalocyanine molecule, the molecule is written with a resonating double bond structure such that one of the benzene rings contains an o-quinonoid structure as suggested originally by Linstead (51). The bonding of copper to the four inner nitrogen atoms is then represented to be

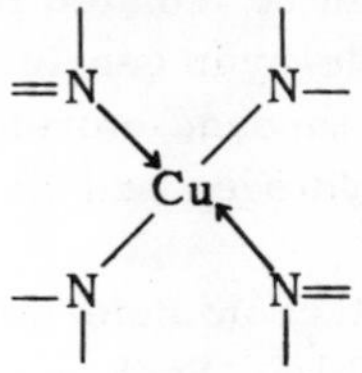

$$
\begin{array}{ccc}
 & | & | \\
=\text{N} & & \text{N}— \\
 & \diagdown \ \diagup & \\
 & \text{Cu} & \\
 & \diagup \ \diagdown & \\
—\text{N} & & \text{N}= \\
 & | & |
\end{array}
$$

That is, the copper atom is bonded to two nitrogen atoms by covalent bonds and to the other two nitrogen atoms by coordinate covalent bonds.

Endermann (66) has represented the phthalocyanine molecule in such a way that there is no quinonoid group:

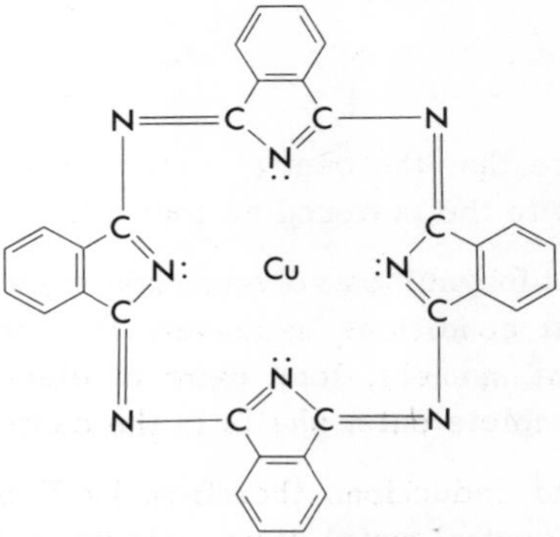

In this instance, each of the four inner nitrogen atoms maintains three covalent and one coordinate covalent bond. The electropositive copper atom is neutralized and bonded, so to speak, by the four pairs of un-shared electrons surrounding it.

Linstead also considered the Endermann representation (51), but did not accept it because "The stability of the copper compound in the vapour phase at 580° would be inconceivable if the metal were held solely by coordinate links." Also, it was argued that if the four inner nitrogen atoms offered coordinate covalent bonds only, then there would be no hydrogen atoms in the center of metal-free phthalocyanine. How-ever, the facts that (1) 2/18 of the total hydrogens are replaced by deuterium under conditions that copper phthalocyanine shows no ex-change (91) and that (2) fission of a molecule of phthalocyanine contain-ing 18 hydrogens requires one atom of oxygen whereas a molecule of phthalocyanine containing 16 hydrogen atoms would require no oxygen demonstrate that phthalocyanine contains two central hydrogen atoms. "Ceric sulphate reacts very rapidly with a suspension of phthalocyanine in dilute sulphuric acid at room temperature. Exactly one atom of oxygen is taken up (for each four C_8 units) and about 90 per cent of the theoretical quantity of phthalimide can be isolated from the product.

"The absence of oxidisable hydrogen in the metallic derivatives and its presence in the parent compound proves that a bivalent metal takes the place of two atoms of hydrogen and is therefore bound by covalencies" (51).

A third possibility is that coordinate covalencies with some central metal atoms may be negligible. Such a condition for copper phthalocyanine would be represented by

$$
\begin{array}{ccc}
\mid & & \mid \\
=N & & N- \\
& \diagdown & \diagup \\
& Cu & \\
& \diagup & \diagdown \\
-N & & N= \\
\mid & & \mid \\
\end{array}
$$

Additional evidence that the central metal atoms are in 4-coordinated position with respect to the surrounding four nitrogen atoms is:

(1) Few metal phthalocyanines solvate upon crystallization.
(2) "The molecular conditions necessary for coordination and chelation are present, namely, lone pairs of electrons on two nitrogen atoms and incomplete outer shells in the central atoms" (8).

X-ray evidence and deductions therefrom by Robertson in 1935 (214) established that the central metal atom—nickel, copper, and platinum—and the four surrounding isoindole nitrogen atoms are coplanar. The question of cis- and trans-configurations did not arise because none of the central atoms investigated would be considered to be in a univalent oxidation state, since only one atom of nickel, copper, and platinum occupy the center of the phthalocyanine molecule.

The distance between successive corners of the square formed by the nitrogen atoms in phthalocyanine was established to be 2.7 Å (215). The diameters of atoms of crystals of copper, nickel, and platinum are 2.6 Å, 2.5 Å, and 2.8 Å respectively (193). These dimensions emphasize the "close fit" of these atoms in the central open portion of the phthalocyanine molecule. In a review of bond lengths, Wells (276) has expressed the opinion that "the apparent abnormal shortness of many bonds cannot be satisfactorily explained in the present state of our knowledge.... A number of bonds are inexplicably short, notably M—F in SiF_4 and PF_3,

M—O in many oxy-ions and molecules, M—C in metallic-carbonyls (and cyanides?), and M—N in phthalocyanines."

Beryllium, manganese, iron, and cobalt phthalocyanines also were shown by X-ray analysis to lie in the center of and in the same plane as the four surrounding nitrogen atoms. The diameters of atoms of crystals of beryllium, manganese, iron, and cobalt are 2.2 Å, 2.6 Å, 2.5 Å, and 2.5 Å respectively (193). Copper, nickel, platinum, beryllium, manganese, iron, and cobalt are all 4-coordinate bivalent metals.

The fact of planar symmetry of these 4-coordinate metals, as well as of other central metal atoms investigated subsequent to Robertson's studies aroused interest in the field of stereochemistry. As Linstead and Robertson pointed out (159) in 1936, it was already known that 4-coordinate bivalent platinum and nickel exhibit planar symmetry. However, that normally tetrahedral copper, cobalt, and beryllium can exhibit planar symmetry as in phthalocyanine was the first demonstration of planar symmetry of these atoms. The stereochemistry of 4-coordinate bivalent iron and manganese apparently had not been studied up to 1936 and the planar symmetry of these metals in phthalocyanines was the first observation of their stereochemical behavior.

"Though the square-planar configuration is fully established for the 4-coordinated complexes of divalent platinum, this stereochemical arrangement is not common with the compounds of other elements" (109).

An index of the stability or type of bonding of the planar configuration of metals within the phthalocyanine molecule is the aptitude of the central metal atom to form hydrates. Of the metals discussed above, "The planar arrangement appears to be very unstable, for the anhydrous beryllium compound readily forms a dihydrate even in moist air. This behavior is not paralleled by other phthalocyanines except the magnesium derivative" (159).

However, steric hindrance in other compounds may prevent these compounds from bonding with the central metal atom in a metal phthalocyanine. Langenbeck, Schubert, and Giesemann (151), interested in the stereochemistry of iron phthalocyanine, have studied steric hindrance in the formation of base complexes of iron phthalocyanine. It was shown that imidazole compounds can complex or coordinate with ferrous phthalocyanine only if there are no spatially impeding substituents on the α-carbon atom adjacent to the tertiary nitrogen of the imidazole molecule.

The stereochemistry of the four nitrogen atoms surrounding the metal atoms is unusual also. "The three valencies from each of these lie in one plane and are inclined to each other at approximately $110°$, $125°$, and $125°$. This is only possible owing to the peculiar 'aromatic' behaviour of the great ring; if the double and single bonds had fixed positions, the third valency of the imino-nitrogen atoms would be inclined to the general plane" (159).

Decomposition of a metal phthalocyanine in acids or water is another index of whether the metal-isoindole nitrogen bond is stable or unstable or, in other words, is covalent or ionic in nature. Phthalocyanine was prepared by Linstead and co-workers by the decomposition of beryllium and magnesium, univalent sodium and potassium, and calcium, barium, manganese, cadmium, tin, and lead phthalocyanines by water or acids (8).

Two additional indices of whether the central metal atom is held to the surrounding nitrogen atoms by covalent or electrovalent bonding are solubility in organic media and tendency to sublime.

Sodium, potassium, calcium, barium, and cadmium phthalocyanines, for example, are insoluble in chloronaphthalene and quinoline and they do not sublime (8).

In addition to bivalent nickel, copper, platinum, beryllium, manganese, iron, and cobalt phthalocyanines, bivalent tin, lead, zinc, and vanadium phthalocyanines and trivalent aluminum phthalocyanine may be considered to be covalent salts (8).

"The fact that the metal in zinc phthalocyanine is held by covalencies, whereas the corresponding cadmium compound is electrovalent, is in keeping with Fajans' principle that in the same periodic group of metals the tendency to form covalent compounds decreases with rise in atomic number. It is also of interest that, where comparison is possible between pairs of metals in the same group, a metal of higher atomic number enters the phthalocyanine complex more reluctantly and leaves it more readily. This is shown by comparing sodium with potassium, beryllium with magnesium, calcium with barium, and tin with lead" (8).

Still another criterion by which to discriminate between covalent and electrovalent bonding is the diameter of the metal atom. In general, metals the diameters of which approximate the dimensions of the square gap between the four isoindole nitrogen atoms form stable or covalent bonds. However, metals the diameters of which are larger or smaller than the central void tend to form electrovalent bonds (8). For example, the diameters of unstable or electrovalent sodium, potassium, calcium, barium, and cadmium atoms in crystals of these elements are respectively (193): 3.7 Å, 4.6 Å, 3.9 Å, 4.3 Å, and 3.0 Å.

Whether univalent atoms such as hydrogen, sodium, potassium, and lithium exist in cis-, trans-isomeric forms is questionable because they are probably not bonded to any one nitrogen atom. "Free phthalocyanine is also centro-symmetrical, and in classical stereochemistry the two hydrogen atoms should be in opposite sides of the great ring (*trans*). It is preferable to assume that the molecules of phthalocyanine exist in a state of resonance and that each hydrogen atom is co-ordinated with two nitrogen atoms. . ." (8).

Many metals which form metal phthalocyanines, it is well known, exist in more than one valence state. However, only few of these metals exhibit more than one valence state in phthalocyanine.

Tin was the first element observed to exhibit variable valency. Stannous phthalocyanine and stannic phthalocyanine were observed by Linstead and his collaborators (8). Stannous phthalocyanine $C_{32}H_{16}N_8Sn$ is normal in the sense that it is bivalent and 4-coordinate in nature. Stannic phthalocyanine $(C_{32}H_{16}N_8)_2Sn$, however, is quadrivalent and is unusual in that it combines with two phthalocyanine rings instead of one. The mixed chloride-phthalocyanine salt dichlorotin phthalocyanine contains tin in quadrivalent 6-coordinate octahedral configuration: two coordinate covalent bonds with two nitrogen atoms, two covalent bonds with two other nitrogen atoms, and two electrovalent bonds with two chlorine atoms.

Trivalent aluminum retains its normal valence in phthalocyanine, forming a mixed halogen-phthalocyanine salt such as chloroaluminum phthalocyanine $C_{32}H_{16}N_8AlCl$, hydroxyaluminum phthalocyanine $C_{32}H_{16}N_8AlOH$, and aluminum phthalocyanine oxide $(C_{32}H_{16}N_8Al)_2O$.

Dilithium and lithium hydrogen phthalocyanines are considered to be electrovalent in nature. Dilithium phthalocyanine is unusual, however, in that it is quite soluble in organic solvents. However, other organic lithium compounds are also easily dissolved in organic solvents (9).

Bivalent mercury phthalocyanine is categorized as a normal electrovalent compound because it is insoluble in organic solvents and it is easily decomposed to phthalocyanine in acidic solution (9).

Silver phthalocyanine may be either bivalent or univalent silver hydrogen phthalocyanine. Analysis has not yet succeeded in clarifying the structure. However, if the silver atom is in the bivalent form, then a rare case of bivalent silver is obtained. The facts that silver phthalocyanine is soluble in organic solvents and sublimes, at reduced pressure, indicate that it is in covalent relation with the inner four nitrogen atoms of phthalocyanine (9).

Bivalent chloropalladium phthalocyanine, $C_{32}H_{16}N_8ClPd$, soluble in organic solvents, may be classed as covalent. The fact that it does not sublime is not unusual of nuclear halogenated phthalocyanines.

Diantimony phthalocyanine, in which the antimony atoms are univalent, which is decomposed by heat, would probably be considered as an electrovalent compound. A univalent assignment to the antimony atom would be unusual. However, if the antimony atoms lie outside the phthalocyanine plane, on either side of the plane, forming the apex of tetrahedra with the four isoindole nitrogen atoms, then a resonating bivalent structure would be formed in which at any time one of the antimony atoms would be in bivalent union with two of the four nitrogen atoms. Or "The compound may have a complex structure such as Pc : Sb · Sb : Sb · Sb : Pc. In this the two terminal antimony atoms are located in the centre of phthalocyanine rings and are joined by a chain of two antimony atoms in the manner shown" (9). Interatomic distances in metal crystals of silver and palladium are 2.9 Å and 2.7 Å respectively. These dimensions are not unexpected for covalent bonding in the central gap of phthalocyanine. Interatomic distances in crystals of lithium and mercury are 3.0 Å. Here the "oversize" of 0.3 Å is a factor that favors electrovalence.

Another criterion for electrovalence or covalence is the rapidity of the reactions in which the metal atoms bound in a molecule are exchanged with free metal atoms such as ions in solution. "If the bonding is predominantly ionic, exchange is expected to occur rapidly, probably too fast to be measured. As the bond type changes towards predominantly covalent linking, the rate of exchange is expected to decrease" (277).

Berezin (21,22) has determined the solubility constants of copper, cobalt, and nickel phthalocyanines in aqueous and acidic solutions. The constant is of the order of 10^{-6}, at 20–70°. Berezin concluded that the slight solubility indicates an extraordinary stability of the metal phthalocyanines studied with the metal-ligand structure exhibiting planar covalent dsp^2-hybrid bonds.

In systems containing radioactive cobalt Co^{60} ion, "No evidence for exchange has been obtained for either the simple complex in pyridine or the water-soluble sulphonic acid derivative in aqueous 0.1 M-sulphuric acid. The bond here may, therefore, be classified as strong covalent."

Another guide for the discrimination between electrovalent and covalent bonding is the magnetic moment of a compound. The smaller the moment, the greater is the tendency to form covalent bonds. In the first study of magnetic moments of phthalocyanines, Klemm and Klemm (135) concluded, on the basis of measured magnetic moments of nickel, cobalt, iron, copper, and zinc phthalocyanines, that the central atoms in these compounds "nicht in salzartiger Form vorliegt."

A recent compilation (26) of magnetic moments of bivalent metal phthalocyanines, Table 2-6, shows that, as a rule, if the theoretical moment for ionic bonding is no less than the actual moment, then the metal probably is covalently bound to the inner four nitrogen atoms.

Chromium phthalocyanines, prepared by Elvidge and Lever (63) in 1956, it was claimed, were the first authenticated instance of these compounds and of octahedral 6-coordinate metal complexes of the phthalocyanine series. Chromium phthalocyanine, $C_{32}H_{16}N_8Cr$, for example, although readily oxidized, is stabilized by coordination with pyridine in "perpendicular conjugation," with two pyridine molecules bound to the

TABLE 2-6. MAGNETIC MOMENTS OF PHTHALOCYANINE COMPLEXES (26).

Metal in Complex	Obs. Mag. Moment in Bohr Magnetons	Theoretical Moment for Ionic Binding
Cu	1.73	1.73
Ni	0	2.83
Co	2.16	3.87
Fe	3.96	4.90
Mn	4.55	5.92

central chromium atom on both sides of the phthalocyanine plane. Manganese phthalocyanine also may be involved in 6-coordinate bonding with oxygen (64). Each manganese atom is bonded to an oxygen atom on either side of the phthalocyanine plane. "Manganese phthalocyanine can combine reversibly with oxygen: it appears to be the first example of a manganese compound that behaves as an oxygen carrier."

Vanadium phthalocyanine may also combine with oxygen atoms about the vanadium atom to form 6-coordinate vanadium complexes (104).

Elvidge and Lever have stated that in pure chromium phthalocyanine (65), the assumed dsp^2 bonding for chromium phthalocyanine places the chromium-ligand linkage in the covalent group.

Recently Elvidge (62) has developed a method for the determination of the valency of a metal in a phthalocyanine molecule by titration with $0.01N$ dichromate which disrupts the great phthalocyanine ring. Phthalocyanines such as iron, chromium, cobalt, copper, nickel, and zinc, for example, were found to have a valence state of two whereas aluminum has a valence state of three, and tin in tin diphthalocyanine has a valency of four.

Watt and Dawes (273) have described the preparation of copper phthalocyanine with the copper atom in the zero oxidation state, as further evidence that the copper-phthalocyanine ligand involves coordinate covalent bonding. Copper (II) phthalocyanine was reduced to copper (O) phthalocyanine with potassium in ammonia. The copper (O) complex is "quite stable in an inert atmosphere even at elevated temperatures" and is "sufficiently stable to permit sublimation at $500°$."

Another index of covalent or electrovalent bonding of the metal-ligand structure is the behavior of the structure in various environments. For example, although ionic copper is destructive to rubber, copper phthalocyanine is commonly mixed with rubber as a colorant (174).

MAGNETIC PROPERTIES

The magnetic properties of compounds give information relating to their structure. In particular, the magnetic properties of the phthalocyanines refer to the bonding of the central metal atom with the surrounding four isoindole nitrogen atoms, which form the corners of a square about the central atom. The advantage of magnetic measurements when used to study chemical bonding relates to the information they give on one atom and its immediate surroundings with no additional information from the rest of the molecule. The magnetic properties of the phthalo-cyanines are of interest also because of the similarity of the central portion of phthalocyanine, chlorophyll, and hemoglobin molecules.

Klemm and Klemm (135) made the first measurements of magnetic properties of phthalocyanines in 1935. They determined the magnetic moments of nickel and copper phthalocyanines to be −0.30 and 1.73 Bohr magnetons per gram at room temperature respectively. Thus, nickel phthalocyanine is diamagnetic in accordance with Pauling's theory for similar compounds with arrangement of the bonds in a plane around the central metal atom and sixteen electrons in the intermediate layer. The copper compound, on the other hand, is paramagnetic because of an unpaired electron in the intermediate layer in which eight electrons are supplied by the four nitrogen atoms and nine electrons are supplied by the copper atom. The molar magnetic susceptibility of copper phthalo-cyanine was calculated to be $\chi = 970 \times 10^{-6}$.

Mellor and Craig (169) also have made magnetic measurements on copper phthalocyanine. They found the moment of copper phthalocyanine to be 1.72 Bohr magnetons, and the molar magnetic susceptibility to be $\chi = 890 \times 10^{-6}$ at room temperature, in agreement with Klemm (135).

Ray and Sen (210) have investigated the magnetic properties of more than thirty copper complexes including copper phthalocyanine, using the Gouy method. The measured molecular moment of copper phthalocyanine at room temperature was 1.68 Bohr magnetons per gram and the magnetic susceptibility was 966×10^{-6} per mole. According to the authors, 4-coordinated copper complexes can be divided into two groups, one with moments between 1.72 and 1.82 Bohr magnetons and the other with moments between 1.90 and 2.20 Bohr magnetons. In compounds in the former group the bond is homopolar of the dsp^2 planar square type and in the latter group the bond is ionic or covalent of the tetrahedral sp^3 or planar sp^2d type, although in both groups the central copper atom con-tains one unpaired electron.

Elvidge and Lever (65) have measured the magnetic moments of chromium phthalocyanine by the Gouy method at 110–295°K. The effec-tive moment at room temperature is 3.49 Bohr magnetons. The theoretical value, assuming inner orbital bonding, is 4.90 Bohr magnetons.

Senff and Klemm (230) have studied the magnetic susceptibility of cobalt, iron, manganese, and vanadyl phthalocyanines. The magnetic moments of these compounds at 20° are respectively: 2.9, 10.5, 15, and 1.6 Bohr magnetons.

Figgis and Nyholm (87) have measured the temperature dependence of the magnetic susceptibility of cobalt phthalocyanine over the range 80–300°K. At 90°K the value is 2.22 Bohr magnetons and at 300°K the value is 2.72 Bohr magnetons.

Lonsdale (162) and Lonsdale and Krishnan (163) have considered the diamagnetic anisotropy of a number of aromatic molecules including phthalocyanine. The diamagnetic anisotropy of phthalocyanine is fifteen times as great as that of benzene (145). By means of the Krishnan anisotropy balance, the principal susceptibilities of single crystals of phthalocyanine were determined. With additional X-ray data available on molecular directional cosines, the principal susceptibilities for individual molecules were calculated. The sizable magnetic anisotropy of phthalocyanines is explained by the authors on the assumption that the π-electrons move only in planar orbits and can precess only in their own plane whereas the valency electrons have spherically symmetrical orbits which are free to precess when any magnetic field is applied.

Selwood (229) has reviewed magnetic susceptibility, diamagnetic anisotropy, and paramagnetism and the methods of measuring magnetic susceptibility. "The largest diamagnetic anisotropies are shown by graphite, and by aromatic compounds, the molecules of which contain benzene, cyanuric, or phthalocyanic rings" (229).

Berthier, Mayot, Pullman, and Pullman (23) have made extended calculations on the determination of diamagnetic anisotropy by the method of molecular orbitals on conjugated hydrocarbons containing at least four aromatic nuclei, including porphyrin and phthalocyanine. The values calculated for phthalocyanine agree well with the experimental results of Lonsdale (162). It is shown there is no simple relation between diamagnetic anisotropy and resonance energy.

Paramagnetic resonance absorption measurements on phthalocyanines have recently been made. Paramagnetic resonance techniques are more sensitive than magnetic susceptibility determinations, and measurements on single crystals are possible.

Lancaster and Gordy (152) have determined paramagnetic resonance properties of more than a hundred salts in powder form, including copper phthalocyanine, in the microwave region, at frequencies from 9000 to 50000 Mc/sec. "The paramagnetic substance is placed in a magnetic field. The resulting Larmor precession of the electron spin gives rise to absorption of radiation. The resonant frequencies are given by the simple formula

$$\nu = g\beta H/h$$

where g is the gyromagnetic ratio, β is the Bohr magneton, h is Planck's constant, and H represents the magnetic field strength" (152).

COPPER PHTHALOCYANINE (152)

Mc/sec	Resonance field strength (gauss)	g factor	Line Width (gauss)	$\dfrac{<(\Delta H)^4> \mathrm{Av}^{\frac{1}{2}}}{<(\Delta H)^2> \mathrm{Av}^{\frac{1}{2}}}$
29650	10410	2.02	250	Asym

Ingram and Bennett have made paramagnetic resonance absorption measurements of crystals of copper, cobalt, iron, manganese, vanadium, and nickel phthalocyanines (125,126). Paramagnetic resonance is also of use to determine nuclear moments and nuclear couplings in paramagnetic substances. Nuclear hyperfine structure in paramagnetic substances was first detected by Penrose, in 1949, in copper sulfate (152). Bennett and Ingram have detected and measured hyperfine structure in copper phthalocyanine (20):

"The diluted crystals show four hyperfine components, due to the $I = 3/2$ of ^{63}Cu and ^{65}Cu. With present sensitivity the linewidth cannot be reduced much below 50 gauss, and so far no fine structure, due to any covalent linkage with the nitrogen atoms, has been observed. The maximum splitting between successive hyperfine components is 210 ± 10 gauss, and the maximum g-value is 2.165 ± 0.004, both occurring along the axis through the copper atom normal to the plane of the four nitrogens. In the plane perpendicular to this axis, that is, the plane of the molecule, the g-value remains isotropic at 2.045 ± 0.003. The hyperfine splitting in this plane collapses to an ill-resolved pattern, as is usual in copper salts, having an approximate value of $B = 30 \pm 10$ gauss. However, there does seem to be a 180° variation of this splitting for rotation in the plane of the molecule. The difference is small but appears to be outside the experimental error, and is being studied more closely, as it may give information which differentiates the individual copper-nitrogen bonds" (20). The g-values obtained by Ingram and Bennett (126) are given in Table 2-7.

TABLE 2-7. G-VALUES AND MAGNETIC MOMENTS OF PHTHALOCYANINES (126).

phthalocyanine	g-values	effective magnetic moment, in Bohr magnetons per gram, from susceptibility measurements (105,152)
Copper	2.045 to 2.165	1.73
Cobalt	1.98 to 2.90	2.16
Ferrous	...	3.96
Chloro-ferric	3.8 ± 0.05	...
Manganese	2.0 ± 0.02	4.55
Vanadyl	2.0 ± 0.02	1.70

Measurements on single crystals were confined to copper and cobalt phthalocyanines. The results indicate that there is likely to be a mixture of both bivalent ionic copper and copper in a sp^2d bond since each has one unpaired electron. The spectrum is similar to that of ionically bound copper but the smaller g-value variation ($g_\perp = 2.045$ to $g_{||} = 2.165$ instead of 2.14 to 2.45) indicates some covalent bonding (126). The paramagnetic absorption spectrum of cobalt indicates little ionic and strong covalent bonding. The results of the polycrystalline spectra of the chloroferric, manganese, and vanadyl phthalocyanines indicate that the chloroferric atom is covalently bound and the manganese and vanadyl atom bonds are mainly ionic in character (126).

Gibson, Ingram, and Schonland (106,219) have determined the paramagnetic resonance of copper phthalocyanine and have discussed in detail the significance of the g-values and hyperfine splitting of copper and cobalt phthalocyanines.

"Although the copper hyperfine structure was observed, no evidence of the nitrogen hyperfine structure appeared. It was supposed that the absence of nitrogen hyperfine structure was due either to poor resolution and the small magnetic moment of nitrogen or to a copper-nitrogen bond of high ionic character" (213). Roberts and Koski determined the electron spin resonance spectrum of 0.001 M solution of copper phthalocyanine in concentrated sulfuric acid at $-137°$. The electron spin resonance measurements were made with a Varian model V 4500 epr spectrometer. The magnetic field was monitored with a Harvey-Wells Model 501 nuclear magnetic resonance gaussmeter. The nitrogen hyperfine structure is observed in this spectrum. Values of $g_{||}$ and $g_\perp$ obtained from the spectrum are 2.180 and 2.037, differing from values of 2.165 and 2.045 previously reported (106).

Griffith (111) has also discussed the theory of electron resonance and magnetic susceptibility measurements in nickel and iron phthalocyanines.

George, Ingram, and Bennett (103) and Gibson and Ingram (105) have used the paramagnetic resonance absorption technique in a study of the oxidation of phthalocyanine, aluminum, copper, and cobalt phthalocyanines.

"The great advantage of electron resonance techniques in such studies as these is that absorption from the unpaired electrons of the intermediate state can be observed independently of the initial and final products, and their coupling to the central metal and other atoms can be calculated from the g-value and width of the absorption line" (105).

In the oxidation of these compounds it is demonstrated that the two-equivalent oxidation of phthalocyanine proceeds by way of a one-equivalent oxidation intermediate with similar properties to the more stable intermediates formed from copper, cobalt, and aluminum phthalocyanines and in which the macrocyclic ring remains intact. All the intermediates are paramagnetic and have g-values close to the free-spin value. In other words, the macrocyclic ring remains intact and the unpaired electron remains in a π-orbital in the ring and not with the central metal atom. These one-equivalent intermediates, in sulfuric acid media in which they are oxidized, are short-lived. However, they are further examples of phthalocyanine *free radicals*, which Cahill and Taube (34) have observed in the oxidation of tetrasulfonated copper phthalocyanine in water by one-electron oxidation agents.

Winslow, Baker, and Yager (279) have compared the magnetic properties of pyrolitic derivatives of polyvinylidene chloride and polyvinylbenzene with phthalocyanine. "For example, the ratio of skeletal (atoms in the ring network, itself) to nonskeletal atoms (H in phthalocyanine) in these structures is nearly five to two, respectively. This suggested examination of pure, metal-free phthalocyanine, in which Eley and simultaneous experiments of our own, found considerable d.c. electrical conduction at elevated temperatures. Surprisingly, highly purified microcrystalline phthalocyanine, which acts diamagnetic (162), showed relatively intense and sharp paramagnetic resonance absorption (125) under the same measurement conditions as the polymers, and further purification increased the effect. Apparently, enough thermal energy is absorbed at room temperature to produce unpaired electrons in crystals of this highly conjugated structure." See Figure 2-9.

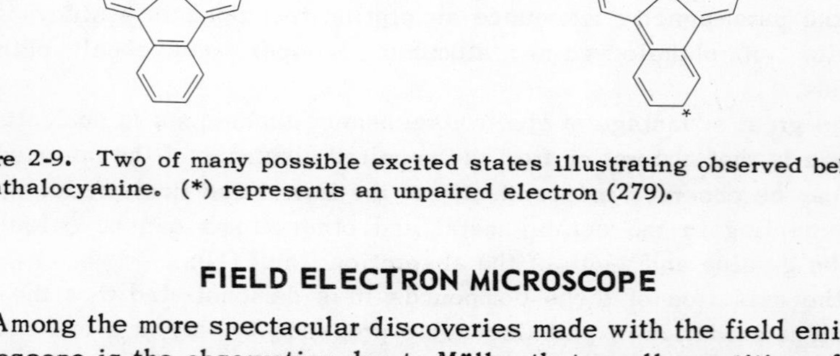

Figure 2-9. Two of many possible excited states illustrating observed behavior of phthalocyanine. (*) represents an unpaired electron (279).

FIELD ELECTRON MICROSCOPE

"Among the more spectacular discoveries made with the field emission microscope is the observation due to Müller that small quantities of such substances as phthalocyanine, hemin or anthracene on the emitter give rise to patterns that can best be explained as 'images' of single molecules" (108).

"Nun konnte aber Müller auch die direkte Abbildung eines adsorbierten Moleküls erhalten, was historisch die erstmalige Sichtbarmachung einzelner Moleküle darstellt" (240).

Single molecules of copper phthalocyanine on a tungsten surface have been photographed by Müller (39,176) using the field electron microscope at an effective magnification of 2.8×10^6. The molecules appear as white discs on a black background. Although the phthalocyanine molecule is roughly 10×10 Å in dimensions, and the normal resolving power of the field electron microscope is 20 Å, the additional magnification is attributed to a spreading of the electron orbits in the observation field because they are emitted from points of high field strength at the edge of the molecule in a direction away from the molecule. "Bright quadruplet patterns, strikingly similar in shape to the actual shape of the phthalocyanine molecule, appeared on the screen. Other bright spots formed doublets and occasionally a doughnut-shaped pattern or some odd-shaped pattern would appear" (171). "Da die Mitten der vier Benzolringe an den Ecken der völlig ebenen Molekel nur etwa 7.7 Å Abstand voneinander haben, konnte man kaum damit rechnen, dass sich das Elektronenbild der Einzelmolekel von dem objektseitig etwa 20 Å grossen Streuscheibchen eines schweren Einzelatoms unterscheiden würde. Überraschenderweise zeigt sich aber die vierteilige Gestalt der Molekel ganz deutlich... Die Erklärung für das unerwartet hohe Auflösungsvermögen von 7.7 Å ergibt sich durch eine schematische Betrachtung des Verlaufes der Elektronenbahnen unmittelbar vor dem Objekt. (Fig. 2-10.) Dabei ist die unterliegende Wolframkathode mit etwa 1000 Å Krümmungsradius als eben anzusehen, auch ihre atomare Oberflächenrauhigkeit braucht nicht berücksichtigt zu werden. Links ist ein hervorstehend adsorbiertes Einzelatom, rechts die Phthalocyaninmolekel, von der Seite gesehen, dargestellt, darüber die Äquipotentialflächen des die Emission bewirkenden Feldes von etwa 4×10^7 v/cm. Die Elektronenbahnen bilden ein schwach divergentes Bündel, dessen auf die Oberfläche zurückprojizierter Rand den objektseitigen Streukreisdurchmesser des Einzelatoms andeutet. Bei der Molekel tritt eine starke Emission nur in den Gebieten hoher Lokalfeldstärken an den Ecken auf. Von dort verlaufen die divergenten Elektronenbündel stark nach aussen durchgebogen, so dass die durch sie erzeugten Streukreise, auf die Objektebene zurückprojiziert, weit ausserhalb der Molekel zu liegen kommen. Auf diese Weise entsteht eine lokale Abbildungsspreizung, die sich sowohl in einer erhöhten Vergrösserung wie in einer gesteigerten Auflösung auswirkt.

"Dieser Effekt wird gegenüber der schematischen Darstellung (in Fig. 2-10) noch wesentlich verstärkt, wenn die Molekel durch zwischenliegende

Atome von der Unterlage etwas abgehoben ist, da dann die Krümmung der Äquipotentialflächen an den Ecken noch ausgeprägter wird.... Während die Vergrösserung der Unterlage in der Wiedergabe etwa 350000 fach ist, erscheinen die Bilder der Molekeln noch maximal um einen Faktor 8 aufgespreizt, so dass ihre Vergrösserung hier 2.8×10^6 beträgt" (176).

Single molecules of phthalocyanine and zinc phthalocyanine (108) are visible also in the field electron microscope (177,275).

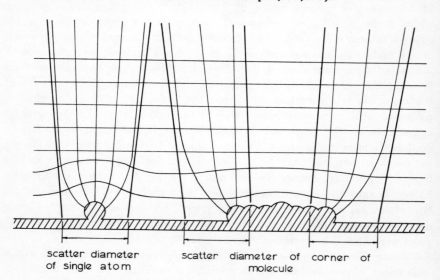

scatter diameter   scatter diameter of corner of
of single atom   molecule

Figure 2-10. Electron flow from the field cathode from around a single atom and a single molecule (176).

In the field electron microscope electrons are emitted from sharply pointed tungsten cathodes about 10^{-5} cm in radius. With an applied voltage of 3000 V, an electric field of forty million v/cm is produced. Electrons emitted perpendicular to the cathode surface with the intermediary of a ring anode pass in straight lines to a fluorescent screen. The velocity distribution of electron flow transverse to the direction of emission has been calculated by Gomer (107). The magnification of the image of the emitting surface is the ratio of the point radius to the screen distance, and is of the order of a million times. See Figure 2-11.

A study of the significance of the doublet and quadruplet images of the phthalocyanines indicates that the image patterns are due to stacks of varying numbers of molecules, viz., from two to six in number, and not to contamination, decomposition products on the tungsten surface, or ion bombardment (171). In this study phthalocyanines were adsorbed on

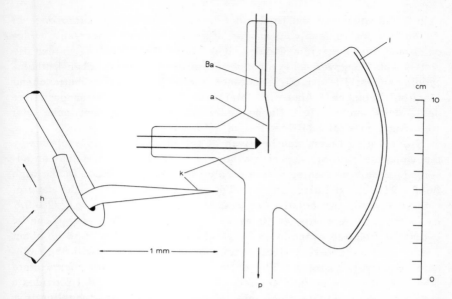

Figure 2-11. Field electron microscope. H: heating current, K: cathode tip, A: anode ring, Ba: barium, L: lightscreen, P: pump (177).

tungsten tips at temperatures as low as $-195°$ and at pressures as low as 10^{-8} mm Hg.

Copper phthalocyanine on tungsten, molybdenum, rhenium, tantalum, iridium, platinum and vanadium shows differences in molecular patterns (170).

The field electron microscope has been used to determine the polarizability of copper phthalocyanine (53). The effective force, K, on an atom or molecule without dipole moment is given by

$$K = \alpha E \frac{dE}{dr}$$

where α is the polarizability, E is the field strength, and dE/dr is the change of the field strength in the direction of the lines of force of the field. The value of α for copper phthalocyanine is:

$$120 \times 10^{-24} \pm 30 \times 10^{-24} \text{ cm}^3$$

Phthalocyanine can be desorbed from the tungsten cathode surface of a field electron microscope by reversing the polarity (178). Phthalocyanine molecules disappear at about 15×10^7 v/cm, presumably as positive ions.

In a discussion of the field electron or field emission microscope in its application to resolving images of phthalocyanines, inorganic molecules and other organic molecules, it is stated that "Zufällig wurden die ersten Abbildungsversuche mit dem vierteiligen symmetrischen Phthalocyanin angestellt und die erhaltenen vierteiligen Bilder überraschend 'ähnlich' befunden. Aber die Untersuchung weiterer Substanzen zeigte bald, dass auch andere flache Moleküle, sogar unsymmetrische oder dreieckige, vierteilige Bilder liefern" (175).

"No detailed theory can be given at the present time to explain why the molecule patterns appear as they do. One can assume that an adsorbed organic molecule, possibly polymerized, is polarized in the high field. With the polarizability as high as 120×10^{-24} cm^3 in the case of phthalocyanine, the polarization contributes approximately $\alpha F^2/2 = 0.6$ ev to the binding energy at 40 mv/cm. The total binding energy can be estimated from the evaporation temperature of 700 to 800°K to be about 2 ev. This indicates an electron transfer from the metal, with the molecule negatively charged. The extra electron is in a low energy state otherwise it would be field emitted. This electron in its orbit provides a negative charge density which interacts with the electrons tunneling from the substrate through the molecule, deflecting them with equal probability, in two or four directions. For example, if the electron is in a π orbital, a doublet would be produced. Two electrons in π orbitals or one electron in a δ orbital would produce a quadruplet. In other words, the adsorbed molecule, inside the barrier, acts as an aperture through which conduction electrons from near the Fermi level may tunnel out more easily, and the specific shape of the pattern is due to the interaction of this electron beam with the charge distribution inside the molecule. This picture would include the fact that a large number of quite dissimilarly structured molecules give only a few types of patterns" (171). In other words, emission of electrons is enhanced from a substrate covered with adsorbed single molecules or stacks of molecules rather than from the substrate alone. The electron beam passing through the molecule may interact with the excess negative charge distribution of the polarized molecule splitting it into two or four equally intense beams (170).

A thorough discussion reviewing the theory and results obtained with the field electron microscope in general has been written recently by Müller (179).

OXIDATION

The remarkable stability of phthalocyanines includes resistance to atmospheric oxidation at temperatures up to 100° or higher depending on the particular metal complex (83). However, in aqueous acid solution strong oxidizing agents oxidize phthalocyanines to phthalic residues, such as phthalimides, while in nonaqueous solution an oxidation product which can be reduced readily to the original pigment is usually formed.

In 1927 de Diesbach and von der Weid (48) in their work on the formation of o-dicyanobenzenes from o-dibromobenzenes with copper cyanide in pyridine, found that hot nitric acid destroyed their complex, presumably copper phthalocyanine, with the formation of a benzene derivative.

In Linstead's initial work, copper phthalocyanine heated with concentrated nitric acid formed an intermediate compound with a strong purple color transitorily (50). The solution was diluted and a small amount of resin was removed by filtration while hot. About 80 per cent of the calculated amount of phthalimide precipitated on cooling and standing for 24 hours.

Oxidation also takes place readily with potassium permanganate or with ceric sulfate. A quantitative method using ceric sulfate for the estimation of copper phthalocyanine, developed by Linstead (51), is described in Appendix II. Linstead found that the oxidation of one molecule of copper phthalocyanine requires one atom of oxygen, which is donated by one molecule of ceric sulfate which is thereby reduced to cerous sulfate.

$$(C_8H_4N_2)_4Cu + 3H_2SO_4 + 7H_2O + O \longrightarrow 4C_8H_5O_2N + CuSO_4 + 2 (NH_4)_2SO_4$$

Copper phthalocyanine is oxidized by aqueous sodium hypochlorite. However, the rate of oxidation of copper phthalocyanine by aqueous sodium hypochlorite is slow because of the negligible solubility of copper phthalocyanine in water (89).

A violet colored precipitate was formed when copper phthalocyanine was dissolved in concentrated sulfuric acid, poured onto ice and treated with cold 3 per cent nitric acid (83). The product was reconverted to copper phthalocyanine when stored as filter cake or when dried. Similar addition products were obtained when dry copper phthalocyanine was treated at room temperature with nitrogen dioxide or nitric oxide. The original pigment was regenerated with the release of nitrogen dioxide when the product was heated. Four to five moles of nitrogen dioxide are readily absorbed by phthalocyanine or by its copper or zinc complexes. The copper phthalocyanine addition product could be dissolved in formic acid to give an intensely violet colored solution. Most phthalocyanines give strongly violet colored solutions when their solution in concentrated sulfuric acid is added to formic acid containing a small amount of nitric acid. The reaction does not take place if the phthalocyanine contains more than four halogen atoms.

In none of the above cases was the oxidation product isolated or analyzed. Pedersen (196–200) finds that copper phthalocyanine can be oxidized by benzoyl peroxide (198) or by other diacyl peroxides, by organic hypochlorites (196), or by chlorine or bromine in methanol (197, 199), to give well defined oxidation products. "More specifically, about 70 per cent of the benzoyl peroxide (initial concentration: 0.14 molar) reacts with an excess of finely divided copper phthalocyanine in U.S.P. chloroform (0.57 per cent by weight of alcohol) at 30° within the first 2 hr. This rate is about 1800 times greater than the rate of spontaneous decomposition of the peroxide in chloroform at the same temperature as determined by Cass. No carbon dioxide is evolved and the rate is not affected by the presence or absence of molecular oxygen. The rate, however, is about 60 per cent lower in pure chloroform and the oxidation product, instead of yielding a bright pigment on reduction as in the case of the product obtained in chloroform containing alcohol, gives a dull, dark blue precipitate" (200).

The product formed with benzoyl peroxide is shown in Figure 2-12 and that formed from the hypochlorite or from the action of chlorine or bromine in methanol is shown in Figure 2-13.

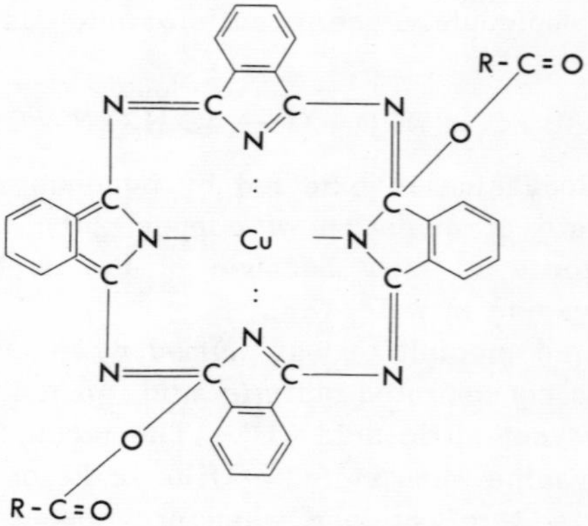

Figure 2-12. Oxidation product of copper phthalocyanine with acyl peroxide (198).

The formation of these structures is supported by infrared spectra and by other data (200). These reversible oxidation products are yellowish or reddish solids of low tinctorial value in contrast to phthalocyanines which are blue or green solids of high tinctorial power.

Pedersen also observed that: "Metal-free phthalocyanine and phthalocyanines of magnesium, zinc, iron, cobalt, and nickel are also reversibly

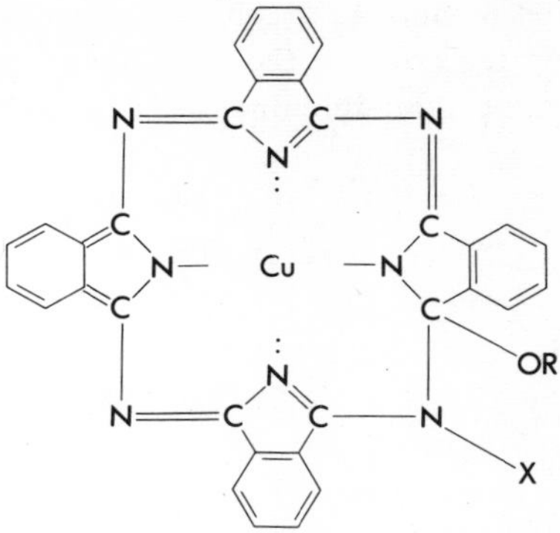

X = halogen atom

Figure 2-13. Oxidation product of copper
phthalocyanine with organic hypochlorite,
or with halogen and alcohol (196,197,199).

oxidized but perchlorinated copper phthalocyanine is resistant to oxidation.

"Phthalocyanines react more readily in the alpha-form than in the beta-form of crystals.

"The relative order of reactivity of the peroxides, estimated by observing the start of the formation of the oxidation products as judged by sight and confirmed by spot-testing with a reducing agent, is: bis(2,4-dichlorobenzoyl) peroxide > bis(4-chlorobenzoyl) peroxide > benzoyl peroxide > lauroyl peroxide > tertiary-butyl hydroperoxide. Perbenzoic acid also oxidizes phthalocyanines. Neither anhydrous nor aqueous hydrogen peroxide gave any measurable quantity of the oxidation product.

"Ether, acetone and 2-alkoxyethanols are satisfactory solvents for use with peroxides. No advantage is gained by deviating from room temperature.

"The oxidation products are stable if protected from reducing agents and hydrolytic conditions. They are brownish solids which do not melt but are converted into phthalocyanines between 140–220°. Any reducing agent will regenerate the phthalocyanines which are always obtained in the alpha-form of crystals."

Baumann and his colleagues (14,16,18) have described products related to those discussed above. They are made by treating a mole of copper or cobalt phthalocyanine with a large excess of an oxidizing agent, viz., 11 moles of bromine in methanol or 15 moles of concentrated nitric acid in nitrobenzene. The final products are soluble in organic solvents and are easily reduced to the starting material. This makes it possible to use them as dyestuffs, impregnating the fibers at 50° with a solution of the oxidation product in alcohol, formamide, or water and then reducing and developing the color in the cloth by steaming. The products formed are derivatives of isoindolenine as illustrated in Figures 2-14 and 2-15.

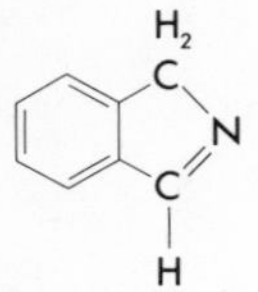

Figure 2-14. isoindolenine

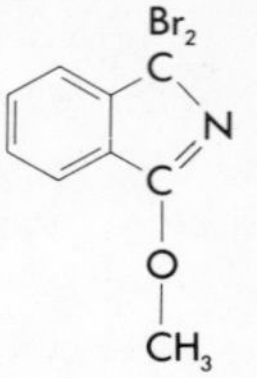

Figure 2-15. 1-methoxy-3-dibromoisoindolenine

The above isoindolenine derivatives can also be produced from phthalonitrile. These and other derivatives (13,15,17,222–226,272) can function as dyes; they are treated in Chapter 5. Other methods for making so-called "phthalocyanine precursors" are also given in Chapter 5.

Linstead found that iron phthalocyanine is decomposed by hot nitric acid or aqua regia forming phthalimide and an iron salt (157).

Brown oxidation products of iron phthalocyanine were observed when the latter was brought in contact with hydrogen peroxide or α-tetralin peroxide (42).

Linstead and Weiss (160) show by analogy that the oxidation of phthalocyanine suspended in sulfuric acid proceeds in steps. "A purple or brown intermediate is first formed. This subsequently undergoes hydrolysis, in the case of phthalocyanine, or further oxidation, in the case of pigments containing methin links. The initial reaction product involves addition of oxygen, probably in the form of hydroxyl groups, and not dehydrogenation...."

Their suggested reaction from the phthalocyanine to the purple intermediate is:

$$PcH_2 + O + H_2O \rightleftharpoons PcH_2(OH)_2$$

(where PcH_2 = phthalocyanine).

The oxidation of magnesium phthalocyanine by benzoyl peroxide gives a colorless product which can be reduced again to the colored pigment with ascorbic acid (139). Magnesium phthalocyanine can also be photochemically oxidized by atmospheric oxygen to a colorless product (138).

Cahill and Taube (34) found that "Oxidation of tetrasulfonated copper phthalocyanine in water by certain agents produced a fugitive red intermediate which has a lifetime of several seconds. One-electron oxidizing agents of sufficient potential produce the intermediate most efficiently.

A similar stage is observed in the oxidation of the Co(II), Fe(III), Al(III) and Zn(II) complexes but not of the unmetallated sulfonated phthalocyanine. In 85 per cent H_3PO_4, the half-life of the intermediate derived from tetrasulfonated copper phthalocyanine is ca. 15 min. at 25°. The spectrum of the red intermediate differs markedly from that of the parent copper complex. It has been shown that a net one-electron change produces the intermediate quantitatively. The red substance disproportionates, regenerating in part the original compound, or if excess oxidizing agent is present, undergoes net oxidation by a further one-electron change. The kinetics of disappearance of the red intermediate in phosphoric acid solvents has been studied, and interpreted recognizing the colloidal nature of the system."

Cahill and Taube also showed that the couple tetrasulfonated copper phthalocyanine TSCP-TSCP$^+$ provides a path for the catalytic decomposition of hydrogen peroxide. The general similarity of the phthalocyanine and porphyrin rings raises the question of whether similar one-electron oxidation processes may not be important in the functioning of porphyrin complexes.

One-electron oxidations of phthalocyanine have been investigated by paramagnetic resonance (103). Aluminum, cobalt, and copper tetrasulfonated phthalocyanines gave more stable intermediates than metal-free tetrasulfonated phthalocyanine, and therefore well defined signals. George (102) has compared the effect of strong oxidizing agents on tetrasulfonated copper phthalocyanine, hemin, and peroxides.

REDUCTION

In terms of the definition of reduction as the addition of electrons to an atom or to a group of atoms, reduction in the phthalocyanine molecule can take place at the central metal atom or at the 16 peripheral carbon atoms of the four phenylene rings. The extent of reduction in the center of the molecule is limited by the number of valency states attainable by a given metal atom and by the phthalocyanine ligand.

The highest valency state that has been attained at the center of the phthalocyanine molecule is four, illustrated by dichlorostannic phthalocyanine, which can be reduced to a valency of two by reduction with hydrogen gas in boiling quinoline (8), and by stannic (IV) phthalocyanine, which is formed by boiling dichlorotin phthalocyanine with disodium phthalocyanine in chloronaphthalene (8). The four valencies of tin in stannic phthalocyanine are satisfied by two parallel molecules of phthalocyanine positioned on each side of the tin atom, each phthalocyanine molecule satisfying two of the four valencies of the tin atom.

Complete reduction of the central metal atom to a valency of zero has been attained by Watt and Dawes in the case of copper phthalocyanine

(273). "The reduction of copper (II) phthalocyanine with potassium in liquid ammonia has been shown to yield an anionic phthalocyanine complex of copper in the zero oxidation state. Evidence is presented for the possible intermediation of copper (I) phthalocyanine and its disproportionation."

Thus both lower limit of zero oxidation state and the probable upper limit of the quadrivalent oxidation state have been demonstrated for the central metal atom-phthalocyanine ligand system.

The simplest reduction of the peripheral carbon atoms of the phthalocyanines has been accomplished by the addition of a hydrogen atom at each of the available 16 carbon atom sites, by synthesis from 3,4,5,6-tetrahydrophthalonitrile giving hexadecahydrophthalocyanine (85):

The effect of this reduction is the addition of 16 electrons to the phthalocyanine molecule.

Therefore, the minimum and maximum limits of reduction of the peripheral carbon atoms have been accomplished. It would appear possible to make phthalocyanine compounds of the intermediate stages of reduction as well. In the reduction of the central metal atom and of the peripheral carbon atoms discussed above, the phthalocyanine molecule retains its identity and preserves its color and other pigmentary properties.

Vatting procedures, on the other hand, reduce phthalocyanine molecules to colorless intermediates or products of undesired color which may be reoxidized to the original phthalocyanines (46). This transient reduction to unstable or stable intermediates may involve hydrogenation at the α- and β-carbon atoms of the pyrrole rings of the phthalocyanine molecule. Also, not all phthalocyanines can be vatted, for example, copper and nickel phthalocyanines. Vatting-reduction of phthalocyanines was recognized as early as 1928 when Dandridge, Drescher, and Thomas wrote (47): "The dyestuff [iron phthalocyanine] may be purified by vatting or by fractional precipitation from sulphuric acid. It forms a practically colourless vat."

Cobalt phthalocyanine can be reduced by a vatting procedure while copper phthalocyanine decomposes under the same conditions (25).

Certain metal phthalocyanines or their sulfonated derivatives form highly colored reduction products when subjected to a treatment with hydrosulfite in dilute alkali. These include the complexes of iron, titanium, chromium, tin and molybdenum. The colored reduction products are fugitive to light. Attempts to determine attachment of an OH group on the central metal atom by alkylation or by esterification have been unsuccessful (83).

The studies of phthalocyanine vatting procedures has led to the use of cobalt phthalocyanine as a vat dyestuff, as it is the complex best suited for this purpose in both application properties and shade. For further discussion of vat dyestuffs see Chapter 5.

Shigemitsu has shown that copper chlorophthalocyanines are reduced to vat compounds by the addition compound of sodium hydrosulfite and formalin. This is indicated by a darkening of the color of the phthalocyanine. It is interesting that although copper phthalocyanine decomposes upon vatting, its chlorine derivatives can be vatted. The maximum reduction takes place with the copper chlorophthalocyanine containing 13 atoms of chlorine. The stability to this agent increases again with copper chlorophthalocyanines containing more than 13 chlorine atoms and the hexadecachloro derivative is again stable. The darkening is caused by a change in composition and not in particle size (232). A later paper by Shigemitsu (233) reports the reduction of copper hexadecachlorophthalocyanine by the same agent. "Thus, the chlorination of copper phthalocyanine seems to facilitate hydrogenation at $C=C$ and $C=N$ bonds of phthalocyanine, and the darkening of color occurs as is observed in the reduced vat dyes." The changes are shown by reflectance curves, X-ray diffraction curves, and infrared spectra.

CATALYSTS

The first mention of phthalocyanines as catalysts is the work of Calvin, Cockbain, and Polanyi (36) who studied the effect of the presence of crystals of phthalocyanine and copper phthalocyanine on the activation of molecular hydrogen. Their initial results indicated that crystals of phthalocyanine and copper phthalocyanine show atomic interchange with molecular hydrogen, catalyze atomic interchange between molecular hydrogen and water vapor, and catalyze formation of water from hydrogen and oxygen although many crystals of phthalocyanine were inactive (201). The activation energy for the interchange between molecular hydrogen and water vapor was computed to be 6000 cal/mole and the activation energy for the formation of water from hydrogen and oxygen was calculated to be 18,000 cal/mole. It was also observed by Calvin, Eley, and Polanyi that para-hydrogen is converted into normal hydrogen by crystals of phthalocyanine and copper phthalocyanine (37). The activation energy of the conversion with phthalocyanine was 5700 cal/mole, and with copper phthalocyanine was 5000 cal/mole. However, not all preparations of phthalocyanine and copper phthalocyanine crystals exhibited catalytic activity (200). The same phthalocyanines yielded no activity in homogeneous solution presumably because of blocking of the active centers by the solvent molecules (35).

Eley studied the heterogeneous conversion of para-hydrogen on hemin, hemetoporphyrin, hematin, phthalocyanine, and copper phthalocyanine (58). The author determined that the conversion is catalyzed by paramagnetic but not by diamagnetic solids.

Rittenberg and Krasna (212) state that solutions of copper phthalocyanine tetrasulfonic acid, like hydrogenase, catalyze the exchange reaction between hydrogen and deuterium oxide. "Clearly the hydrogen molecule cannot complex with the copper by displacing one of the nitrogen atoms of the tetrapyrrole; it must interact with an excited state of the 18 member conjugated system of the tetra-azo-pyrrole. In this respect it reminds one of cytochrome c in which the iron uses all its six coördination bonds to bind itself to the porphyrin and the specific protein. The function of the iron in hydrogenase or the cytochromes and of the copper in the phthalocyanine may be to supply suitable electron levels in a manner similar to that of impurities in semi-conductors."

Cook studied several reactions of biochemical interest with iron phthalocyanine, chloroiron phthalocyanine, and chromium phthalocyanine, in particular, and investigated catalytic properties of manganese, molybdenum, hydroxyaluminum, platinum, cerium, diiodotin, copper 4-chloro, mercury, magnesium, chloroaluminum, beryllium, nickel, lead, copper 4-nitro, and copper phthalocyanines (42–45). It was found that iron phthalocyanine catalyzes the decomposition of hydrogen peroxide, in 75 per cent pyridine solution, and in aqueous suspensions of the pigments deposited on wood charcoal, barium sulfate, and silica gel. The result was of note because of the structural relationship between phthalocyanines on the one hand and porphyrins and chlorophylls on the other hand. The catalytic properties of iron porphyrins such as the enzyme catalase are well-known. Magnesium, beryllium, zinc, chloroaluminum, and metal-free phthalocyanines did not catalyze the decomposition of hydrogen peroxide under similar conditions. Therefore the origin of the catalytic activity stems from the central metal atom, iron, and not from the surrounding organic skeleton, unlike the hydrogen-activating properties of the phthalocyanine ring (36). The similar activities of the iron porphyrins and bivalent and trivalent iron phthalocyanine was the first indication that it is the association of the iron atom with the four pyrrole nitrogen atoms that leads to catalytic activity. Results similar to the decomposition of hydrogen peroxide were observed in the oxidation of hydrogen iodide, unsaturated compounds such as oleic acid, polyphenols, aromatic chromogens, and benzaldehyde in the presence of free iron phthalocyanine and iron phthalocyanine deposited on inorganic carriers. Rate of reaction was largely independent of the amount of catalyst employed. Phthalocyanines enumerated above did not exhibit any significant catalytic activity in the oxidation of benzaldehyde (43). Organic peroxides are also readily decomposed in the presence of iron phthalocyanine. The peroxide of tetralin was readily decomposed by iron phthalocyanine and to a less extent by hemin at room temperature (44). It is claimed that numerous other metal phthalocyanine compounds were examined but that they did not show catalytic activity except chromium and cobalt phthalocyanines which showed only slight activity. Tetralin peroxide itself does not decompose at temperatures at least up to $100°$. Iron phthalocyanine also decomposes the peroxide Δ^2-octalin. α-Pinene and cyclohexene are oxidized with air or oxygen in the presence of iron phthalocyanine. Compounds containing a reactive methylene group are oxidizable by oxygen in the presence of iron phthalocyanine, e.g., diphenylmethane is oxidized to benzophenone (44).

Also in common with hemin, iron phthalocyanine catalyzes the chemiluminescent oxidation of luminol, 5-aminophthalaz-1 : 4-dione. The luminescence, red in color, is best observed in relatively high boiling hydrocarbons in the presence of a trace amount of catalyst. Near the boiling point the liquid "glows with a bright crimson color clearly visible in daylight; the luminescence persists for 30 secs. or more, the time depending upon the amounts of pigment and peroxide originally present" (45). The luminescence effect was confirmed by Tamamushi and Tohmatsu (251) using chloroiron phthalocyanine as catalyst. There was only a feeble luminescence when magnesium or copper phthalocyanine was used in lieu of the iron pigment. Chloroiron phthalocyanine also catalyzes the air drying of linseed oil and methyl linoleate. At $50°$ in air, linseed oil mixed with catalyst (0.05 gm per 1 cm^3 oil) dried in 3 hours with cobalt-lead-naphthenate, in 7 hours with chloroiron phthalocyanine, and in 25 hours with copper or magnesium phthalocyanine. Similar results were obtained with the oxidation of methyl linoleate.

George (101) has made a detailed kinetic study of the decomposition of hydrogen peroxide for reaction mixtures of hydrogen peroxide and the following catalysts: hemin, ferrous phthalocyanine, ferrous ion (ferrous ammonium sulfate) and ferric ion (ferric sulfate), and horse liver catalase. The course of the reaction was determined by measurement of the rate of oxygen evolution. Ferrous iron and catalase bring about a reaction in which there is an initial rapid evolution of oxygen followed by a much slower decomposition. Hemin, ferrous phthalocyanine, and ferric ion do not give an initial rapid evolution but only the steady rate.

Ferrous phthalocyaninediazonium sulfate, coupled with ovalbumin has been tested for its catalase-like action (56). It is claimed that the iron phthalocyanine azoprotein has a considerable catalase activity. Copper phthalocyanine azoprotein, on the other hand, exhibits no catalase activity.

Iron phthalocyanine also catalyzes the oxidation of d-limonene (227).

Paquot, following upon the initial work of Cook, and co-workers have studied the oxidizing properties of the phthalocyanines on a number of organic compounds (49,185–192). Cobalt and nickel phthalocyanines, for example, as well as iron phthalocyanine catalyze oxidation of α-pinene. α-Pinene oxidized with 2.5–5 per cent iron, cobalt, and nickel phthalocyanines at 50–100° for 8–40 hours yields 10–25 per cent verbenone, 1–3 per cent pinacol hydrate, and 40–70 per cent α-pinene (185). Oxidation of cyclohexene with 0.4 per cent nickel phthalocyanine for 60 hours at 65° yields 17 per cent 3-cyclohexen-1-one, 6 per cent 3-cyclohexen-1-ol, 2 per cent 1,3-cyclohexadiene, 2 per cent epoxy-cyclohexane, and 4 per cent 1,2-cyclohexanediol (185). In the oxidation of cyclohexane and α-pinene, it is the α-carbon of the double bond that is mainly attacked and the α-ethylenic ketone is the principal product. The metallic phthalocyanines thus appear to be interesting catalysts for the oxidation by oxygen of ethylenic hydrocarbons into α-ethylenic ketones (185). Nickel phthalocyanine also catalyzes the oxidation of 1-ethyl-1-cyclohexene giving 29 per cent 1-ethyl-1-cyclohexene, 25 per cent 1-ethyl-cyclohex-1-en-6-one, 15 per cent 1-ethyl-1,2-epoxycyclohexane, and 8 per cent 1-ethylcyclohex-1-en-6-ol. The catalytic effect of nickel phthalocyanine is to hasten the oxidation and to direct it about 60 per cent to the carbon atom in the α-position to the double bond, 15 per cent to the —C≡C— bond itself and 4 per cent to break the side chain (186). The oxidation of benzene hydrocarbons is also accelerated by nickel phthalocyanine (187). Ethylbenzene oxidized with 0.75 per cent nickel phthalocyanine at 125° for 240 hours yields 18 per cent acetophenone, 2 per cent benzoic acid, and 70 per cent unoxidized ethylbenzene. The oxidation of toluene, diphenyl methane, benzyl alcohol, and phenylethyl alcohol are also affected by the presence of nickel phthalocyanine. The nature and distribution of the reaction products indicate that the activation due to the benzene nucleus is analogous to that produced by ethylene hydrocarbons (187).

Nickel phthalocyanine also catalyzes the autoxidation of saturated ketones such as 2-octanone, 4-heptanone, and cyclohexanone at 120–130°, yielding α-diketones, and aldehyde and acid scission products (188). 4-Heptanone on oxidation, for example, for 75 hours at 120° with 0.8 per cent nickel phthalocyanine gives 47 per cent 4-heptanone, 4 per cent hepta-3,4-dione, 2 per cent butyraldehyde, 23 per cent butyric acid, and 19 per cent propionic acid (188). Oxidation of saturated fatty acid esters is also catalyzed by nickel phthalocyanine. In air oxidation of

ethyl palmitate and ethyl caprate at 120° using 1 per cent nickel phthalocyanine as catalyst, from 40 to 50 per cent of the initial ester is recovered unchanged, 0.5 per cent is lost as carbon dioxide, and 5 per cent
is entrained in the air as lower acids and ketones. The saponification
and acid numbers rise as the oxidation progresses, indicating the presence of monoesters of di-acids and lactonic acids (49). Ethyl caprate,
ethyl palmitate, and palmitic acid were oxidized 200–300 hours at 100°
with a current of air using 1 per cent nickel phthalocyanine as catalyst
(189). The oxidation products indicate that the principal reaction route
is β-oxidation with acid scission yielding oxalic acid and lower acids
and with ketonic scission or decarboxylation. The same results apply to
the oxidation of long-chain saturated fatty acids (190–192). Oxidation
by molecular oxygen of the homologue series of saturated acids and their
esters from caproic acid to stearic acid at 100° with 1 per cent nickel
phthalocyanine give as principal oxidation products oxalic acid and
lower fatty acids containing an even number of carbon atoms. Lower
acids oxidize more difficultly than acids of higher molecular weight.
Small amounts of methyl ketones are found in the oxidation products. It
is indicated that main oxidation is β-oxidation accompanied by a ketonic
scission (190–191). Nickel phthalocyanine appears to be a better catalyst
than alkali metals in the form of sodium and potassium soaps of the
acids used. Nickel phthalocyanine appears to favor the formation of
acids; the alkali metal soaps appear to favor the formation of ketones
and lactones (190,191). The oxidation of methyl oleate in air is catalyzed not only by nickel phthalocyanine but also by magnesium and iron
phthalocyanines (192).

The aerobic oxidation of unsaturated fatty acids catalyzed by iron and
cobalt phthalocyanines has been reported by Uri (262). Under the conditions investigated, the ratio of the catalyzed to the uncatalyzed rate was
10:1. The kinetic expression for the aerobic oxidation with these cata-
lysts in organic solvents was considered to be $\dfrac{d[\text{ROOH}]}{dt} = k[\text{RH}]$ [cata-
lyst].

Phthalocyanines also are catalysts for the autoxidation of cumene,
methylbenzene, p-xylene, ethylbenzene, diphenylmethane and p-cymene
(121). The autoxidation of cumene, with manganese, iron, cobalt, nickel,
copper, zinc, and magnesium phthalocyanines yields cumene hydroperoxide, 2-phenyl-2-propanol, and acetophenone. The ratios of the amounts
of the three products depend on the particular phthalocyanine used. Zinc
and magnesium phthalocyanines are the least effective catalysts.

Kropf has made an extensive study of the kinetics and reaction mechanism of the autoxidation of cumene, with copper, cobalt, and nickel

phthalocyanines (146). The kinetics of the autoxidations of m-diisopropyl benzene, phenylcyclopentane, and phenyl cyclohexane in the presence of copper phthalocyanine have also been studied. The decomposition of cumene hydroperoxide by cobalt phthalocyanine in nonane and by copper phthalocyanine in cumene has been studied also. In the cumene and benzene compound studies, free radical reaction mechanisms were proposed.

Krasnovskiĭ and Brin studied the catalytic action of phthalocyanine, and of magnesium and copper phthalocyanines in the oxidation of aqueous solutions of ascorbic acid (142). Reactions were carried out both in darkness and in the light of a 200-w incandescent lamp placed 5 cm from the bottom of the flat container. Reactions were carried out at 20, 30, and 40° and the container was oscillated 100 times/min through an arc amplitude of 7 cm. Into the side arm of the container was introduced 0.75 cc 1 per cent solution ascorbic acid and into the middle portion 3 cc thrice-distilled water and 30 mg powdered catalyst. The amount of oxygen absorbed versus time was measured by the manometric technique of Warburg and Bancroft. Reactions carried out in the dark conformed satisfactorily to the Arrhenius equation. Illumination greatly accelerated the process. In the presence of light, catalytic and photosensitizing effects were superimposed. Except for copper phthalocyanine, the reaction in light obeys the Arrhenius equation. With copper phthalocyanine, the rapid photoprocess may be limited by a secondary chemical reaction, the value of the effective energy of activation being lower than that when the reaction is carried out in darkness.

Schenck and Musche confirmed that ascorbic acid is oxidized by visible light more readily in the presence than in the absence of copper phthalocyanine (228).

Manganese (II) phthalocyanine is an oxygen carrier (64). It may be the first example of a manganese compound to behave as an oxygen carrier. Manganese phthalocyanine is an effective catalyst for the air oxidation of benzaldehyde and aniline. In pyridine manganese phthalocyanine absorbs oxygen reversibly. The structure PcMnO-pyridine (Pc = phthalocyanine) for the isolated product is supported by polarographic evidence.

Copper, magnesium, zinc, iron, cobalt, and nickel phthalocyanines are also oxidized, reversibly, in organic solvents (200). Irreversible oxidation of phthalocyanine catalysts was observed during the course of initial work on phthalocyanines as oxidation catalysts (42).

In addition to acting as catalysts in activation of hydrogen, oxidation, and decomposition of peroxides, phthalocyanines act as polymerization catalysts. Iron phthalocyanine accelerates the isomerization of dimethyl maleate to dimethyl fumarate (250). Copper and magnesium phthalocyanines are virtually ineffective.

Methyl methacrylate is polymerized in the presence of magnesium and zinc phthalocyanines while illuminated with a light of 600 mμ (146).

SEMICONDUCTORS

Eley and Vartanyan were the first to observe semiconductivity in phthalocyanines (59,265). "Probably the earliest studies of organic substances as intrinsic semiconductors were started in 1948 when Eley and Vartanyan discovered the unusual temperature dependence of the resistivities of the phthalocyanines and their metal derivatives" (31). Crystals of phthalocyanine and copper phthalocyanine were examined in a Hysil conductivity cell between platinum electrodes of area 2 cm^2 spaced 2 mm apart (59). As packed the cell had a bulk density of about 0.2. Both materials were found to be semiconductors over the range 300–500° and the curves were reversible, obeying the exponential expression

$$\sigma = \sigma_0 \exp\left(-E/RT\right)$$

where σ is the specific conductivity at temperature T, in ohm^{-1} cm^{-1}, σ_0 is the specific conductivity at infinite temperature, E is an "activation energy," and R is the gas constant (59). Powders of phthalocyanine, copper phthalocyanine, magnesium phthalocyanine, and evaporated aqueous solutions of sulfonated phthalocyanine were examined between gold electrodes spaced 0.5 mm from each other. The electrodes were 10 mm long. Film thickness of the pigments rubbed onto quartz plates carrying the gold electrodes was 10–28μ (265). The range of temperature was –80 to +200°. Phthalocyanines were also examined deposited from alcoholic solutions with a film thickness of 0.1–1.0μ on quartz plates carrying gold or platinum electrodes 1 mm apart (263). The currents were measured with a Hartmann and Braun mirror galvanometer and the applied voltages were measured with a class 0.5 voltmeter. For measurements in vacuum, the specific conductivity of phthalocyanine, copper phthalocyanine, and sulfonated phthalocyanine is about 5×10^{-8} ohm^{-1} cm^{-1} (265). The specific conductivity of magnesium phthalocyanine is about 10^{-6} ohm^{-1} cm^{-1}. Visible and ultraviolet light cause no increase in the conductivity. Conditioning the compounds in a hydrogen atmosphere at 400° and in vacuum at 100° affects the conductivity (59,265). Heating magnesium phthalocyanine in oxygen causes a 100 fold increase in conductivity. Thus impurities may have a rôle in the semiconductivity of phthalocyanines. At 20° and 100° the phthalocyanines obey Ohm's Law up to 3000 volts/cm (265).

The semiconductivity of zinc phthalocyanine has also been measured (267). The conductivity of thin films of zinc phthalocyanine is 10^{-12}–10^{-13} ohm^{-1} cm^{-1} and the activation energy is 1.7–1.8 ev.

Using the exponential equation in the form $\sigma = \sigma_0 \exp\left(-E/RT\right)$, values of E for phthalocyanine and copper phthalocyanine are about 29 kcal/mole. In the uncompressed state E is influenced by crystal contacts. Under compression, a lower value of E is obtained which may be characteristic of the crystals themselves (61). Using the equation in the form $\sigma = \sigma_0$ $\exp\left(-\dfrac{U}{2kT}\right)$, where U is considered to be the energy of dissociation of an electron, the average values of U for phthalocyanine, copper, zinc, magnesium, and sulfonated phthalocyanines are 0.87, 1.2, 0.79, 0.78, and 0.9 ev respectively (264,265). The "energy of activation" and the "energy of dissociation" are to be expected to be related in large measure to the mobile π-electrons in the conjugated double bonds of the phthalocyanine ring.

Kleitman and Goldsmith have measured the electrical conductivity of films and crystals of phthalocyanine and of films and a single crystal of copper phthalocyanine (133,134). The electric field was applied along the crystal b-axis or growth axis with behavior agreeing with Ohm's Law, in fields of 2000 v/cm. "The temperature behavior indicated that the relation $\sigma = \sigma_0 \exp(-E/RT)$ applied between room temperature and 420°C. obtains. The results were reproducible and independent of applied field and helium pressure... For different samples the E-values ranged between 0.7 and 1.0 ev, and could be altered in a sample by heating to temperatures greater than 420°. Defects in the crystal structure or impurity effects might account for this behavior. Films were found sensitive to atmospheric effects and temperature behavior of the conductivity was not reproducible.... Similar behavior was observed with copper phthalocyanine films and crystals" (134).

The semiconductivity of the phthalocyanines is considered to be intrinsic (60,166) although variations or results indicate that impurities, anisotropic strains, crystal imperfections, contacts, and surface conditions may influence the values observed (133). Eley and Parfitt have measured the semiconductivity of phthalocyanine with a.c. voltage to short out the contact resistances (60). With intrinsic semiconductivity, the current carriers are mobile π-electrons. The energy gap which these electrons must traverse in the conduction of current is related to the energy required to make an electron pass from the highest filled to the lowest filled energy level of the molecule (60).

Fielding and Gutman (86) have studied the electrical conductivity of single crystals of phthalocyanine, copper, nickel, and cobalt phthalocyanines at 50–390°. The average values of the activation energies are 1.71 ev for phthalocyanine, 1.60 ev for cobalt and nickel phthalocyanines, and 1.64 ev for copper phthalocyanine. Many, Harnik, and Gerlich list 1.20 ev for phthalocyanine and 1.30 ev for copper phthalocyanine (166). No significant difference in the activation energy of phthalocyanine is observed between directions parallel and perpendicular to the face of the crystal. The authors believe these compounds are intrinsic semiconductors and the introduction of a metal atom into the molecule produces little change in the activation energy of conduction. Ohm's Law is obeyed by these compounds at fields up to 1000 v/cm (86). Felmayer and Wolf (82) give values for the electrical resistance of powders of platinum phthalocyanine, highly chlorinated copper phthalocyanine, and polymers of copper phthalocyanine in a nitrogen atmosphere. These compounds are semiconductive. Highly chlorinated copper phthalocyanine and platinum phthalocyanine have approximately the same conductivity as copper phthalocyanine whereas the phthalocyanine polymers have a higher conductivity. Brenner (31) has also discussed the fact that phthalocyanine polymers exhibit semiconductivity. More recently Vartanyan and Karpovich have made additional measurements on the electrical conductivity of phthalocyanine, copper, magnesium, and zinc phthalocyanines (268). Films outgassed under vacuum presumably are intrinsic semiconductors with thermal activation energies of 1.7–1.8 ev and a specific conductivity of 10^{-12}–10^{-13} ohm^{-1} cm^{-1}. The authors discuss variations in reported measurements on various phthalocyanines made by different investigators and the fact that the electrical conductivity of a film of metal phthalocyanine is increased in the presence of oxygen whereas the activation energy is decreased.

Kleitman (133) and Haak and Nolta (113) have observed rectification in phthalocyanines. In Haak's and Nolta's work compressed powders of phthalocyanine, copper, nickel and molybdenum phthalocyanines initially purified by vacuum sublimation were cut into thin slices of these compounds $1/4 \times 1/4 \times 1/8$ inch and were sandwiched between gold, aluminum or tin metal foil or between silver electrodes. To samples equipped with contacts of dissimilar metals a d.c. voltage was applied and the resulting current was measured. Forward and reverse conductivities were measured by switching the applied voltage. The highest rectification ratio observed is 500 and is obtained with copper phthalocyanine between platinum-silver or platinum-gold electrodes.

Kleitman tested rectification in a 1/4-inch diameter pill of compressed phthalocyanine with one side painted with "Aquadag" and the other side in contact with a copper wire. No rectification was observed (133).

Garrett has presented an interesting summary of present theory concerning organic semiconductors of which the phthalocyanines represent a class (100).

PHOTOCONDUCTIVITY

Electrical conductivity in the phthalocyanines can be induced by the impingement of light as well as by application of an electrical field on a phthalocyanine body. Phthalocyanine was shown to exhibit photoelectric sensitivity by Putseiko in 1949 (203). Powdered phthalocyanine was pressed between thin, transparent insulating pads and was placed in a condenser. The electrical conductivity was greater at a potential of + 70 volts than at −70 volts at the transparent electrode of the condenser. The electrical conductivity also was greater with no field than at an applied potential of −70 volts. Illumination was by white light and by monochromatic light. On the basis of these results it is postulated that phthalocyanine exhibits hole conductivity rather than electronic conductivity (203). It is reported Lobanova (81) also made preliminary measurements of photoelectrochemical effects on films of magnesium phthalocyanine deposited by electrophoresis on platinum in 1949. In 1951 Evstigneev and Terenin showed that a photopotential is produced on illumination of an inert electrode bearing a film of phthalocyanine and magnesium phthalocyanine powder and immersed in an electrolyte (81). The films were deposited on the electrodes by sublimation in vacuum. The potential decreases sharply in an electrolytic solution of $2N$ potassium chloride and $0.1N$ potassium hydroxide when the imposed illumination of visible or ultraviolet light is extinguished. See Figures 2-16 and 2-17. The role of oxygen in the creation of a photopotential was confirmed upon evacuation

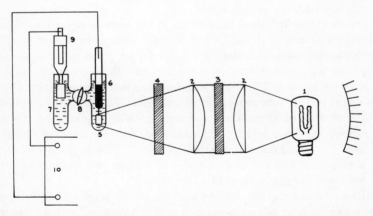

Figure 2-16. Schematic diagram of apparatus of Evstigneev and Terenin used to measure photoconductivity of phthalocyanines (81).

1. Projector lamp 300 w.
2. Condenser
3. Light filter, absorbing infrared rays
4. Light filter
5. Platinum electrode

6. Electrolyte
7. Saturated solution of potassium chloride
8. Stop cock
9. Calomel electrode
10. Lamp potentiometer

(Accuracy of Measurement—1-2 mv)

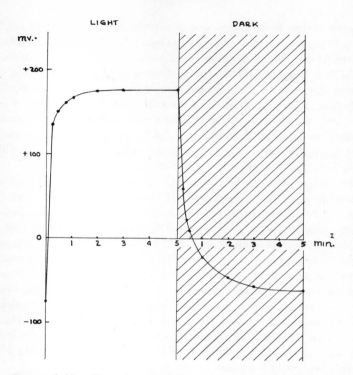

Figure 2-17. The change of the potential of phthalocyanine film (deposited by a distillation in a vacuum, electrolyte $2N$ KCL + 0.1N KOH) during illumination and when the light is cut off (81).

of air from aqueous or alcoholic electrolyte solution. The pumping out gave rise to a significantly lower positive photopotential. In presence of reducing media the positive photopotential was diminished. The photopotential was greater in alkaline media than in acid media.

Photosensitivity of magnesium phthalocyanine, sulfonated copper phthalocyanine, and phthalocyanine in the form of thin films, powders, and films adsorbed on quartz and in organic compounds has been measured by the condenser method. Spectral sensitivity curves were determined by means of a quartz monochromator with mercury and krypton lamps (207).

The photoelectric conduction of inorganic semiconductors is sensitized by phthalocyanine amines (204,207). The photoelectric sensitivity of zinc oxide colored by magnesium phthalocyanine exhibits a reversible reduction in sensitivity when air is removed. At a pressure of 10^{-14} mm Hg, the photo-emf in the sensitized region of 680 mμ is from 10 to 20 per cent of the initial sensitivity in air. Passing a weak discharge through dry oxygen at low pressures strongly affects the photo-emf of zinc oxide pigmented by magnesium phthalocyanine. It is indicated that oxygen atoms are formed in the discharge and are adsorbed on zinc oxide. Oxygen, which has great affinity for electrons, acts as an electron trap by prolonging the life of the photoelectrons in the conduction band. The photoelectric effect is ascribed to the expulsion of the electrons by light quanta from excess zinc cations. The sensitization of the photoelectric effect on zinc oxide by magnesium phthalocyanine is due to transmission of light energy absorbed by the pigment to oxygen traps; the electrons are brought out of the traps into the conduction band (204).

Unlike magnesium phthalocyanine, phthalocyanine does not give a sensitized photoeffect to zinc oxide (208).

Baba, Chitoku, and Nitta (5) and Meier (168) have shown that copper phthalocyanine is photoconductive and that the photocurrents obey Ohm's Law within the range studied up to 100 v/cm. The photocurrents are proportional to the square roots of the light intensities. Experiments were conducted in vacuum at room temperature using crystal films prepared by vacuum sublimation. Light sources were a tungsten filament lamp, and mercury and sodium vapor lamps. Photoelectric phenomena occurred upon the illumination with ultraviolet, visible, and near infrared light. Conductance was measured by means of a surface cell. The phthalocyanine crystal was deposited by sublimation on the surface of a quartz plate between the two gold electrodes of the cell.

"The cell used in measuring the electromotive force was of the sandwich type; that is, the crystal to be tested was first deposited on the surface of a platinum disk and then a thin translucent film of gold was prepared by evaporation upon the organic crystal. When the photocell was illuminated without imposing any external voltage, an electromotive force was generated, and the film of gold became negative" (5). The authors also observed photoconductivity in phthalocyanine (6). The photocurrent could be induced by ultraviolet light and infrared radiation. The photocurrent was proportional to the k-th power of the intensity of light with the value of $k = 0.67–0.71$. The surface potential of phthalocyanine and copper phthalocyanine was also found to be sensitive to illumination (5,6).

Kleitman and Goldsmith also observed photoconductivity in phthalocyanine and copper phthalocyanine (134). "Photoconductivity was observed in both films and crystals. No saturation was indicated and ohmic behavior observed. The transmissivity of films and the dependence of photoconductivity on wavelength was measured over the visible range and to 1 micron."

Putseïko and Terenin (208) have studied in detail the rôle of the central atom in photoconductivity. They have obtained the remarkable result that phthalocyanine has a greater photoeffect than magnesium, zinc, and copper phthalocyanines. The photoeffect of phthalocyanine is resistant to the action of vapors and gases in the temperature range 20–100°.

Phthalocyanine, zinc, copper, and magnesium phthalocyanines all show hole type conductivity in air at room temperature on irradiation with visible or near infrared light. The photoelectric sensitivity of layers of microcrystalline powders of these materials has been measured with material sublimed onto mica, quartz, or glass supports, and with layers deposited from acetone, pyridine, and ether solutions. The photo-emf and the absorption of light are both at a maximum in the region 600–700 mμ for zinc, copper, and magnesium phthalocyanines (208).

Although the photoconductivity of phthalocyanine does not change under external influences such as exposure to oxygen at elevated temperature, the photoconductivity of zinc and copper phthalocyanines does respond to treatment in oxygen which enhances the photoconductivity of these compounds. Thermal activation in oxygen is presumably brought about by combination of oxygen with the zinc and copper atoms of the phthalocyanine. Also, copper and zinc phthalocyanines exhibit decreased photoconductivity when exposed to water vapor whereas phthalocyanine itself is not affected (208). Phthalocyanine, copper, and zinc phthalocyanines have a positive temperature photo-emf coefficient. The photo-emf is 2–3 times greater at 100° than at room temperature. Zinc phthalocyanine deposited on zinc oxide enhances the photoconductivity of zinc oxide whereas copper phthalocyanine deposited on zinc oxide decreases the photoconductivity of zinc oxide. This difference is attributed to the deposition of zinc phthalocyanine in the molecular state and of copper phthalocyanine in the microcrystalline state.

Magnesium phthalocyanine shows a very weak photoeffect. Heating in oxygen has no effect on the photo-emf of magnesium phthalocyanine. However, molecules which form a coordinate link with metal ions and which may be hydrogen donors such as glycerin, phenylhydrazine, and hydrogen sulfide activate the photoeffect of magnesium phthalocyanine. Water vapor does not suppress the photoeffect of magnesium phthalocyanine. Although magnesium phthalocyanine in air or oxygen has a very weak photoeffect, zinc oxide coated with magnesium phthalocyanine shows a definite photoeffect (208) and magnesium phthalocyanine sensitizes the photoeffect of mercuric oxide (206).

Iron and cobalt phthalocyanines do not show noticeable photoeffects as crystals or as vacuum sublimed layers in air or oxygen at room temperature or upon heating to 200°, or in water vapor.

In summary, in zinc and copper phthalocyanines which show hole conductivity, adsorption of electronegative oxygen into the crystal enhances the photosensitivity. The necessity of treatment of magnesium phthalocyanine with vapors of substances capable of entering into the coordinate link for observation of the photoeffect indicates that the magnesium atom makes sufficiently deep traps for electronic conductivity and must be blocked by adducts (208).

According to Vartanyan and Karpovich (267), the photocurrent, i_{ph}, of films of phthalocyanine varies with intensity of illumination, L, as

$$i_{ph} = KL^n$$

n is 1 for oxygen-free films and decreases to 0.5 as the oxygen content rises. In the metal phthalocyanines, the photocurrents in oxygen are proportional to a power of the light intensity which varies from 0.15 to 1 (27). The relative photosensitivity varies with wavelength in a manner parallel to the absorption spectra of phthalocyanine. The optical activation energy of photoconductivity in films of phthalocyanine, copper, zinc, and magnesium phthalocyanines is 1.51–1.65 ev (267).

Bornmann (27,28) states that the photocurrents in cobalt and copper phthalocyanines approximately follow a Langmuir adsorption isotherm versus oxygen pressure. In the region between 300 and 1000 mμ the spectral response of photocurrent corresponds to the optical absorption curves. The photocurrents as well as dark currents of phthalocyanines in oxygen obey Ohm's Law.

Phthalocyanine (282) photosensitizes cuprous emulsions such as mixtures of gelatin solution, agar-agar, and polyvinyl alcohol ground with cuprous bromide.

Magnesium phthalocyanine (74) in solution is photoconductive as discussed earlier. Measurements of the electrical conductivity have been made in a vacuum electrode vessel equipped with platinum electrodes, 5×5 mm, spaced 7 mm apart. The electrical conductivity was measured with a universal bridge. The solvent used was pyridine. Phenylhydrazine was incorporated as reductant. Illumination was by incandescent lamp. Absorption maximum occurred at 560 mμ in a 10^{-4} M solution at $-40°$ with a photoconductivity of 0.19×10^{-6} ohm^{-1}. After photoreduction to the red reduced product of magnesium phthalocyanine the photocurrent dropped to 0.16×10^{-6} ohm^{-1}.

In the region of maximum absorption with visible light, the ratio of σ_{photo}/σ, where σ_{photo} is the photoconductivity and σ the dark conductivity, is not less than 10^{-2}–10^{-3} for outgassed films of phthalocyanine (268).

The decay of photocurrent of phthalocyanine, copper, zinc, and magnesium phthalocyanines after illumination ceases is governed by a hyperbolic law:

$$1/i_t = 1/i_0 + at$$

where i_0 is the photocurrent at the moment illumination ceases, i_t is the photocurrent at time t, and a is a constant (268).

The relation between photocurrent and temperature for carefully out-gassed films is given by the expression:

$$i_{photo} = a \exp \left(-E_{photo}/2\, kt\right)$$

over the range 0 to 150°. Values of E_{photo} for phthalocyanine, copper, zinc, and magnesium phthalocyanines are 0.55, 0.5, 0.5, and 0.4 ev respectively. They are about one-third of the thermal activation energy E. The activation energy of photoconductivity is independent of the wavelength of the exciting light (268,269).

The theory of photoconduction in phthalocyanines, in phthalocyanines in solution, and in inorganic semiconductors treated with films of phthalocyanines is discussed by Terenin and Putseĭko (256). The fact that a p-type semiconductor such as magnesium phthalocyanine sensitizes a n-type semiconductor such as an inorganic oxide indicates that the energy transfer is by excitons.

Kearns and Calvin (130) have found that magnesium phthalocyanine disks coated with a thin film of air oxidized tetramethyl-p-phenylene-diamine are organic systems which show the photovoltaic effect.

"...a suggestion has been made that the primary quantum conversion process in photosynthetic tissues involves the creation and separation of charge to opposite sides of an asymetrically constructed lamina followed by the trapping of both the electrons and the holes which then lead to their respective chemical processes; namely, reduction of carbon dioxide and oxidation of the water to oxygen. This has led us to study model systems as semiconductors with a view to creating an organic photovoltaic junction.

"We have found that magnesium phthalocyanine disks coated with a thin film of air-oxidized tetramethyl p-phenylenediamine are organic systems which do show the photovoltaic effect" (130). Maximum voltage developed is 200 mv. The magnesium phthalocyanine layer has a positive potential with respect to the air-oxidized tetramethyl-p-phenylenediamine layer. Magnesium phthalocyanine alone exhibits no photovoltaic effect. Air-oxidized tetramethyl-p-phenylenediamine exhibits only a very small photovoltaic effect.

Suhrmann (241) states that adsorbed foreign molecules affect photoemission from metals. The author observed that copper phthalocyanine adsorbed on platinum increases the photoelectric emission of platinum more at low than at room temperature.

Relaxation of photoconductivity in vacuum sublimed layers of phthalocyanines containing copper and magnesium as well as phthalocyanine has been studied (205,267,268). The layers of pigments, 0.1 to several microns thick, were deposited by sublimation in a vacuum on quartz or mica base surfaces which had on their surface platinum or gold electrodes at 1 mm separation. A voltage of 100–300 v was applied between the electrodes. Photoconductivity relaxation was studied by the taumeter method which permitted simultaneous observation on the oscillograph of the entire process of the growth and the fall-off of photocurrent, permitting measurement of periods of relaxation from 5×10^{-6} to 10^{-2} sec (205). Illumination was given by visible light from a mercury lamp.

The processes of growth and fall-off of photocurrent in the case of all phthalocyanines progresses within the time interval 10^{-5} to 10^{-2} second. The photoconductivity kinetics depend on the illumination level and in general do not fall into simple exponential dependence. The fall-off curves fall into simple hyperbolic dependence in the first stages as well as in the remote stages from 10 seconds to 5 minutes after cessation of illumination. The short term progress of about 10^{-5} second of photoelectric processes indicates the electronic nature of photoconductivity by the phthalocyanines. The hyperbolic fall-off points to the bimolecular process of recombination.

PHOTOCHEMICAL REACTIONS

Knowledge of the photochemical properties of chlorophyll has stimulated interest in the photochemical properties of the phthalocyanines and of magnesium phthalocyanine in particular. Krasnovskii, Evstigneev, and Gavrilova at the Bakh Institute of Biochemistry have studied this subject in detail (71–77,138–144). Participation of chlorophyll in photosynthesis may be related to its oxidation-reduction properties.

Krasnovskiĭ found that benzoyl peroxide, but not hydrogen peroxide, oxidized $10^{-5} M$ solutions of magnesium phthalocyanine in 95 per cent ethyl alcohol (138,139). The oxidized products can be partially reduced by ascorbic acid or phenyl hydrazine. Oxalic acid, maleic acid, acetic acid and oleic acid are inactive. The dark reaction also gives similar oxidation products. Illumination was with a Schott RG-2 red filter. Photooxidation of magnesium phthalocyanine by atmospheric oxygen yields colorless products and in 18 minutes the extinction coefficient of magnesium phthalocyanine at 665 mμ drops from 0.96 to 0.04. Boiling the solution of oxidation products of magnesium phthalocyanine leads to partial regeneration of magnesium phthalocyanine. Ascorbic acid also helps the reverse process at room temperature, giving 6–8 per cent regeneration at 24–30 per cent concentration of ascorbic acid in solution. Long irradiation leads to irreversible oxidation, however.

Magnesium phthalocyanine is also reduced photometrically in a vacuum in pyridine solution containing ascorbic acid (140), or containing 10 per cent water or deuterium oxide (76). Illumination at 400–500 mμ produces a red-violet reduced form of magnesium phthalocyanine. It was observed that the rate of its formation is slower in deuterium oxide than in hydrogen oxide.

Evstigneev and Gavrilova (75) have demonstrated that the possibility of obtaining identical reduction products of chlorophyll, magnesium phthalocyanine, and their analogs by dark and photochemical methods shows the reversible reducing character of the photochemical reaction of chlorophyll and magnesium phthalocyanine with ascorbic acid and other weak reductants, not capable of reducing chlorophyll or magnesium phthalocyanine in the dark. The reduction proceeds in two stages (73). As a result of the initial photochemical change there is formed a reactive form of pigment that may be a negatively charged free radical. The primary reduced ionized form is then converted to a secondary slightly ionized or nonionized form. The conversion from primary reduced form to secondary reduced form probably proceeds by a dark reaction. The changes in electrical conductivity of 10^{-5} M solutions of chlorophyll and magnesium phthalocyanine during reduction supports this conclusion (75). After cessation of illumination, there is a rapid drop in conductivity.

Chlorophyll and magnesium phthalocyanine are oxidized photochemically or in the dark more rapidly than pheophytin and phthalocyanine (71,144). On the other hand, pheophytin and phthalocyanine are reduced faster than chlorophyll or magnesium phthalocyanine. Reduction in the dark is slower than the photochemical reduction (144). It is concluded that the presence of magnesium in chlorophyll or in magnesium phthalocyanine increases the capacity for photooxidation while the capacity for photoreduction is more pronounced in the absence of magnesium.

The photoreduction of chlorophyll and of magnesium phthalocyanine in pyridine solution containing ascorbic acid has been traced by measurement of the potential of inert metal electrodes immersed in the reacting solution (72). A system of a calomel electrode and a gold electrode, the latter immersed in pyridine solution containing chlorophyll or magnesium phthalocyanine, evacuated and briefly illuminated, shows a rapid drop of potential of the gold electrode to the negative side when pyridine and ascorbic acid are present. When the illumination is extinguished, the potential rapidly rises and levels off at a value lower than the original value. After long irradiation the potential drops to a minimum then begins to change in the positive direction for about thirty minutes. If irradiation ceases at this time the potential rises rapidly to the dark reaction value. The relative photopotentials are -0.294 volt for chlorophyll a + b and -0.291 volt for magnesium phthalocyanine.

Evstigneev and Terenin state that the method of measurement of photoelectrochemical potentials may be the simplest and may become the only method for the solution of a number of problems connected with the oxidation-reduction function of chlorophyll during the primary photochemical act of photosynthesis (139). In the photoelectrochemical system, the electrode potential during irradiation changes toward the positive direction for chlorophyll and magnesium phthalocyanine; the photopotential is proportional to the intensity of the light absorbed. The spectrum of the photoelectrochemical effect coincides with the absorption spectrum of the films in the visible and near ultraviolet portion of the spectrum; the photopotential does not result from the heating of the films by the energy of the light absorbed; the photoelectrochemical effect is determined by the surface interaction between the film and the electrolyte. The sign and magnitude of the photopotential are closely connected with the oxidation-reduction properties of the electrolyte surrounding the pigment film deposited on the electrode; in the presence of oxidizing agents, a positive photopotential is generally observed; in the presence of reducing agents, the positive value decreases or the sign of the photopotential changes to negative. The sign and magnitude of the photopotential are the same in aqueous and alcoholic solutions indicating that the primary importance in the generation of a photopotential belongs not to the electrolyte but to the neutral molecules such as oxygen, quinone, and hydroquinone, as well as to the ions fulfilling an oxidizing or reducing function. The pH of the electrolyte also influences the photoelectric effect. The photopotential of phthalocyanines in an alkaline medium in the absence of reductants is positive and greater than the photopotential in an acid medium. All these phenomena are reproduced using pigment films deposited on platinum, carbon, and graphite electrodes (81).

PHOTOSENSITIZERS

In addition to entering photochemical oxidation or reduction reactions, phthalocyanines may act as photosensitizers in reactions involving the oxidation or reduction of other compounds.

Photochemical reduction of riboflavin and safranin T, in 10^{-5} M solution, in ethyl alcohol and in pyridine, by 10^{-2}–10^{-3} M solutions of ascorbic and pyruvic acids can be sensitized by chlorophyll or magnesium phthalocyanine in the red region of the spectrum. Sensitizer concentration was 10^{-5} M; illumination period was five minutes, and light was filtered through the Schott RG-2 red filter. The reactions, carried out at 480 mμ and at 520 mμ, were followed with a Beckman spectrophotometer by the change of the absorption coefficient. In the anaerobic photoreduction of riboflavin and safranin T dyes at room temperature, the change in optical density, ΔE, for the sensitizer reductant systems magnesium phthalocyanine-ascorbic acid, and magnesium phthalocyanine-pyruvic acid is given in Table 2-8.

TABLE 2-8. ANAEROBIC PHOTOREDUCTION OF DYES SENSITIZED BY CHLOROPHYLL $a + b$ AND BY MAGNESIUM PHTHALOCYANINE AT 20° (141).

sensitizer and reductant	in ethanol		in pyridine	
	riboflavin ΔE at 480 mμ	safranin T ΔE at 520 mμ	riboflavin ΔE at 480 mμ	safranin T ΔE at 520 mμ
magnesium phthalocyanine + ascorbic acid	0.065	0.070	0.260	0.250
magnesium phthalocyanine + pyruvic acid	metal-free phthalocyanine is formed		0.020	0.015

Phthalocyanine, magnesium phthalocyanine, and copper phthalocyanine act as catalysts in the oxidation of aqueous solutions of ascorbic acid (142). The dark reaction is accelerated in the presence of light (200-watt incandescent lamp). With illumination, catalytic and photosensitizing effects of the phthalocyanines are superimposed on one another.

Ascorbic acid is also oxidized more readily under infrared illumination as well as by visible light than in the dark (228). Oxidation takes place in the solvents catechol and protocatechualdehyde. The extent of oxidation was determined colorimetrically.

It has been shown that although numerous dyes sensitize the photoelectric effect in silver halides, chlorophyll and magnesium phthalocyanine have no sensitization effect (1).

Magnesium and zinc phthalocyanines act as photosensitizers in the polymerization of methyl methacrylate under illumination at 600 mμ (137).

Magnesium phthalocyanine and chlorophyll exert photosensitizing action in the oxidation of oleic acid as well as of ascorbic acid (143). The process appears to be a chain reaction with no temperature dependence, indicating that the photochemical stage is the rate-determining step.

Chlorophyll and magnesium phthalocyanine act as photosensitizers in the reduction of Methyl Red by ascorbic acid in pyridine (77). Concentrations of chlorophyll and magnesium phthalocyanine in pyridine were 10^{-5} M and of ascorbic acid in pyridine were 10^{-2}–10^{-3} M. Rates of sensitized reduction of the hydrogen or electron acceptor Methyl Red were compared under illumination in the absence of oxygen with light absorbed only by the pigment sensitizer (light filter RG-5) after addition of 10 per cent hydrogen oxide or deuterium oxide to the pyridine. The course of the reduction was traced in the case of the magnesium phthalocyanine system by decrease in absorption of the pigment at 430 mμ. There was no significant reduction of the reaction rate by addition of hydrogen oxide or deuterium oxide. The formation of a protonic reduced form of the sensitizing agent is not a necessary step in the sensitized reduction reaction, and the primary reduced form of the sensitizer evidently reacts with the dye under reduction. In the following reaction scheme, therefore, reactions (4) and (5) probably are subordinate

$$XI + RH \rightleftharpoons X1^- + RH^+ \tag{1}$$

$$X1^- + Z \rightleftharpoons X1 + Z^- \tag{2}$$

$$Z^- + RH^+ \longrightarrow ZH + R \tag{3}$$

$$X1^- + RH^+ \longrightarrow X1H + R \tag{4}$$

$$X1H + Z \longrightarrow X1 + ZH \tag{5}$$

where X1 = pigment, such as magnesium phthalocyanine
    RH = reductant, such as ascorbic acid
     Z = oxidant, such as Methyl Red
  X1$^-$ = primary reduced form
 X1H = secondary reduced form

The presence of phthalocyanine accelerates the photolysis or photochemical decomposition of cuprous chloride but not of cuprous bromide in the spectral range 550–650 mμ (281).

LUMINESCENCE

In addition to taking part in photochemical reactions, acting as photosensitizers, exhibiting the photovoltaic effect, and photoconductive properties, certain of the phthalocyanines also participate in reactions in which luminescence is observed and take part in reactions which are characterized by fluorescence. "A reciprocal relation between photochemical and chemiluminescent reactions is to be expected. In one case, absorbed light leads to chemical action, and in the other, chemical processes result in light emission" (156).

In 1938 Helberger observed the luminescence of magnesium and zinc phthalocyanines in boiling tetralin containing small amounts of benzoyl peroxide, hydrogen peroxide or air (118). A certain amount of the phthalocyanine is destroyed with intense red luminescence which persists several minutes. The luminescence of magnesium phthalocyanine is greater than the luminescence of zinc phthalocyanine:

"Bei dem Versuch, das komplexe Magnesiumsalz des Phthalocyanins in siedendem käuflichem Tetralin zu lösen, wurde die Beobachtung gemacht, dass eine gewisse Menge des Farbstoffs unter Auftreten einer intensiv roten Leuchterscheinung zerstört wird; besonders effektvoll ist der Versuch, wenn in einem verdunkelten Raum Magnesiumphthalocyanin in kleinen Portionen in schwachsiedendes Tetralin eingetragen wird. Das Leuchten hält einige Zeit an, wird dann schwächer und hört nach einigen Minuten ganz auf. Durch erneutes Eintragen von Farbstoff lässt sich die Erscheinung reproduzieren, bis schliesslich unverändertes Magnesiumphthalocyanin mit grüner Farbe in Lösung geht. Gibt man nunmehr etwas Benzoylperoxyd, oder einen Tropfen Perhydrol zu oder leitet Luft ein, so leuchtet die kochende Flüssigkeit erneut auf. Somit ist wohl das in käuflichem Tetralin immer enthaltene Peroxyd für die Chemiluminiscenzerscheinung verantwortlich zu machen.''

Also in 1938 Thielert and Pfeiffer observed luminescence of an iron phthalocyanine (258).

The luminescence of phthalocyanines in boiling organic solvents requires the presence of an oxidant impurity (119). For example, a suspension of magnesium phthalocyanine in boiling benzene luminesces when treated with a small amount of tetralin peroxide. Magnesium phthalocyanine luminesces in boiling commercial toluene. However, magnesium phthalocyanine does not luminesce in boiling toluene purified by distillation unless air is passed through or tetralin peroxide is added to the toluene. Soon after boiling begins water and ammonia are formed. Apparently the magnesium atom is removed and is converted to magnesium oxide, the phthalocyanine decomposes to phthalic residues and ammonia, and tetralin is converted to α-tetralone. The water is formed by the decomposition of tetralin peroxide into tetralone and water.

Lead phthalocyanine luminesces in boiling toluene but to a lesser extent than magnesium phthalocyanine (119).

Magnesium phthalocyanine also luminesces in commercial xylene and in commercial cymene (119). Peroxide-containing turpentine and commercial decalin are also active. Chlorobenzene and bromobenzene are inactive unless tetralin peroxide is added. No or only trace luminescence is found in aliphatic alcohols, amyl acetate, dioxane, pyridine, quinoline, piperidine, and acetic acid anhydride (119). The mixture of 2 mg magnesium phthalocyanine dissolved in 5 cc vegetable oils when heated in the dark gives only a ruby luminescence (259). Active vegetable oils are soybean oil and cottonseed oil. In purified soybean oil there is no luminescence. The luminescence is thought to be due to a peroxide formed in the oil during storage with the magnesium phthalocyanine.

Ferrous phthalocyanine luminesces in luminol to which hydrogen peroxide is added (274). Under the given reaction conditions, the duration of luminescence for the emission of about 99 per cent of the total energy was between 2 and 17 minutes.

Neporent and Klochkov have made a detailed study of the luminescence spectra of magnesium phthalocyanine in the region of 200 to 1000 mμ using a quartz window photomultiplier and a Ag—O—Cs photomultiplier with a grating monochromator with a grating 150 × 120 mm with 600 lines/mm and a resolution of 3–5 Å (182,183). See Figure 2–18.

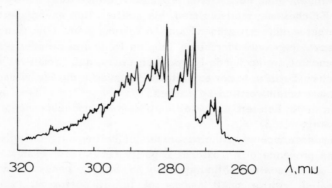

Figure 2-18.   Record of luminescence spectrum of a solution of magnesium phthalocyanine in acetone (182).

Using an impulse apparatus, the effect of strong light impulses on cobalt, copper, iron, magnesium, and zinc phthalocyanines dissolved in alcohol, acetone, ether, pyridine, and toluene has been studied (255). Luminescence was observed in the case of magnesium and zinc phthalocyanines but was not observed in the case of cobalt, copper, and iron phthalocyanines.

Phosphorescence has been found in chlorophyll-b. However, no phosphorescence in phthalocyanines in the region of the photographic infrared to 9000 Å has been detected (19).

Detection was attempted with a Steinheil Universal Spectrograph GH, with f/3 coated glass optics, using three prisms. "The exciting light was the AH-6 high-pressure 1 kw. water-coated mercury arc, monochromatized by suitable filters. Both steady excitation with filtered light, and intermittent excitation with a phosphoroscope of 10^{-4} sec resolving time was used."

FLUORESCENCE

In their studies on the properties of chlorophyll, Evstigneev and Krasnovskiĭ investigated the fluorescence of chlorophyll and its phthalocyanine analogue, magnesium phthalocyanine (80). The fluorescence of chlorophyll is of interest in connection with the mechanism of energy transfer from the light-excited chlorophyll molecule. They found that magnesium phthalocyanine does fluoresce with absorption in the red band, in alcoholic solution, and with emission as a narrow red band in the region 670–675 mμ, about 5 mμ beyond the main fluorescence band of chlorophyll. Observation of the fluorescence was through a Zeiss spectrometer. Fluorescence intensity was measured with a Pulfrich photometer. Fluorescence was excited in the red region and not by ultraviolet light to avoid undue photochemical effects.

In the apparatus shown in Figure 2-19 the light from an incandescent lamp (a) passed through a red filter, RG-2, (b), and was focused on a test tube (c) containing the fluorescent solution. The fluorescent light passed through the objective (d), into the left diaphragm of the Pulfrich photometer. Its intensity was compared with that of the light from the frosted glass pane (f), illuminated by a beam from the same lamp (a) through the red filter (b), by partial reflection from a glass plate (g). The intensity of fluorescence was expressed in divisions on the per cent scale on the right drum of the photometer, noted when the left drum was set on 100 per cent, and the two illuminated fields were equalized. The maximum fluorescence intensity was obtained by using solutions of an optical density of about 0.5 in the red absorption maximum (668 mμ for magnesium phthalocyanine), corresponding to a 10^{-5} M concentration.

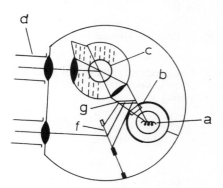

Figure 2-19. Apparatus for measuring fluorescence quenching. Tubes on left belong to a Pulfrich photometer (80).

Quenching of fluorescence was measured in solutions of ethanol by oxygen, quinone, and hydroquinone. Oxidizing molecules, with an affinity for electrons, such as quinone and oxygen, have a strong quenching effect on the fluorescence of chlorophyll and magnesium phthalocyanine; reductants such as hydroquinone, ascorbic acid, and alkali iodides are

considerably less effective. The nature of the solvent also was found
to have an effect on the intensity of fluorescence, as shown in Table 2-9.

TABLE 2-9. SOLVENT DEPENDENCE OF INTENSITY OF
FLUORESCENCE (80).

E = Optical density in red peak
F = Fluorescence in relative units measured at $7 \pm 0.5\,^{\circ}C$.

Solvent	Magnesium phthalocyanine		Chlorophyll (a + b)	
	E	F	E	F
95% ethanol	0.415	61.5	0.418	40.5
acetone	0.413	70.5	0.417	50.5
pyridine	0.412	35.5	0.416	32.0

Rackow and König have also studied the quenching of fluorescence of
chlorophyll and magnesium phthalocyanine in the presence of ascorbic
acid in pyridine solution (209).

Measurements of the fluorescence of phthalocyanine and of magnesium
phthalocyanine ether solutions dissolved in toluene followed by evaporation in vacuum have been made at an optical density as high as 1.3 at
the red peak of 672 mμ (69). Changes in the intensity of fluorescence
and the value of the absorption coefficient upon evacuating and re-admitting air are shown in Table 2-10 and in Figure 2-20.

TABLE 2-10. CHANGES IN THE INTENSITY OF FLUORESCENCE AND THE
MAGNITUDE OF THE ABSORPTION COEFFICIENT UPON
EVACUATING AND RE-ADMITTING AIR (69).

Compound, dissolved in toluene	Intensity of Fluorescence (in relative units)			Absorption Coefficient (at the wavelength of the absorption maximum)			Wavelength of absorption max.
	Initial	After evacuating air	After re-admitting air	Initial	After evacuating air	After re-admitting air	
Mg Phthalocyanine	49	27	45	0.700	0.314	0.557	672 mμ
Mg Phthalocyanine	30	23	30	0.268	0.165	0.226	672
Mg Phthalocyanine	27	19	36	0.186	0.095	0.200	672
Phthalocyanine	21	22	22	0.327	0.300	0.290	690
Pheophytin (a plus b)	30	31	32	0.900	0.895	0.892	670
Pheophytin (a plus b)	24	27	28	0.345	0.346	0.341	670

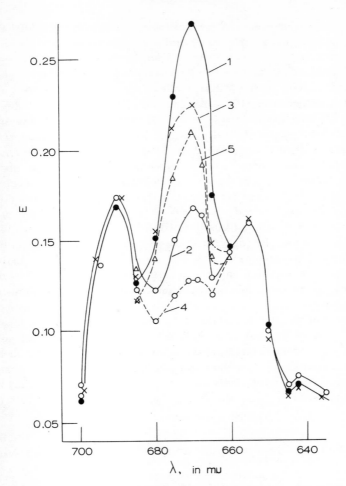

Figure 2-20. Changes in absorption spectrum of a mixture of phthalocyanine and magnesium phthalocyanine dissolved in toluene, caused by evacuation and readmission of air. Curve 1 —Original solution; Curve 2—After first evacuation; Curve 3 —After admission of air; Curve 4—After renewed evacuatiom; Curve 5—After renewed admission of air (69).

The curves in Figure 2-20 show that the maxima at 655 and 690 mμ of phthalocyanine are changed hardly at all whereas the maximum at 672 mμ of magnesium phthalocyanine decreases upon evacuation and increases upon re-admission of air. Chlorophyll and pheophytin behave similarly. The difference in behavior between the metal-free and the magnesium bearing pigments is indicated to be due to the magnesium atom. Compounds which enhance the fluorescence of chlorophyll probably form co-ordination complexes with the central magnesium atom.

The quenching of fluorescence of solutions of chlorophyll and magnesium phthalocyanine in ethanol, pyridine, and toluene by a variety of compounds added to the solution shows that oxidants exert a stronger quenching effect than other substances and that there is no direct connection between the quenching effect of extraneous molecules and their ability to react photochemically with chlorophyll. Strong quenchers such as oxygen and quinone are practically without effect on the absorption spectrum whereas iodine and dinitrobenzene decrease the absorption maximum markedly. The absence of a relation between quenching and photochemical reactivity indicates that photoreactivity is not determined by the electronic excited state with a life of 10^{-7}–10^{-8} sec but is determined by the long lived biradical triplet state (70). Compounds added to the solutions of chlorophyll and magnesium phthalocyanine in ethanol, pyridine, and toluene were nitrobenzene, m-dinitrobenzene, iodine, ascorbic acid, benzoic acid, aniline, dimethylaniline, phenol, benzaldehyde, catechol, pyrogallol, phenylhydrazine hydrochloride, p-quinone, and hydroquinone.

The life of the excited state of chlorophyll pigments and of phthalocyanine, magnesium and zinc phthalocyanines, of the order of 10^{-9} seconds, in ethyl ether, ethanol, acetone, pyridine, hexane, and toluene, has been measured directly by the extinguishing of fluorescence by means of the phase fluorometer designed by Bonch-Bruevich, Molchanov, and Shirokov (52). The phase fluorometer has a resolving power with respect to time of 2×10^{-11} seconds. See Table 2-11.

TABLE 2-11. LIFE OF THE EXCITED STATE OF PIGMENTS IN SOLUTIONS FROM MEASUREMENTS OF THE EXTINGUISHING OF FLUORESCENCE (IN 10^{-9} SEC) (52).

Life of the excited state of pigments in solutions from measurements of the extinguishing of fluorescence (in 1×10^{-9} seconds). Excitation by mercury lines at 436 mμ. Receiver FEU-22.

Pigment	Solvent					
	ethyl ether	ethanol	acetone	pyridine	dioxane	toluene
magnesium phthalocyanine	8.6	7.6	7.2	8.1	6.5	6.9
zinc phthalocyanine	4.5	4.4	3.0	...	3.9	...
phthalocyanine	...	...	...	...	6.7	...

Excitation of the fluorescence was effected by the mercury line 436 mμ. Concentration of the solutions did not exceed 10^{-5} M. The time of the extinguishing of fluorescence depends only slightly on the solvent.

The extinguishing time is greater for phthalocyanines than for pheophytins of the corresponding metals. The extinguishing time of fluorescence of zinc phthalocyanine is half the extinguishing time of magnesium phthalocyanine. The same relationship is true for chlorophyll and zinc pheophytin. The presence or absence of oxygen has little or no effect on the extinguishing time.

Gachkovskiĭ has conducted a series of investigations on the fluorescence of magnesium phthalocyanine and of chlorophyll in the solid state as adsorbates. Absorption and fluorescence spectra of magnesium phthalocyanine and of chlorophyll adsorbed on magnesium oxide from ethanol solution and outgassed in vacuum have been determined (92). Small amounts of oxygen produce a flare-up of the fluorescence of magnesium phthalocyanine. At higher oxygen pressures, however, quenching is produced. Fluorescence of the magnesium phthalocyanine adsorbate, measured at $20°$, decreases in intensity with the increase of the temperature at which the preparation is outgassed in vacuum, and disappears if the adsorbate is outgassed at $400°$ (93). Adsorbates of magnesium phthalocyanine on magnesium oxide produced by passing magnesium phthalocyanine vapor outgassed at $150°$ over magnesium oxide outgassed 4–6 hours at $350–400°$, and kept 2 hours at $250–300°$ under constant pumping show no fluorescence (94). Fluorescence arises if the originally non-fluorescent adsorbate is treated with gaseous oxygen, water, ethanol, ethyl ether, acetone, carbon dioxide, phenol, ammonia, hydrogen sulfide, chlorine, or iodine. Vapors of benzene, toluene, or tetralin are ineffective. The fluorescence is due to a complex between the adsorbate and the added compound. All these fluorescence spectra have three to four bands, falling off on the long wave side and separated from each other by $500–900$ cm^{-1}. The distance between the principal band and the second, third, and fourth bands are, for the complex with oxygen, 899, 1451, and 2263 cm^{-1}, for the complex with chlorine, 823, 1365, and 2234 cm^{-1}, and for the complex with iodine, 738, 1245, and 1978 cm^{-1}. The distances decrease with increasing mass of the molecule entering the complex. The fluorescence spectra of these complexes correspond to transitions from the excited electronic level to different vibrational levels of the ground state (94). Chlorophyll and magnesium porphyrin adsorbates on magnesium oxide exhibit fluorescence phenomena similar to magnesium phthalocyanine. In analogy with the spectrum of magnesium phthalocyanine, the difference of the wave number of bands corresponds to vibration quanta, and the fluorescence and absorption spectra are related by specular reflection, with the intensities decreasing with decreasing frequency (95). A mechanism is proposed for the primary reaction on the change in the fluorescence spectra of magnesium phthalocyanine and chlorophyll adsorbed on magnesium oxide with the formation of complexes with oxygen, permitting an interpretation for the mechanism of the oxidation-reduction reactions in the photosynthesis process (99).

Absorption spectra as well as fluorescence spectra of monolayers of magnesium phthalocyanine obtained from solutions of magnesium phthalocyanine in ethanol or ether adsorbed on magnesium oxide are sensitive to environment (96). Absorption was studied by diffuse reflection using an incandescent 45 watt lamp. The absorption spectra were determined after heating the mixture to 375° to remove the red fluorescence. Adsorption of oxygen, oxygen and water vapor, and vapors of ether and alcohol produces shifted spectra with a maximum in the region 650–690 mμ. Phthalocyanine adsorbed on magnesium oxide and treated to vapors and oxygen similarly to magnesium phthalocyanine does not fluoresce at all.

Adsorbates of magnesium phthalocyanine on magnesium oxide, obtained from ethanol solution, after retention in the dark, in air, change in fluorescence color from clear red to milky violet accompanied by shifts in absorption and fluorescence spectra (97). It is indicated a slow dark heterogenous reaction involving oxygen is taking place. This shift in the maximum varies depending on whether the adsorbed layer of magnesium phthalocyanine is complexed with solvent molecules, oxygen, or complexes of unknown nature. The respective spectral maxima are 673 mμ, 659 mμ, and 684 mμ.

Adsorbates of magnesium phthalocyanine on zinc oxide, alumina, and crushed glass have also been prepared and studied with an electron microscope (98). Monomolecular layers are formed by adsorbing the phthalocyanines from solution. It is indicated that the fluorescence of molecules of magnesium phthalocyanine can be lost as a result of the aggregation on various substrates and as a result of reaggregation with moist air. For example, fluorescence of magnesium phthalocyanine adsorbates on catalytically active adsorbents such as alumina and zinc oxide disappears when the solvent is evaporated in air.

The fluorescence of magnesium and zinc phthalocyanines adsorbed on silica gel, after each compound is degassed under vacuum, leads to a shifting and widening of the fluorescence spectrum compared to the corresponding spectra in ethanol, ether, and acetone solutions (129). Traces of oxygen cause normal quenching of fluorescence of the adsorbates. The introduction of water or organic solvent vapors to the degassed adsorbates affects the fluorescence similarly to the fluorescence of the corresponding solutions.

It is stated that fluorescence of magnesium phthalocyanine deposited from 10^{-5}–10^{-6} M solutions in ethanol from −180° to 20° does not occur when adsorbed on lead oxide, silver halides, or tellurium halides but does occur on magnesium oxide, barium oxide, titania, paper, cotton, gelatin, and polyvinyl lacquer (2).

Vapors of magnesium phthalocyanine sensitized by naphthalene show a red fluorescence (254). Thus, fluorescence of magnesium phthalocyanine has been observed in the dissolved, solid, and vapor states. Magnesium phthalocyanine vapor does not fluoresce alone or mixed with benzene in the absence of naphthalene, presumably because of the slight volatilization of magnesium phthalocyanine. The fluorescence of magnesium phthalocyanine vapor was determined by magnesium spark and mercury vapor lamps and recorded by a Fuss glass spectrograph with exposure of eight hours.

The state of polarization of a fluorescent molecule may play a role in determining the wavelength of the emission (112). Polarization should decrease towards the long-wave end of the emission band and in case of mirror symmetry of excitation and emission bands the polarization should decrease on both sides of the electron transition. Measurements on 3-methyl-aminophthalimide, fluorescein, rhodamine B, and magnesium phthalocyanine confirm this dependence.

NEUTRON IRRADIATION

A number of phthalocyanines have been examined with respect to their suitability for use in the Szilard-Chalmers process for the preparation of radioactive isotopes of the central metal atom.

In the Szilard-Chalmers process, the target material or compound containing the atom, the radioactive isotope of which is wanted, is bombarded with slow or thermal neutrons. For the Szilard-Chalmers process to be effective, upon neutron capture the newly-formed isotope atom must separate from the parent molecule; it must not recombine with the molecular fragment from which it separates; and a chemical method for the separation of the isotope from the residual target compound must be available. An effective Szilard-Chalmers separation produces radioactive isotopes of high specific activity, high enrichment or concentration, and high yield of separable activity. The specific activity of a preparation is the ratio of the number of radioactive atoms of the element to the total number of atoms of the element present. Enrichment or concentration is the ratio of the specific activity of a preparation after separation to that of the unseparated target. The yield of separable activity gives the percentage of the radioactivity that may be separated from the bombarded target.

$$E = S_1/S_2 = \frac{Y \times a}{100 \times b} \quad (194)$$

where E = enrichment

S_1 = specific activity of separated material

S_2 = specific activity of compound before separation
Y = yield of separable activity
a = total amount of metal in the compound
b = amount of metal in the separated material

In the first Szilard-Chalmers reaction, an ethyl iodide target, after bombardment with thermal neutrons, was extracted in water containing a trace of iodine and precipitated to silver iodide. Ethylene chloride, ethyl iodide, and ethyl bromide have also been used as targets for the preparation of Cl^{38}, I^{128}, and Br^{80}. After neutron irradiation, the targets were extracted in water and in benzene successively, to remove the isotopic atoms in the water and the residual molecular target material in the benzene (7,90).

Nath and Shankar (180,181) applied the Szilard-Chalmers technique to the preparation of the radioactive cobalt isotope Co^{60}, from cobalt phthalocyanine, for radiotherapeutic use. High specific activity and enrichment were reported. Cobalt phthalocyanine was bombarded with thermal neutrons in the Harwell BEPO nuclear reactor, dissolved in concentrated sulfuric acid, reprecipitated in water containing a small amount of cobalt sulfate, filtered out, and decomposed by treatment with fuming nitric and sulfuric acids. "'Equal Weight' cobalt samples of separable and retentive activity were obtained, by electrodeposition from ammoniacal solutions of cobalt sulfate, containing hydrazine sulfate and ammonium sulfate. An electrodeposition cell with rotating carbon anode was used. The samples were measured at fixed geometry by means of an end-window G. M. Tube.

"The yield of the separable activity was about 95.5 per cent. The small obtention retained is in harmony with the fact that the phthalocyanines have a planar structure, thus offering little hindrance to the recoil cobalt atom" (180).

In an extensive investigation Payne, Scargill, and Cook (194) have irradiated cobalt phthalocyanine, as well as copper, gallium, iron, palladium, and zinc phthalocyanines in the BEPO reactor at Harwell, with a neutron flux of $10^{12}n/cm^2$-sec. Separable activity and enrichment factors were measured as a function of time. The effect of γ-radiation in the decomposition and of postirradiation heating of the phthalocyanine metal complexes was considered. "Despite the reported high chemical stability of these compounds some decomposition of the complexes was observed and consequently the enrichment factors are not high, although the yield may be as high as 98 per cent."

The authors conclude that "the Szilard-Chalmers process in phthalocyanines can be very useful for obtaining high specific activity radioisotopes of short half-life when the irradiation time is relatively short.

In the case of isotopes of long half-life the method is not attractive as the small gains in specific activity are offset by the rather intractable nature of the compounds.''

Sharp, Schmitt, Suffredini, and Randolph (231) have measured yield and enrichment in the Szilard-Chalmers production of 12-hr Cu^{64} from copper phthalocyanine and of 14-hr Zn^{69m} from zinc phthalocyanine. In the case of copper phthalocyanine, at less than 10 kw-hr exposure, the yield was 70 per cent with enrichment greater than 350. At less than 100 kw-hr exposure of zinc phthalocyanine, the yield was greater than 50 per cent and the enrichment exceeded 35.

Herr (120) applied the Szilard-Chalmers technique to the separation of 42-sec Rh^{104} and 4.34-min Rh^{104}, using rhodium (Rh^{103}) phthalocyanine as the target compound. 4.34-Min Rh^{104}, upon emission of γ-rays, reverts to the ground state 42-sec Rh^{104}. Rhodium phthalocyanine (100 mg) and phthalodinitrile (3 mg) were sealed in a quartz tube, bombarded with slow neutrons for five minutes, producing Rh^{104} isotope, and the contents heated at 320° for two minutes to assure withdrawal by the phthalocyanine ring of any rhodium released by the neutron bombardment. The material was dissolved in hot, concentrated sulfuric acid, and was kept standing eight to ten minutes. Water containing a few milligrams rhodium trichloride was added, and the precipitated rhodium phthalocyanine was filtered. The filtrate contained the 42-sec $(Rh^{104})^{+++}$ ion, and the residue contained the excited 4.34-min Rh^{104} atom in the phthalocyanine nucleus.

Atkins and Garner (4) have shown that there is only a slight exchange of radioactive zinc 250-day Zn^{65}, in the form of $0.002N$ zinc acetate, and of $0.002N$ zinc phthalocyanine, after a 35-day reaction time at 25° in pyridine solution. After the reaction period of 35 days, the reaction was stopped and separation was effected by addition of a water-chloroform mixture. Most of the zinc phthalocyanine separated into the chloroform-pyridine layer and the zinc acetate separated into the water-pyridine layer. After the layers were separated, the chloroform-pyridine layer was shaken with chloroform. The chloroform layers were combined and the water layers were combined. Other zinc chelate compounds *did* give measurable exchange; zinc diphenylthiocarbazone, zinc 8-hydroxyquinolate, zinc anthranilate, zinc salicylaldehyde-o-phenylenediimine, zinc salicylaldehyde-methylimine, zinc acetylacetonate, zinc benzoylacetonate, and zinc nicotinylacetonate. Among these zinc chelate complexes, only zinc phthalocyanine exhibits a planar configuration. Only the zinc phthalocyanine is suitable "for use in Szilard-Chalmers concentration of radio-zinc, assuming that the inorganic recoil zinc is separated by the pyridine-chloroform-water procedure used in the exchange separations.''

Robinson and Klein (221) have observed that radiation of α-form copper phthalocyanine in the form of a thermal neutron flux of 10^{18}–10^{19} n/cm^2

sec. in the ORNL Graphite Reactor results in conversion of the irradiated material to crystalline, presumably β-form, copper phthalocyanine. The crystallization began during or shortly after exposure and the material became highly crystalline after standing six months at room temperature. The continued crystallization may have taken place in the presence of residual solvent material used in the preparation of the sample.

"The next few years will see a great expansion in radioisotope applications in industry, research, and medicine. Until recently, the major emphasis has been on the use of radioisotopes with half-lives greater than a few days.... There are many situations, particularly in medical therapy and in consumer-product industries, where short-lived radioisotopes would be extremely useful. Short-lived activities also present a considerably reduced hazard, since spills or errors are corrected by merely waiting for the activity to decay away.

"The use of short-lived radioisotopes necessarily implies a local source of supply. This requirement is being met by the installation of many small, inexpensive research and training reactors at leading laboratories and institutions throughout the world.... Although such small reactors are capable of producing substantial *quantities* of radioisotopes, the *specific activities* produced are often too low for the intended application" (231). The Szilard-Chalmers process is noteworthy, therefore, since it is a general method for obtaining high specific activity targets of both short and long half-lives.

OTHER PROPERTIES

Flocculation

A property of phthalocyanines that has been investigated thoroughly because of its practical significance is their tendency to flocculate in paint systems. While this property is influenced by all factors of the system in which flocculation occurs, the phthalocyanine particles appear to have a marked influence on flocculation. Flocculation of pigments in paint systems, however, is a problem not limited to phthalocyanine pigments, having been recognized many years before the discovery of the phthalocyanines (110).

Dispersion of a finely divided solid in a liquid results in a two phase system with the solid as the discontinuous phase and the liquid as the continuous phase. The freedom of the particles to migrate is determined in part by (1) the solid, its chemical properties, polarity, and particle size, (2) the liquid, its chemical properties, polarity, and viscosity and (3) the effect of other substances such as resins and surfactants on the system. According to Fischer (88) "Flocculation may be defined as the formation of clusters of particles which are disturbed and broken by relatively weak mechanical forces or by a change in the physical forces at the interface between the solid and the suspending medium. The term flocculation derives from the Latin *floccus*, implying a woolly, soft massing of fibers or particles." Industrially the term flocculation may have a more variable meaning. Green (110) considers the term flocculation to have the following implications: (1) the units composing the flocculate were originally separately dispersed in the continuous phase, (2) the floccule is formed by movement of the particles within the liquid, and (3) adherence of the particles occurs.

Flocculation accompanies low values of the adhesion tension of solid for liquid (11). Shur (236) has made an excellent literature review on flocculation and has studied (237) the effect of variation in the composition of the organic dispersing medium on the flocculation of copper phthalocyanine pigments. Although experimental results indicate that the polarity of the dispersing phase is not the sole factor affecting the flocculation of copper phthalocyanine, solvent media in the absence of surfactants are shown to have a profound influence on flocculating tendencies. Alkyl acetate esters have been found to be superior to most other commonly used media in their deflocculating effect on the copper phthalocyanine pigment tested. The above studies were made using sedimentation volume, rheological and photomicrographic methods.

The economic importance of flocculation is great because of its effect on application properties and reproducibility of color in coatings and films (235). In a flocculated system the particles adhere to each other because of surface forces causing the formation of a "structure" of particles which gives a high yield value to the rheological system. In a finished paint flocculation may also cause the final film to have less hiding power as shown in Figure 2-21.

Methods of reducing flocculation in systems containing phthalocyanine pigments are discussed in Chapter 4. Flocculation in paint systems is also considered in Chapter 6. Flocculation tests are given in Appendix II.

Solubility

Phthalocyanine and its metal derivatives are insoluble in water and in most common organic solvents. They vary from insolubility to slight solubility in 1-chloronaphthalene, pyridine, pyridine-ether, and quinoline, but have a strong tendency to precipitate to some degree on standing. Lead phthalocyanine and dichlorotin phthalocyanine can be purified by crystallization from quinoline (8). Magnesium phthalocyanine is sufficiently soluble in boiling naphthalene for the determination of its molecular weight (158). Lithium phthalocyanine is very soluble in amyl alcohol. See Chapter 3 for other solubility data.

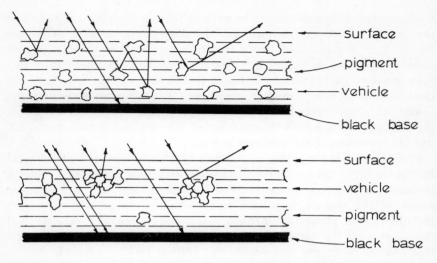

Figure 2-21. A larger proportion of incident light is reflected by a deflocculated system (above) providing better hiding power than a flocculated system (below) (235).

Phthalocyanines are soluble in concentrated phosphoric and sulfuric acids and in chlorosulfonic, anhydrous hydrofluoric, ethylsulfuric, and trichloroacetic acids (46). They are reprecipitated by dilution with water. Phthalocyanines with electrovalent metal bonds lose their metal atoms upon hydrolysis.

Some phthalocyanines such as hydroxyaluminum, chloroaluminum (8), beryllium, and magnesium phthalocyanines (159) form hydrates.

The solubility of zinc, nickel and metal-free phthalocyanines in concentrated sulfuric acid at 25°, cobalt phthalocyanine at 25° and 40°, and copper phthalocyanine at 18°, 25°, 50° and 70° was determined by Berezin (21,22), according to the reaction

$$(MPc)_{solid} + H_2SO_4 \rightleftharpoons MPcH^+ + HSO_4^-$$

The solubility of copper phthalocyanine in anhydrous liquid ammonia at $-33.5°$ is approximately 20 mg/100 ml of solution (273).

The metal phthalocyanines in which the metal atom is held by electrovalent bonds are insoluble in organic solvents (8).

A procedure for increasing the solubility of metal phthalocyanines has been reported by Pedersen (200) who subjected these compounds to reversible oxidation with certain oxidizing agents, and who found that the oxidized form is soluble in some organic solvents to as much as 68 per cent for copper phthalocyanine. These products are described in the Oxidation section of this chapter.

Molecular Weights

Robertson, Linstead, and Dent (216) used cell dimensions of the phthalocyanine crystal to determine its maximum molecular weight:

$$\text{Molecular weight} = \frac{\text{volume of cell} \times \text{density}}{\text{number of molecules per cell}}$$

"The metallic phthalocyanines appear to offer an almost unique example of a class of compound in which an unequivocal determination of the *true* molecular weight can be made from the crystal data combined with an elementary analysis of the percentage of metal in the compound. The results have proved of considerable importance in deciding the structure of these compounds, because their low solubility renders ordinary methods of molecular weight determination difficult or impossible to apply, except in the case of the magnesium compound."

The percentage of metal in the compound by elemental analysis gives the minimum possible molecular weight, viz., that of a molecule containing only one atom of the metal.

Since the determinations of molecular weights by these two methods (for maximum and minimum molecular weight determination) agree, it follows that these figures represent the true molecular weights, as shown in Table 2-12.

TABLE 2-12. MOLECULAR WEIGHTS OF PHTHALOCYANINES (216).

	Nickel Phthalocyanine	Copper Phthalocyanine	Platinum Phthalocyanine
Minimum molecular wt.	559	573	720
Maximum molecular wt.	586	583	712
Calculated molecular wt.	571	576	707

In earlier work, Linstead and Lowe (158) used the ebullioscopic method with a sensitive platinum resistance thermometer to determine the molecular weight of magnesium phthalocyanine. The solvent used was naphthalene.

The molecular weights of acid stable phthalocyanines have been determined by a cryoscopic method using sulfuric acid as the solvent (239).

Extinction Coefficient

In a study of thin films of chlorophyll, magnesium and iron phthalocyanines and magnesium naphthalocyanine, Hughes observed that films of the latter compound less than 30 Å in mean thickness can be seen with the naked eye to possess a greenish-blue color. "A comparative test with an alcoholic solution showed that the remarkably high molecular extinction coefficient possessed by this compound is of the same order in the unimolecular film as in the bulk solution" (124).

Dielectric Properties

The dielectric constant for commercial copper phthalocyanine as an air-packed powder is 4.85 (271). Dielectric constants of pigment dispersions have been compared with theoretical values as calculated from Boettcher's equation for the dielectric constant as a function of volume-concentration. The predicted linear relation was observed at concentrations below 10 per cent for copper phthalocyanine. The observed slopes of the linear plots were in only fair agreement with calculated values probably because the particles were non-spherical in shape.

Copper phthalocyanine was used by Hamon (115) as an "impurity" in studying its effect on the dielectric properties of hard paraffins.

REFERENCES

1. Akimov, I. A., *Zhur. Fiz. Khim.*, **30**, 1007–18 (1956).
2. Akimov, I. A., *Zhur. Nauch. i Priklad. Fot. i Kinematographii*, **4**, 64–6 (1959).
3. Anderson, J. S., Bradbrook, E. F., Cook, A. H., and Linstead, R. P., *J. Chem. Soc.*, **1938**, 1151–6.
4. Atkins, Jr., D. C., and Garner, C. S., *J. Am. Chem. Soc.*, **74**, 3527–9 (1952).
5. Baba, H., Chitoku, K., and Nitta, K., *Nature*, **177**, 672 (1956).
6. *Ibid.*, *Hokkaidô Daigaku Ôyô Denki Kenkyûjo Ihô*, **8**, 127–43 (1956).
7. Barnes, J. W., and Burgus, W. H., in Wahl and Bonner, ed., "Radioactivity Applied to Chemistry," New York, John Wiley & Sons, 1951.
8. Barrett, P. A., Dent, C. E., and Linstead, R. P., *J. Chem. Soc.*, **1936**, 1719–36.
9. Barrett, P. A., Frye, D. A., and Linstead, R. P., *J. Chem. Soc.*, **1938**, 1157–63.
10. Barrett, P. A., Linstead, R. P., Rundall, F. G., and Tuey, G. A. P., *J. Chem. Soc.*, **1940**, 1079–92.
11. Bartell, F. E., and Osterhof, H. J., *Ind. Eng. Chem.*, **19**, 1277 (1927).
12. Basu, S., *Indian J. Phys.*, **28**, 511–21 (1954).
13. Baumann, F., and Bienert, B. (to Farbenfabriken Bayer A.-G.), U. S. Patent 2,768,867 (Oct. 30, 1956).
14. Baumann, F., Bienert, B., and Rösch, G. (to Farbenfabriken Bayer A.-G.), U. S. Patent 2,683,643 (July 13, 1954).
15. *Ibid.*, U. S. Patent 2,778,819 (Jan. 22, 1957).
16. Baumann, F., Bienert, B., Rösch, G., Vollmann, H., and Wolf, W., *Angew. Chem.*, **68**, 133–50 (1956).
17. Baumann, F., Bienert, B., Vollmann, H., and Rösch, G. (to Farbenfabriken Bayer A.-G.), U. S. Patent 2,897,039 (July 28, 1959).
18. Baumann, F., Bienert, B., and Rösch, G., German Patent 888,837 (Sept. 3, 1953).
19. Becker, R. S., and Kasha, M., *J. Am. Chem. Soc.*, **77**, 3669–70 (1955).
20. Bennett, J. E., and Ingram, D. J. E., *Nature*, **175**, 130–1 (1955).

21. Berezin, B. D., *Izvest. Vysshikh Ucheb. Zavedenii, Khim. i Khim. Tekhnol.*, **2**, 10-14 (1959).

22. Berezin, B. D., *Izvest. Vysshikh Ucheb. Zavedenii*, *Khim. i Khim. Tekhnol.*, **2**, 165-72 (1959).

23. Berthier, G., Mayot, M., Pullman, A., and Pullman, B., *J. phys. et radium*, **13**, 15-20 (1952).

24. Beynon, J. H., and Humphries, A. R., *Trans. Faraday Soc.*, **51**, 1065-71 (1955).

25. Bigelow, N. M., and Perkins, M. A., in Lubs, ed., "The Chemistry of Synthetic Dyes and Pigments," pp. 577-606, New York, Reinhold Publishing Co., 1955.

26. Block, B. P., Johnson, R. D., Nielsen, N. C., and Parry, R. W., in Bailar, ed., "Chemistry of the Coordination Compounds," pp. 223, 243, 361, 370, 741, and 760-1, Reinhold Publishing Corp., New York, 1956.

27. Bornmann, Jr., J. A., *J. Chem. Phys.*, **27**, 604-5 (1957).

28. Bornmann, Jr., J. A., Ph.D. Thesis, "Photoconductive Properties of Some Phthalocyanine Complexes," Indiana University, 1958.

29. Bowden, F. P., *Rev. mét.*, **55**, 1126-32 (1958).

30. Bradbrook, E. F., and Linstead, R. P., *J. Chem. Soc.*, **1936**, 1744-8.

31. Brenner, W., *Materials in Design Eng.*, **51**, No. 4, 12-13 (1960).

32. Brouillard, R. E., *Am. Ink Maker*, **35**, No. 3, 36-40, 73 (1957).

33. Buerger, M. J., "Crystal Structure Analysis," p. 523, New York, John Wiley & Sons, 1960.

34. Cahill, A. E., and Taube, H., *J. Am. Chem. Soc.*, **73**, 2847-51 (1951).

35. Calvin, M., *Trans. Faraday Soc.*, **34**, 1181-91 (1938).

36. Calvin, M., Cockbain, E. G., and Polanyi, M., *Trans. Faraday Soc.*, **32**, 1436-43 (1936).

37. Calvin, M., Eley, D. D., and Polanyi, M., *Trans. Faraday Soc.*, **32**, 1443-6 (1936).

38. Cannon, C. G., and Sutherland, G. B. B. M., *Spectrochim. Acta*, **4**, 373-95 (1951).

39. *Chem. Eng. News*, Feb. 5, 1962, p. 54.

40. Chikayama, A., Ooshika, Y., Itch, R., and Oshida, I., *J. Phys. Soc. Japan*, **12**, 1316 (1957).

41. Colaitis, D., *Compt. rend.*, **242**, 2555-7 (1956).

42. Cook, A. H., *J. Chem. Soc.*, **1938**, 1761-8.

43. *Ibid.*, 1768-74.

44. *Ibid.*, 1774-80.

45. *Ibid.*, 1845-7.

46. Dahlen, M. A., *Ind. Eng. Chem.*, **31**, 839-47 (1939).

47. Dandridge, A. G., Drescher, H. A. E., Thomas, J., and Scottish Dyes Limited, British Patent 322,169 (Nov. 18, 1929).

48. de Diesbach, H., and von der Weid, E., *Helv. Chim. Acta*, **10**, 886-8 (1927).

49. De Goursac, F., and Paquot, C., *Oléagineux*, **2**, 564-7 (1947).

50. Dent, C. E., and Linstead, R. P., *J. Chem. Soc.*, **1934**, 1027-31.

51. Dent, C. E., Linstead, R. P., and Lowe, A. R., *J. Chem. Soc.*, **1934**, 1033-9.

52. Dmietrievskiĭ, O. D., Ermolaev, V. L., and Terenin, A. N., *Doklady Akad. Nauk S.S.S.R.*, **114**, 751-3 (1957).

53. Drechsler, M., and Müller, E. W., *Z. Physik*, **132**, 195-211 (1952).

54. Eastes, J. W. (to American Cyanamid Co.), U. S. Patent 2,770,629 (Nov. 13, 1956).

55. Ebert, Jr., A. A., and Gottlieb, H. B., *J. Am. Chem. Soc.*, **74**, 2806–10 (1952).
56. Egami, F., Yamamoto, A., and Doi, S., *Science (Japan)*, **21**, 94 (1951).
57. Eigenmann, G., and Kern, F., *Textil-Rundschau*, **16**, 167–76 (1961).
58. Eley, D. D., *Trans. Faraday Soc.*, **36**, 500–5 (1940).
59. *Ibid.*, *Nature*, **162**, 819 (1948).
60. Eley, D. D., and Parfitt, G. D., *Trans. Faraday Soc.*, **51**, 1529–39 (1955).
61. Eley, D. D., Parfitt, G. D., Perry, M. J., and Taysum, D. H., *Trans. Faraday Soc.*, **49**, 79–86 (1953).
62. Elvidge, J. A., *J. Chem. Soc.*, **1961**, 869–71.
63. Elvidge, J. A., and Lever, A. B. P., *Proc. Chem. Soc.*, **1959**, 123–4.
64. Elvidge, J. A., and Lever, A. B. P., *Proc. Chem. Soc.*, **1959**, 195.
65. *Ibid.*, *J. Chem. Soc.*, **1961**, 1257–65.
66. Endermann, F., *Z. physik Chem.*, **190**, 162–3 (1942).
67. Espagne, H., *Compt. rend.*, **247**, 992–5 (1958).
68. *Ibid.*, 2318–21.
69. Evstigneev, V. B., Gavrilova, V. A., and Krasnovskii, A. A., *Doklady Akad. Nauk S.S.S.R.*, **70**, 261–4 (1950).
70. *Ibid.*, **74**, 315–18 (1950).
71. Evstigneev, V. B., and Gavrilova, V. A., *Doklady Akad. Nauk S.S.S.R.*, **74**, 781–3 (1950).
72. *Ibid.*, **92**, 381–4 (1953).
73. *Ibid.*, **98**, 1017–20 (1954).
74. *Ibid.*, **103**, 97–100 (1955).
75. *Ibid.*, **108**, 507–10 (1956).
76. *Ibid.*, **115**, 530–3 (1957).
77. *Ibid.*, **119**, 125–8 (1958).
78. Evstigneev, V. B., and Krasnovskii, A. A., *Doklady Akad. Nauk S.S.S.R.*, **58**, 417–20 (1947).
79. *Ibid.*, 1399–1402.
80. *Ibid.*, **60**, 623–6 (1948).
81. Evstigneev, V. B., and Terenin, A. N., *Doklady Akad. Nauk S.S.S.R.*, **81**, 223–6 (1951).
82. Felmayer, W., and Wolf, L, *J. Electrochem. Soc.*, **105**, 141–5 (1958).
83. FIAT Final Report 1313, PB 85172 (Feb. 1, 1948), U. S. Dept. of Commerce, Vol. III, 343–4.
84. *Ibid.*, pp. 446–8, 462.
85. Ficken, G. E., and Linstead, R. P., *J. Chem. Soc.*, **1952**, 4847–54.
86. Fielding, P. E., and Gutman, F., *J. Chem. Phys.*, **26**, 411–19 (1957).
87. Figgis, B. N., and Nyholm, R. S., *J. Chem. Soc.*, **1959**, 338–45.
88. Fischer, E. K., "Colloidal Dispersions," p. 104, John Wiley & Sons, New York, 1950.
89. Fleysher, M. H., and Ogilvie, J. (to Allied Chemical & Dye Corp.), U. S. Patent 2,276,175 (Mar. 10, 1942).
90. Friedlander, G., and Kennedy, J. W., "Radiochemistry," New York, John Wiley & Sons, 1949.
91. Frigerio, N. A., *J. Org. Chem.*, **26**, 2115–6 (1961).
92. Gachkovskii, V. F., *Doklady Akad. Nauk S.S.S.R.*, **70**, 51–4 (1950).
93. *Ibid.*, **71**, 509–11 (1950).
94. *Ibid.*, **73**, 963–6 (1950).
95. *Ibid.*, **75**, 407–10 (1950).
96. *Ibid.*, **82**, 739–42 (1952).

97. *Ibid.*, **93**, 511-4 (1953).
98. *Ibid.*, **110**, 408-10 (1956).
99. Gachkovskiĭ, V. F., *Zhur. Fiz. Khim.*, **26**, 1713-15 (1952).
100. Garrett, C. G. B., "Organic Semiconductors," Hannay, N. B., ed., in "Semiconductors," pp. 662-673, New York, Reinhold Publishing Corp., 1959.
101. George, P., *Biochem. J.*, **43**, 287-95 (1948).
102. *Ibid.*, *Arch. Biochem. Biophys.*, **45**, 21-30 (1953).
103. George, P., Ingram, D. J. E., and Bennett, J. E., *J. Am. Chem. Soc.*, **79**, 1870-3 (1957).
104. George, P., and Irvine, D. H., *Nature*, **173**, 1148-9 (1954).
105. Gibson, J. F., and Ingram, D. J. E., *Nature*, **178**, 871-2 (1956).
106. Gibson, J. F., Ingram, D. J. E., and Schonland, D., *Discussions Faraday Soc.*, **26**, 72-80 (1958).
107. Gomer, R., *J. Chem. Phys.*, **20**, 1772-6 (1952).
108. Gomer, R., and Speer, D. A., *J. Chem. Phys.*, **21**, 73-80 (1953).
109. Graddon, D. P., "Co-ordination Chemistry," p. 11, London, Pergamon Press, 1961.
110. Green, H., *Ind. Eng. Chem.*, **15**, 122-6 (1923).
111. Griffith, J. S., *Discussions Faraday Soc.*, **26**, 81-95 (1958).
112. Gurinovich, G. P., and Sevchenko, A. N., *Izvest. Akad. Nauk S.S.S.R., Ser. Fiz.*, **22**, 1407-11 (1958).
113. Haak, F. A., and Nolta, J. P., Proc. Princeton Univ. Conf. on Semiconduction in Molecular Solids, February, 1960.
114. Hamm, F. A., and Van Norman, E., *J. Appl. Phy.*, **19**, 1097-1109 (1948).
115. Hamon, B. V., *Australian J. Phys.*, **16**, 304-15 (1953).
116. Hasimoto, H., and Yotsumoto, H., *Nature*, **183**, 1001-2 (1959).
117. Hazato, G., *Science (Japan)*, **17**, 213 (1947).
118. Helberger, J. H., *Naturwissenschaften*, **26**, 316-7 (1938).
119. Helberger, J. H., and Hevér, D. B., *Ber.*, **72B**, 11-5 (1939).
120. Herr, W., *Z. Naturforsch.*, **9a**, 180-1 (1954).
121. Hock, H., and Kropf, H., *J. prakt. Chem.*, **9**, 173-86 (1959).
122. Huggins, M. L., *Ann. Rev. Biochem.*, **11**, 27-50 (1942).
123. *Ibid.*, *Nature*, **155**, 18-19 (1945).
124. Hughes, A., *Proc. Roy. Soc. (London)*, **A155**, 710-1 (1936).
125. Ingram, D. J. E., and Bennett, J. E., *J. Chem. Phys.*, **22**, 1136-7 (1954).
126. *Ibid.*, *Discussions Faraday Soc.*, **19**, 140-6 (1955).
127. Karasek, F. W., and Decius, J. C., *J. Am. Chem. Soc.*, **74**, 4716-17 (1952).
128. Kartha, G., and Ramachandran, G. N., *Acta Cryst.*, **8**, 195-9 (1955).
129. Karyakin, A. V., and Shablya, A. V., *Optikai Spektroskopiya*, **5**, 655-62 (1958).
130. Kearns, D., and Calvin, M., *J. Chem. Phys.*, **29**, 950-1 (1959).
131. Kendall, D. N., *Anal. Chem.*, **25**, 382-9 (1953).
132. Kenney, M. E., *J. Inorg. & Nuclear Chem.*, **11**, 167-9 (1959).
133. Kleitman, D., PB 111419, August, 1953.
134. Kleitman, D., and Goldsmith, G., *J. Phys. Rev.*, **98**, 1544 (1955).
135. Klemm, L., and Klemm, W., *J. prakt. Chem.*, **143**, 82-9 (1935).
136. Kolthoff, I. M., and Bowers, R. C., *J. Am. Chem. Soc.*, **76**, 1503 (1954).
137. Korsunovskiĭ, G. A., *Zhur. Fiz. Khim.*, **32**, 1926-7 (1958).
138. Krasnovskiĭ, A. A., *Doklady Akad. Nauk S.S.S.R.*, **58**, 617-20 (1947).
139. *Ibid.*, 835-7.
140. *Ibid.*, **60**, 421-4 (1948).
141. *Ibid.*, **61**, 91-4 (1948).

142. Krasnovskii, A. A., and Brin, G. P., *Doklady Akad. Nauk S.S.S.R.*, **53**, 443–6 (1946).
143. *Ibid.*, **58**, 1087–90 (1947).
144. Krasnovskii, A. A., and Gavrilova, V. A., *Doklady Akad. Nauk S.S.S.R.*, **81**, 1105–8 (1951).
145. Krishnan, K. S., and Banerjee, S., *Phil. Trans. Roy. Soc. (London)*, **A234**, 265–98 (1935).
146. Kropf, H., *Annalen der Chemie*, **637**, 73–118 (1960).
147. Kuhn, H., *J. Chem. Phys.*, **17**, 1198–1212 (1949).
148. *Ibid.*, *Z. Electrochem.*, **55**, 165–78 (1949).
149. Kuhn, H., "Analogiebetrachtungen und Analogrechner zur quantenmechanischen Behandlung der Lichtabsorption der Farbstoffe," Jenny, ed., in "Symposium über Farbenchemie," Aarau, Sauerländer & Co., 53–62 (1961).
150. Labaw, L. W., and Wyckoff, R. W. G., *Koninkl. Ned. Akad. Wetenschap. Proc. Ser. B.*, **59**, 449–50 (1956).
151. Lagenbeck, W., Schubert, H., and Giesemann, H., *Ann.*, **585**, 68–90 (1954).
152. Lancaster, F. W., and Gordy, W., *J. Chem. Phys.*, **19**, 1181–91 (1951).
153. Laruelle, P., *Rev. gén. sci.*, **57**, 161–82 (1950).
154. Lawton, E. A., *J. Phys. Chem.*, **62**, 384 (1958).
155. Lecher, H. Z., Brouillard, R. E., and Giambalvo, V. A. (to American Cyanamid Co.), U. S. Patent 2,524,672 (Oct. 3, 1950); British Patent 662,386 (Dec. 5, 1951).
156. Linschitz, H., and Abrahamson, E. W., *Nature*, **172**, 909–10 (1953).
157. Linstead, R. P., *J. Chem. Soc.*, **1934**, 1016–7.
158. Linstead, R. P., and Lowe, A. R., *J. Chem. Soc.*, **1934**, 1031–3.
159. Linstead, R. P., and Robertson, J. M., *J. Chem. Soc.*, **1936**, 1736–8.
160. Linstead, R. P., and Weiss, F. T., *J. Chem. Soc.*, **1950**, 2981–7.
161. Livingston, R., and Fujimori, E., *J. Am. Chem. Soc.*, **80**, 5610–13 (1958).
162. Lonsdale, K., *Proc. Roy. Soc. (London)*, **A159**, 149–61 (1937).
163. Lonsdale, K., and Krishnan, K. S., *Proc. Roy. Soc. (London)*, **A156**, 597–613 (1936).
164. Lyons, L. E., *J. Chem. Soc.*, **1958**, 1347–51.
165. Lyons, L. E., Walsh, J. R., and White, J. W., *J. Chem. Soc.*, **1960**, 167–75.
166. Many, A., Harnik, E., and Gerlich, D., *J. Chem. Phys.*, **23**, 1733–4 (1955).
167. Marculaitis, W. J., *J. Colloid Sci.*, **12**, 581–93 (1957).
168. Meier, H., *Z. Electrochem.*, **58**, 859–67 (1954).
169. Mellor, D. P., and Craig, D. P., *J. Proc. Roy. Soc. N. S. Wales*, **75**, 27–30 (1941).
170. Melmed, A. J., "A Study of Phthalocyanine and Some Other Planar Molecules in the Field Emission Microscope," Ph.D. Thesis, Pennsylvania State University, 1958.
171. Melmed, A. J., and Müller, E. W., *J. Chem. Phys.*, **29**, 1037–41 (1958).
172. Menter, J. W., *Proc. Roy. Soc. (London)*, **A236**, 119–35 (1956).
173. Merritt, Jr., L. L., *Anal. Chem.*, **25**, 718–21 (1953).
174. Morley, J. F., *J. Rubber Res.*, **16**, 31–3 (1947).
175. Müller, E. W., *Ergeb. exakt. Naturw.*, **27**, 290–360 (1953).
176. *Ibid.*, *Naturwissenschaften*, **37**, 333–4 (1950).
177. *Ibid.*, *Naturforsch.*, **5a**, 473–9 (1950).
178. *Ibid.*, *Phys. Rev.*, **102**, 618–24 (1956).
179. *Ibid.*, in Berl, ed., "Physical Methods in Chemical Analysis," Vol. 3, pp. 135–82 (1956).

180. Nath, A., and Shankar, J., *Current Sci. (India)*, **22**, 372–3 (1953).
181. *Ibid.*, **24**, 267 (1955).
182. Neporent, B. S., and Klochkov, V. P., *Izvest. Akad. Nauk S.S.S.R.*, Ser. *Fiz.*, **20**, 545–8 (1956).
183. *Ibid.*, 601–4.
184. Nyburg, S. C., "X-Ray Analysis of Organic Structures," pp. 109–11, New York, Academic Press, 1961.
185. Paquot, C., *Compt rend.*, **209**, 171–3 (1939).
186. *Ibid.*, *Bull. soc. chim.*, **8**, 695–9 (1941).
187. *Ibid.*, *Compt. rend.*, **214**, 173–5 (1942).
188. *Ibid.*, *Bull. soc. chim.*, **12**, 450–2 (1945).
189. Paquot, C., and de Goursac, F., *Compt. rend.*, **226**, 258–60 (1948).
190. *Ibid.*, *Bull. soc. chim.*, *France*, **1950**, 172–3.
191. *Ibid.*, *Oléagineux*, **5**, 349–63 (1950).
192. Paquot, C., and Galletaud, C., *Olii minerali, grassi e saponi, colori e vernici*, **34**, 330–2 (1957).
193. Pauling, L., "The Nature of the Chemical Bond," Ithaca, New York, Cornell University Press, 1948.
194. Payne, B. R., Scargill, P., and Cook, G. B., *Radioisotopes Sci. Research, Proc. Intern. Conf., Paris, 1957*, **2**, 154–66 (1958).
195. PB 73758, frames 3527-8.
196. Pedersen, C. J. (to E. I. du Pont de Nemours & Co.), U. S. Patent 2,662,895 (Dec. 15, 1953).
197. *Ibid.*, U. S. Patent 2,662,896 (Dec. 15, 1953).
198. *Ibid.*, U. S. Patent 2,662,897 (Dec. 15, 1953).
199. *Ibid.*, U. S. Patent 2,681,347 (June 15, 1954).
200. *Ibid.*, *J. Org. Chem.*, **22**, 127–32 (1957).
201. Polanyi, M., *Trans. Faraday Soc.*, **34**, 1191 (1938).
202. Poraĭ-Koshits, M. A., *Trudy Inst. Krist. Akad. Nauk S.S.S.R.*, **10**, 117–35 (1954).
203. Putseĭko, E. K., *Doklady Akad. Nauk S.S.S.R.*, **67**, 1009–12 (1949).
204. *Ibid.*, **91**, 1071–4 (1953).
205. *Ibid.*, **132**, 1299–1302 (1960).
206. *Ibid.*, *Radiotekh. i Electron.*, **1**, 1364–73 (1956).
207. Putseĭko, E. K., and Terenin, A. N., *Doklady Akad. Nauk S.S.S.R.*, **90**, 1005–8 (1953).
208. *Ibid.*, *Zhur. Fiz. Khim.*, **30**, 1019–27 (1956).
209. Rackow, B., and König, H., *Z. Electrochem.*, **62**, 482–8 (1958).
210. Ray, P., and Sen., D. N., *J. Indian Chem. Soc.*, **25**, 473–82 (1948).
211. Ringer, A., *Pharmazie*, **6**, 44–8, 103–7, 156–61 (1951).
212. Rittenberg, D., and Krasna, A. I., *Discussions Faraday Soc.*, **20**, 185–9 (1955).
213. Roberts, E. M., and Koski, W. S., *J. Am. Chem. Soc.*, **83**, 1865–7 (1961).
214. Robertson, J. M., *J. Chem. Soc.*, **1935**, 615–21.
215. *Ibid.*, **1936**, 1195–1209.
216. Robertson, J. M., Linstead, R. P., and Dent, C. E., *Nature*, **135**, 506–7 (1935).
217. Robertson, J. M., and Woodward, I., *J. Chem. Soc.*, **1937**, 219–30.
218. *Ibid.*, **1940**, 36–48.
219. Robertson, R. E., in Nachod and Phillips, ed., "Determination of Organic Structures by Physical Methods," Vol. 2, pp. 640–1, New York, Academic Press, 1962.

220. Robinson, M. T., and Klein, G. E., *J. Am. Chem. Soc.*, **74**, 6294–5 (1952).
221. *Ibid.*, *J. Phys. Chem.*, **61**, 1004 (1957).
222. Rösch, G., Wolf, W., and Vollmann, H. (to Farbenfabriken Bayer A.-G.), U. S. Patent 2,727,043 (Dec. 13, 1955); British Patent 698,049 (Oct. 7, 1953).
223. *Ibid.*, U. S. Patent 2,739,154 (Mar. 20, 1956); British Patent 698,049 (Oct. 7, 1953).
224. *Ibid.*, U. S. Patent 2,739,155 (Mar. 20, 1956); British Patent 698,049 (Oct. 7, 1953).
225. *Ibid.*, U. S. Patent 2,739,151 (Mar. 20, 1956); British Patent 698,049 (Oct. 7, 1953).
226. *Ibid.*, U. S. Patent 2,752,346 (June 26, 1956); British Patent 698,049 (Oct. 7, 1953).
227. Royals, E. E., and Horne, Jr., S. E., *J. Am. Chem. Soc.*, **77**, 187–8 (1955).
228. Schenck, G., and Musche, R., *Arch. Pharm.*, **288**, 352–5 (1955).
229. Selwood, P. W., *J. Research Natl. Bur. Standards*, **41**, 151–62 (1948).
230. Senff, H., and Klemm, W., *J. prakt. Chem.*, **154**, 73–81 (1940).
231. Sharp, R. A., Schmitt, R. A., Suffredini, C. S., and Randolph, D. F., *U. S. Atomic Energy Comm.*, **GA-910**, 40 pp. (1959).
232. Shigemitsu, M., *Bull. Chem. Soc. Japan*, **32**, 502–5 (1959).
233. *Ibid.*, 544–47.
234. *Ibid.*, 607–16.
235. Shur, E. G., *Adhäsion*, **2**, 53–9 (1957); *Interchemical Review*, **15**, No. 2, 31–9 (1956).
236. *Ibid.*, Paint and Varnish Production, **45**, No. 5, 30–3 (1955).
237. *Ibid.*, No. 6, 30–9, 70 (1955).
238. Sidorov, A. N., and Terenin, A. N., *Doklady Akad. Nauk S.S.S.R.*, **104**, 575–8 (1955).
239. Sirur, M. V., Muthanna, M. S., Bhattacharyya, S. K., and Ghosh, J. C., *Proc. Natl. Inst. Sci. India*, **13**, 141–50 (1947).
240. Stranski, I. N., *Trans. Chalmers Univ. Technol.*, Gothenburg, **114**, 21 pp. (1951).
241. Suhrmann, R., *Arbeitstag. Festkörperphysik*, **2**, Dresden, **1954**, 188–96.
242. Suito, E., and Ueda, N., *J. Electronmicroscopy (Chiba)*, **6**, 24–8 (1958).
243. *Ibid.*, *Proc. Japan Acad.*, **32**, 182–7 (1956).
244. *Ibid.*, **33**, 398–402 (1957).
245. Suito, E., Ueda, N., and Takiyama, K., *J. Electronmicroscopy*, **5**, 14–18 (1957).
246. Suito, E., Ueda, N., Watanabe, H., and Komoda, T., *Nature*, **181**, 332–3 (1958).
247. Susich, G., *Anal. Chem.*, **22**, 425–30 (1950).
248. Susich, G. v., U. S. Dept. of Commerce PB 85172-S-93 (Sept. 1, 1935).
249. Szabo, R., *Acta Univ. Szegediensis, Acta Chem. et Phys.* (N. S.), **1**, 52–69 (1942).
250. Tamamushi, B. I., *Bull. Chem. Soc. Japan*, **17**, 417–19 (1942).
251. Tamamushi, B. I., and Tohmatu, S., *Bull. Chem. Soc. Japan*, **15**, 223–6 (1940).
252. Tarantino, F. R., Stubbs, D. H., Cooke, T. F., and Melsheimer, L. A., Calco Technical Bulletin, No. 902, (American Cyanamid Co.).
253. Taylor, C. A., and Lipson, H., *Nature*, **167**, 809–10 (1951).
254. Terenin, A. N., and Karyakin, A. V., *Doklady Akad. Nauk S.S.S.R.*, **96**, 269–72 (1954).

255. Terenin, A. N., Karyakin, A. V., Lynbomerdrov, E. B., Dmitrievskiĭ, O. D., and Sushinskiĭ, P. E., *Optika i Spektroskopiya*, 1, 456–62 (1956).
256. Terenin, A. N., and Putseĭko, E. K., *J. chim. phys.*, 55, 681–7 (1958).
257. Terenin, A. N., and Sidorov, A. N., *Spectochim. Acta Suppl.*, 573–8 (1957).
258. Thielert, H., and Pfeiffer, P., *Ber.*, 71B, 1399–1403 (1938).
259. Tsunoda, Y., *Science (Japan)*, 13, 129 (1943).
260. Tsutsumi, K., Hayase, A., and Sawada, M., *J. Phys. Soc. Japan*, 12, 793–801 (1957).
261. Ubbelohde, A. R., and Woodward, I., *Proc. Roy. Soc. (London)*, A181, 415–27 (1943).
262. Uri, N., *Nature*, 177, 1177–8 (1956).
263. Vartanyan, A. T., *Izvest. Akad. Nauk S.S.S.R.*, Ser. Fiz, 16, 169–85 (1952).
264. *Ibid.*, 20, 1541–7 (1956).
265. *Ibid.*, *Zhur. Fiz. Khim.*, 22, 769–82 (1948).
266. *Ibid.*, 30, 1028–43 (1956).
267. Vartanyan, A. T., and Karpovich, I. A., *Doklady Akad. Nauk S.S.S.R.*, 111, 561–3 (1956).
268. *Ibid.*, *Zhur. Fiz. Khim.*, 32, 178–86 (1958).
269. *Ibid.*, 274–81.
270. Venkataraman, K., "The Chemistry of Synthetic Dyes," Vol. II, New York, Academic Press, 1952.
271. Voet, A., and Suriani, L. R., *J. Colloid Sci.*, 7, 1–10 (1952).
272. Vollmann, H., Baumann, F., and Bienert, B. (to Farbenfabriken Bayer A.-G.), U. S. Patent 2,701,252 (Feb. 1, 1955).
273. Watt, G. W., and Dawes, J. W., *J. Inorg. Nucl. Chem.*, 14, 32–4 (1960).
274. Weber, K., and Schulz, K. F., *Arhiv. kem.*, 26, 173–81 (1954).
275. Weiser, M., *Röntgen Bl.*, 4, 188–93 (1951).
276. Wells, A. F., *J. Chem. Soc.*, 1949, 55–67.
277. West, B., *J. Chem. Soc.*, 1952, 3115–22.
278. Whalley, M., *J. Chem. Soc.*, 1961, 866–9.
279. Winslow, F. H., Baker, W. O., and Yager, W. A., *J. Am. Chem. Soc.*, 77, 4751–6 (1955).
280. Wiswall, Jr., R. H., (to American Cyanamid Co.), U. S. Patent 2,486,351 (Oct. 25, 1949).
281. Wojtczak, J., *Zeszyty Nauk Univ. Poznan Mat. Chem.*, 1, 25–31 (1957).
282. *Ibid.*, 32–9.

CHAPTER 3

PREPARATION

Phthalocyanines containing central metal atoms from every group in the Periodic Table have been prepared. Commercial and patented procedures for preparing phthalocyanine and copper phthalocyanine are described in Chapter 4. In the present chapter methods used to prepare all known metal phthalocyanines in the laboratory are outlined. The forty-six metals that have formed known phthalocyanine complexes are listed by valence groups in Table 3-1.

Reviews of methods of preparation of phthalocyanines are given by Perkins and Bigelow (7) and Venkataraman (77) and in the journal articles listed in Appendix I.

While there is no one method that may be used to prepare all metal phthalocyanines, some methods can be used to form at least several metal complexes. These methods include (1) the reaction of phthalonitrile with a metal or metal salt, (2) the reaction of phthalic anhydride, phthalic acid, or phthalamide, urea, metal salts, and a catalyst, (3) the reaction of o-cyanobenzamide with a metal and (4) the reaction of phthalocyanine or replaceable metal phthalocyanine with a metal forming a more stable phthalocyanine.

In method 1, one mole of phthalonitrile is heated with the stoichiometric amount of metal chloride (one-quarter mole) to 180–190° for two hours in quinoline or a mixture of quinoline and trichlorobenzene (60). Cobalt, nickel, chromium, iron, vanadyl, chloroaluminum, lead and titanium phthalocyanines have been made by this method (2,4,60). The reaction may be written:

104

TABLE 3-1. METALS FORMING KNOWN PHTHALOCYANINE DERIVATIVES

GROUP I	GROUP II	GROUP III	GROUP IV	GROUP V	GROUP VI	GROUP VII	GROUP VIII
Hydrogen	Beryllium	Aluminum	Titanium	Vanadium	Chromium	Manganese	Iron
Deuterium	Magnesium	Gallium	Tin	Antimony	Molybdenum		Cobalt
Lithium	Calcium	Indium	Hafnium		Uranium		Nickel
Sodium	Zinc	Lanthanum	Lead				Rhodium
Potassium	Cadmium	Neodymium	Thorium				Palladium
Copper	Barium	Samarium					Osmium
Silver	Mercury	Europium					Platinum
		Gadolinium					
		Dysprosium					
		Holmium					
		Erbium					
		Thulium					
		Ytterbium					
		Lutecium					

The reaction may also take place in the presence of urea, instead of quinoline. Either quinoline or the urea decomposition products act as acceptors for the halogen atoms which enter the phthalocyanine molecule to an appreciable extent when the acceptors are not present.

Method 2 uses phthalic anhydride, a metal salt, urea, and a catalyst. The reaction is usually complete after four hours heating at 170–200° (60). The higher temperature should be reached at the end of the heating period. A reaction medium such as trichlorobenzene or chloronaphthalene may be used. Copper, cobalt, nickel, iron and tin phthalocyanines have been made by this procedure.

The yields range from 70 to 98 per cent depending on the reaction conditions. In a liquid medium the yields are usually above 85 per cent (60). Again the urea decomposition products probably act as halogen acceptors when metal halides are used to supply the central metal atom. Ammonium molybdate (62) is an effective reaction catalyst. Arsenic pentoxide, ferric chloride (60), zirconium tetrachloride (55) and boric acid (84) have also been used.

In the third general method o-cyanobenzamide and a metal are heated to 250° for 4 to 6 hours. The product is freed of phthalamide and o-cyanobenzamide by heating it with concentrated sodium hydroxide. After filtration, washing, drying and grinding, the product is freed of excess metal by mechanically removing the metal, flotation of the pigment in a suitable solvent, or chemical means. Iron, nickel, cobalt, magnesium, and copper phthalocyanines have been made by this method (2,4,33, 54,74,75).

The fourth method involves boiling phthalocyanine and a metal in quinoline or benzophenone (16,49).

A variation of the last method for the preparation of metal phthalocyanines relates to a double decomposition reaction with a labile metal phthalocyanine and a salt of a less labile metal. Barrett, Frye and Linstead (4) first used this method to prepare more stable metal derivatives from dilithium phthalocyanine. This complex is particularly useful because of its solubility in alcohol. Copper phthalocyanine is immediately precipitated when alcoholic solutions of dilithium phthalocyanine and anhydrous cupric chloride are mixed. Phthalocyanine derivatives of silver, mercury, calcium, zinc, lead, manganese, and cobalt have been similarly prepared. The reaction does not take place with metal chlorides subject to alcoholysis, such as those of tin, thorium, bismuth, or tungsten oxychloride. A number of rare metal phthalocyanines have been prepared from lithium phthalocyanine by double decomposition with liquid Lewis-base-type organic compounds as the reaction medium, such as dimethyl formamide or methyl sulfoxide. Heavy metal phthalocyanines of uranium, lead, thorium, lanthanum, neodymium, gadolinium, dysprosium, samarium, holmium, erbium, europium, thulium, lutecium, ytterbium and hafnium have been made in this manner (30). In place of lithium phthalocyanine, phthalocyanines of sodium, potassium, magnesium, or beryllium may be used.

The chemistry of the formation of phthalocyanines, which involves the union of four isoindole units symmetrically about a central metal atom in one reaction system, is indeed a remarkable process. In the reaction involving phthalic anhydride, urea, cuprous chloride, and catalysts in the formation of copper phthalocyanine, the phthalic anhydride is converted to phthalimide, which, in turn, is converted to monoiminophthalimide and diiminophthalimide. The reaction sequences starting from phthalic acid anhydride involve addition of nitrogen atoms to the carbon atoms of the maleic anhydride residue of phthalic anhydride. The source of the nitrogen may be urea but the urea molecule decomposes and polymerizes at the elevated temperature at which copper phthalocyanine and other phthalocyanines are made. Therefore, the source of nitrogen is probably a mixture of urea, urea decomposition products, and urea polymers. The stages in which the phthalic residue passes prior to condensing to form phthalocyanine probably are:

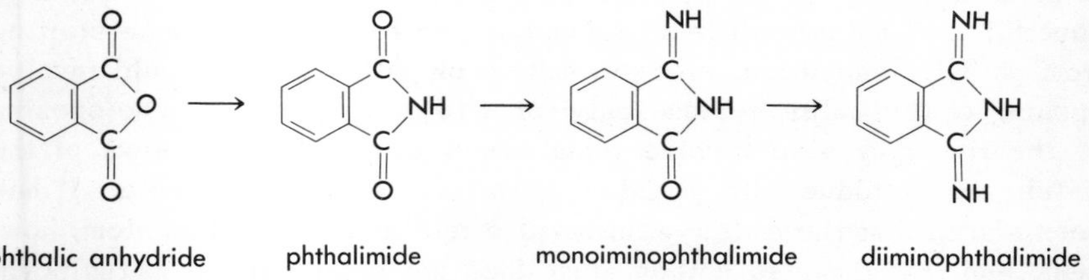

phthalic anhydride   phthalimide   monoiminophthalimide   diiminophthalimide

Either the monoiminophthalimide molecule or the diiminophthalimide molecule condenses with itself to form, for example

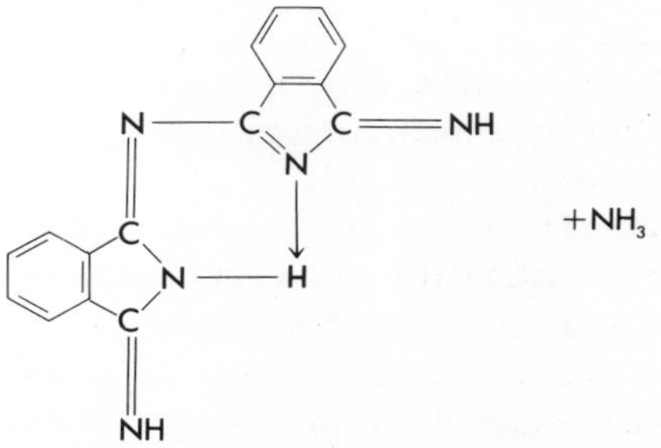

$+NH_3$

(I)

followed by reaction with cuprous chloride to form

(II)

followed by subsequent condensation of (I) and (II) to form copper phthalocyanine and ammonia.

Indeed, phthalocyanines have been made from mixtures of phthalimide and urea, monoiminophthalimide, and diiminophthalimide (5,6,63–67,78). Also, phthalimide and monoiminophthalimide have been isolated from the reaction mass in the formation of phthalocyanines (4,84).

Phthalocyanines may also be made by condensation of four molecules of phthalonitrile. However, although this reaction does take place, it is doubtful that phthalonitrile is formed in the reaction sequence starting from phthalic anhydride, since formation of phthalonitrile would involve opening of the maleic residue only for it to reclose again. The opening of the ring may also involve replacement of an α-carbon atom of the maleic acid residue with a carbon atom from the urea molecule. It has been shown that the maleic acid residue retains its α-carbon atom, however, and that the urea carbon atom does not enter into the phthalocyanine molecule (15).

The infrared absorption spectra of phthalocyanine, copper phthalocyanine and a number of other metal phthalocyanines have been determined (3).

Group I

Phthalocyanine refers to metal-free or dihydrogen phthalocyanine. Not all general methods for the preparation of metal phthalocyanines apply to the preparation of phthalocyanine.

There are two methods for the preparation of phthalocyanine. One is its preparation from phthalonitrile or o-cyanobenzamide and the second is its preparation from a labile metal phthalocyanine.

Because phthalocyanine is a commercial pigment in Europe and because it was manufactured in the United States at one time, its manufacture according to commercial and patented procedures is discussed in Chapter 4. However, some laboratory procedures are included in this chapter.

Byrne, Linstead, and Lowe (16) first developed procedures for its preparation. It may be prepared from magnesium phthalocyanine as follows: The magnesium complex freed from traces of metal or oxide is slowly stirred into 10 times its weight of 96 per cent sulfuric acid, stirred, and kept at $-3°$. The solution is filtered through a coarse sintered glass funnel and is washed with more acid. The sulfuric acid solution is then run slowly into ice made from distilled water. The blue precipitate is collected on a filter, washed acid free, and dried. In this manner 25 g of phthalocyanine is obtained from 42 g of the magnesium derivative.

Phthalocyanine is also prepared (16) by heating 40 g o-cyanobenzamide, 10 g powdered antimony metal, and 20 g naphthalene at 260° for 1 hour. The powdered product is extracted with boiling acetone, caustic soda solution, and hot water, until free from naphthalene and phthalamide. A yield of 11 g of a lustrous purple powder is obtained. The antimony is removed by repeated flotations in ethyl iodide, in which it sinks. The product dissolves in quinoline much less readily than the magnesium complex. Allowing the quinoline solution to cool slowly from 230° in an insulated furnace deposits beautiful long needles with a purple luster.

Reprecipitation from concentrated sulfuric acid gives 3.3 g of product from 3.45 g of phthalocyanine (16). If the solution is heated, no color is recovered on dilution of the acid.

Boiling 2 g phthalocyanine with 30 cc of 20 per cent nitric acid for 15 minutes destroys the color (16). Phthalimide (0.5 g), m p 232°, deposits on cooling the solution.

Phthalocyanine has been prepared by decomposition by means of acids or water on the following metallic derivatives: beryllium, sodium, magnesium, potassium, calcium, manganese, cadmium, tin, barium, and lead (2).

"Heating of 3 g of phthalonitrile with 0.25 g of platinum (prepared by ignition of the oxide) for 45 hours at 360° produced some charring and a 79 per cent yield of phthalocyanine (after extraction with boiling acetic acid). After sublimation this was ash-free" (2).

Phthalonitrile (41 g) is dissolved in 125 g decahydronaphthalene and 125 g benzyl alcohol, heating the mixture to 130° (79). Discontinue heating and add 2 g sodium about 0.1 g at a time during 40–60 minutes. Cool to 130° after each addition. When all the sodium has been added, the reaction mass is heated to 180° for 40 minutes. The pigment is separated from the solvent mixture yielding 26.5 g metal-free phthalocyanine.

Phthalocyanine has been prepared in 75 per cent yield by heating 14.5 g diiminoisoindolenine in 50 g trichlorobenzene at 200° for 2 hours. It is either directly filtered or steam distilled (9). Similarly, 5-nitro-1,3-diiminoisoindolenine in refluxing nitrobenzene gives 90 per cent of tetra-4-nitrophthalocyanine.

The α-, β-, and γ-forms of phthalocyanine are discussed in Chapters 2 and 4.

Sodium phthalocyanine (2,34,51) has been prepared by the addition of 10 g phthalonitrile to a solution of 1.8 g sodium in 100 cc amyl alcohol and refluxing the mixture for 10 minutes. The product is filtered hot and is washed with absolute alcohol and dry ether. The disodium phthalocyanine is a dull greenish blue powder with a purple reflex. The yield is 70 per cent. It decomposes on being heated under reduced pressure.

On heating sodium phthalocyanine with water at 90° for 15 hours the sodium content drops from 8 to 2.5 per cent. Further heating for 3 days reduces it to 0.3 per cent. It also yields free phthalocyanine on treatment with methyl iodide, mineral acids (2), or methanol (21).

Sodium phthalocyanine (39,51) is also prepared by the action of sodium metal on molten phthalonitrile or from 10 g phthalonitrile dissolved in 30 cc amyl alcohol and 3.5 g sodamide added in small portions. The heat of the reaction keeps the alcohol boiling. Absolute alcohol does not boil at a sufficiently high temperature to complete phthalocyanine formation.

In a similar process sodium hydride can be used in place of sodamide (80).

Phthalonitrile, 50 g, 18.6 g sodium cyanamide and 25 g sodium chloride are ball milled (39). The powdered product is heated to 250° for an hour. After cooling and grinding, the product is converted from the sodium complex to the metal-free phthalocyanine by boiling it in hot dilute hydrochloric acid.

Sander (69) postulated that phthalonitrile and sodium react to form a labile addition product of the type of a metal ketyl, viz.,

and that this compound polymerizes with three additional nitrile molecules to form the stable tetramer ring system.

Sander states "Jedenfalls dürfte die bei der Einwirkung von metallischem Natrium auf Nitril-Lösungen auftretende tief rote Färbung für solche Reaktionen sprechen. Kocht man z. B. ein benzolische Lösung von Phthalonitril mit einem Stückchen Natrium-Metall, so färbt sich die Lösung nach Zugabe einiger Tropfen Butylalkohol rasch purpurrot und geht dann über Violett und Blau nach Grün über, wobei sich das Metall mit einer dunkelviolett gefärbten Farbstoffschicht bedeckt. Sorgt man durch Reiben mit dem Glasstab für eine blanke Oberfläche des Metalls, so scheiden sich bei weiterem Erhitzen, gegebenenfalls nach Zufügen weiterer geringer, zum Lösen des Metalls ungenügender Butanolmengen, kupferglänzende Kristalle des metallfreien Phthalocyanins ab, das unter den Reaktionsbedingungen offenbar durch Abspaltung des Metalls aus der Dinatrium-Verbindung entstanden ist. Mit Natriumalkylat allein beobachtet man diese auf labile Zwischenstufen hindeutenden Farberscheinungen weniger gut'' (69).

However Borodkin (8) is not convinced that this is the case since phthalocyanine is not found in the absence of the alcohol. "It would be more probable to assume that in the given case it is sodium butylate that reacts with the phthalonitrile forming the unstable addition product (IV),

which gives phthalocyanine either by reaction with other phthalonitrile molecules or through the intermediate compound

the isoindolenine derivative (V).

"That it is possible to form isoindoline derivatives is indicated in the patent literature."

In seeking proof of his mechanism, Borodkin (8) heated a solution of 5 g of phthalonitrile in 50 cc of benzene under reflux with 0.5 g of sodium metal for 1 hour. Neither the solution nor the sodium appeared to change. Then 5 cc methanol was added to the boiling solution through the reflux condenser. The sodium reacted vigorously with the alcohol, and sodium phthalocyanine was formed immediately. It was impossible to follow the separate steps or to isolate any intermediates because of the rapidity of the overall reaction. The benzene solution was observed to become yellow when the methyl alcohol was added.

If, instead of sodium metal, 0.5 g of sodium methylate was used and the benzene solution of phthalonitrile was boiled for 3 hours, then the solution gradually became yellow-brown in color. The solution, after cooling and removal of partially unreacted sodium methylate, deposited a yellow-brown precipitate on standing. Phthalocyanine was formed when this precipitate was boiled in methyl alcohol or in a mixture of methyl alcohol and benzene. When the dry precipitate was heated, it gave sodium phthalocyanine without melting. The water extract from the precipitate was alkaline. Analysis indicated that it was the sodium methylate addition product of phthalonitrile.

"A product of similar structure (IV) is obtained when butyl alcohol is added to a benzene solution of phthalonitrile in the presence of sodium" (8).

Borodkin also studied the course of the reaction in methanol. "To a solution of 2 g of sodium metal in 70 ml of methyl alcohol, contained in a flask fitted with reflux condensor and stirrer, was added 10 g of phthalonitrile at 25°. The phthalonitrile went into solution on stirring, the temperature of the mixture rose slowly at first, and then rapidly, and the solution assumed by stages a yellow, brown, and then a green color.

"The solution on boiling gave phthalocyanine. If the temperature of the solution was kept below 40°, then colorless rectangular crystals deposited from the yellow-brown solution. After filtering, washing with water to remove alkali, and drying in the air, these crystals have a characteristic odor, inherent to methyl ethers.

"The crystals melt at 116–118°, and are sparingly soluble in cold water; the aqueous extract shows an alkaline reaction. In the air, especially when exposed to sunlight, the crystals turn blue. Phthalocyanine is formed when the product is heated" (8).

A quantitative determination of the amount of carbon, nitrogen and hydrogen indicated that the substance was the sodium derivative of methoxyiminoisoindolenine:

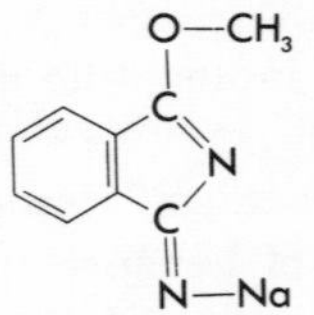

"Heating of the product with alcoholic ammonia in a sealed tube at 100° gave 1,3-diiminoisoindoline with m.p. 196°" (8).

Thus Borodkin concludes that alkoxyiminoisoindolenine is an intermediate in the formation of sodium phthalocyanine from phthalonitrile in the presence of an alcohol, and that in the presence of an excess of alcohol phthalocyanine is formed.

Dipotassium phthalocyanine (2,34,51) has been prepared by refluxing 20 g phthalonitrile for an hour with a solution of 5 g potassium in 200 cc amyl alcohol. The formation of the pigment was slower than in the case of sodium. The product was filtered, washed with dry ether and dried in a vacuum desiccator. Crude dipotassium phthalocyanine (10 g) was obtained as a blue powder, which was insoluble in all solvents and which could not be sublimed. Treatment of the potassium complex with boiling absolute alcohol, or with methyl iodide led to the formation of phthalocyanine.

Lithium phthalocyanine has been prepared (4) by adding 60 g of phthalonitrile to a solution of 4 g lithium in 300 cc amyl alcohol. A green color appeared and a vigorous exothermic reaction took place when the mixture was warmed. The color changed to deep blue and some lithium phthalocyanine precipitated. The mixture was boiled for 30 minutes, cooled, diluted to 1 l with benzene and was allowed to stand for 3 hours. After filtration the dull blue lithium phthalocyanine, 36 g, was extracted with dry acetone. Evaporation of the acetone gave 30 g dilithium phthalocyanine in 50 per cent yield as crystals with a purple luster.

—"The dilithium compound is freely soluble in alcohol, amyl alcohol, and acetone, but not in ether or benzene. On cautious addition of benzene to hot alcoholic solution it separates in plates or needles with a purple lustre, which are solvated and lose alcohol at 250–300°. The unsolvated compound is completely soluble in alcohol. The powder is greenish-blue" (4).

The high solubility of dilithium phthalocyanine in alcohol and the lability of the central metal atoms combine to make a most useful reagent since it is possible to make metallic phthalocyanines by double decomposition at room temperature as described earlier in this chapter.

Lithium hydrogen phthalocyanine (4) is obtained upon extracting the dilithium complex with boiling chloronaphthalene for 9 hours. The green solution becomes gray on cooling and black crystals with a silver luster are deposited on cooling. The same compound is obtained by Dent by adding 52 g of phthalonitrile to a solution of 0.7 g lithium in 300 cc alcohol. The solution becomes brownish-red and then gray. After 25 minutes the black precipitate of lithium hydrogen phthalocyanine was filtered and crystallized from chloronaphthalene. It could be converted to the dilithium complex by dissolving it in lithium amyloxide giving a blue solution.

A solution of dilithium phthalocyanine in absolute alcohol can be hydrolyzed to phthalocyanine by the addition of water, by dilute acids, or by methyl iodide.

Lithium phthalocyanine (80) is prepared by adding a suspension of 1.4 g lithium hydride in 50 g decalin to a mixture of 125 g decalin, 125 g benzyl alcohol, and 41 g phthalonitrile at 175°. After 40 minutes the temperature was raised to 180°, the product was filtered off, washed with benzene, and dried to yield 34 g lithium phthalocyanine.

While Braun and Tcherniac (11) in 1907, de Diesbach and von der Weid (24) in 1927, and Dandridge, Drescher, and Thomas (19) in 1929 had prepared phthalocyanine and copper phthalocyanine, the first determination of the structure of copper phthalocyanine was given by Dent and Linstead (22).

Copper phthalocyanine is prepared by heating a mixture of 4 g-moles of phthalonitrile and 1 g-atom of copper bronze at 270° for 15 minutes. A green color first forms at 190°, the mass becomes viscous at 220° and cannot be stirred at 270°. The powdered product is boiled with alcohol until the washings contain no phthalonitrile. It is then dried to give a yield of from 75 to 90 per cent of the weight of nitrile. The product contains some copper-bronze, which can be removed with sulfuric acid.

The finely powdered pigment is dusted into 10 times its weight of concentrated sulfuric acid at room temperature and with stirring. After an hour the solution is filtered through sintered glass and the filtrate and washings are poured in a thin stream onto 100 times the pigment weight of ice. The blue precipitate is allowed to stand for 2 hours, the solution filtered, the precipitate washed with boiling water, reslurried in boiling alcohol, and filtered and dried at 100° to obtain 90–95 per cent of the weight of the crude pigment. The sulfuric acid solution was stable. A sample kept at room temperature for two days gave a 92 per cent recovery of copper phthalocyanine.

The reaction between phthalonitrile and copper also proceeds well in boiling quinoline or α-methylnaphthalene. The pigment precipitates as it is formed as a crystalline product with a beautiful bronze reflex.

"The tendency to form this compound is great and the readiness with which the various compounds of copper react appears to be determined by the ease with which they can supply the metal. This is clearly illustrated by the reaction between phthalonitrile and the two chlorides of copper. When cuprous chloride (1 equivalent of CuCl) and 4 molecules of the nitrile were heated together without special precautions, a copper phthalocyanine was obtained which contained chlorine. To determine the fate of the chlorine, the reaction was repeated under carefully controlled conditions in a stream of nitrogen, the issuing gas being passed through silver nitrate solution. Pigment formation commenced at 150°, but hydrogen chloride was not eliminated below 200°. Much heat was then evolved and hydrogen chloride came off in quantity. The pigment formed contained chlorine but the uncombined phthalonitrile did not, and the recovered copper chloride was mainly in the cupric state. The quantities of the products and their content of chlorine and copper suggested that the reaction was a combination of the two processes:

(A) at 150–180°: $4C_8H_4N_2 + Cu_2Cl_2 = (C_8H_4N_2)_4Cu + CuCl_2$

(B) above 200°: $4C_8H_4N_2 + CuCl_2 = (C_8H_4N_2)_3Cu(C_8H_3N_2Cl) + HCl$

"This was proved to be correct by the experimental realisation of the two isolated reactions (A) and (B). Cuprous chloride combined smoothly with phthalonitrile at about 170° in the ratio 2CuCl: $4C_8H_4N_2$ and one half of the copper remained behind as cupric chloride. The pigment formed was copper phthalocyanine, practically free from chlorine and identical with that prepared from metallic copper. Cupric chloride reacted only above 200° with the evolution of one half of the chlorine as hydrogen chloride and the formation of *copper monochlorophthalocyanine* $C_{32}H_{15}N_8ClCu$.

"In the second process the chlorine undoubtedly enters one of the benzene nuclei in the phthalocyanine complex and cannot be removed without complete disruption of the molecule. Fission with nitric acid yields a mixture of phthalimide and a chlorophthalimide but no chloride ion, showing the independence of the chlorine from the copper. The chlorine is probably in the 4-position.

"The readiness with which cuprous chloride combines with phthalonitrile is due without doubt to the ease with which it can supply metallic copper, whereas the only way in which cupric chloride can act as a source of copper is by losing chlorine simultaneously. It is a clear indication of the great tendency for the formation of the phthalocyanine complex that so unlikely a reaction as nuclear halogenation should take place in this way. The almost explosively exothermic nature of the reaction also illustrates the tendency for the production of the phthalocyanine.

"The formation of copper phthalocyanine from copper oxides, acetate, sulphide, and sulphate does not call for special comment, but it is worthy of note that copper sulphide appeared to provide copper for the reaction by liberating sulphur, there being no nuclear substitution. Similarly, the use of the sulphate did not give any nuclear sulphonation. None of these substances was as satisfactory in practice as the metal or the chlorides.

"The relationship between copper phthalocyanine and the other members of the group, which is indicated by their general resemblance in physical properties and mode of formation, is proved by the following facts: (1) Free phthalocyanine, when heated with metallic copper in boiling quinoline, yields a copper compound identical with that prepared from phthalonitrile. (2) Nitric acid decomposes copper phthalocyanine to give phthalimide in good yield, together with copper and ammonium nitrates. (3) A similar decomposition is effected by dilute acid permanganate.

"Copper phthalocyanine is even more stable than the other compounds of this series and in this respect must be classed among the most remarkable of organic compounds. It resists the action of molten potash and of boiling hydrochloric acid. It dissolves in concentrated sulphuric acid and is precipitated unchanged and in almost quantitative amount by dilution with water. It is exceptionally resistant to heat and at about 580° it may be sublimed at low pressure in an atmosphere of nitrogen or carbon dioxide. The sublimate is beautifully crystalline and analytically pure. The substance also sublimes with some decomposition in air at atmospheric pressure. It is an indication of the remarkable nature of the compound that an apparatus of hard glass or silica is necessary for these operations. In contrast with this, the monochloro-copper compound cannot be sublimed, but is decomposed with the evolution of hydrogen chloride. This supports the formula assigned to the substance and renders it improbable that it is an inseparable mixture of one part of a fully chlorinated copper phthalocyanine with three parts of unsubstituted copper phthalocyanine" (22).

Lecher, Lacey and Orem (44) observed that pure cuprous halides or copper powder do not react with phthalonitrile in boiling pyridine if air is excluded.

Oxygen oxidizes cuprous halides dissolved in pyridine or copper powder suspended in boiling pyridine. In the halide system, cupric halide-pyridine complexes precipitate and a colloidal solution of cupric oxide is formed. In addition, cupric oxyhalides may be present.

"The conversion of phthalonitrile into copper phthalocyanine in boiling pyridine requires cupric compounds, preferably in the presence of a mild reducing agent such as cuprous halide or copper. Cuprous halides in the presence of oxygen are reactive. So are finely dispersed cupric oxide, cupric oxyhalides or mixtures of cupric halides and cupric oxide. In the absence of any reducing agent part of the pigment formed assumes this function."

In the first patent on a phthalocyanine Dandridge, Drescher, and Thomas (19) made copper phthalocyanine by heating 100 g of phthalic anhydride and 10 g of cuprous chloride to 220–260° and 12 g of ammonia were introduced while agitating the mass. During the second hour another 12 g of ammonia were passed into the mass. The mass was cooled, ground, extracted with 10 times its weight of 2 per cent soda ash twice and with 3 per cent hydrochloric acid twice. It has a strong blue color with a coppery luster. "It contains 10.27 per cent of copper which appears to be combined."

A number of methods for preparing copper phthalocyanine and its derivatives is given in PB 85172, FIAT Final Report 1313, Feb. 1, 1948 (60).

Lich and Schoniger (45) have used the following method for the preparation of a small quantity of copper phthalocyanine: Heat a mixture of 0.25 g phthalic anhydride, 0.05 g cupric chloride, 1.3 g urea and a speck of ammonium molybdate to 180° in a short test tube in an oil bath for one-half hour. The product is ground with dilute hydrochloric acid, boiled, centrifuged and decanted. It is stirred with cold dilute sodium hydroxide, centrifuged and decanted. It is again boiled with dilute hydrochloric acid and then is thoroughly washed with water. After the final decanting the remaining water is removed with a filter paper and the product is vacuum dried. Yield: 0.3 g copper phthalocyanine; time: 1.5 hours.

Refluxing 5-nitro-1,3-diiminoisoindolenine in nitrobenzene in the presence of cuprous chloride gave an 89 per cent yield of copper tetra-4-nitrophthalocyanine, and 4,5,6,7-tetrachloro-1,3-diiminoisoindolenine in the presence of cuprous chloride gave copper hexadecachlorophthalocyanine (9).

α-, β-, and γ-Forms of copper phthalocyanine are defined and their properties are discussed in Chapters 2, 4, and 6.

α-Copper phthalocyanine (26) has been made by heating 82 g of phthalonitrile, 10.6 g of copper-bronze, and 400 cc of ethylene glycol at 137–140° for 24 hours, while agitating the mass. After cooling to 80° the reaction was drowned in ethyl alcohol, filtered, and the precipitate extracted with ethyl alcohol to remove the unreacted phthalonitrile. The alcohol was displaced by water and the aqueous presscake was slurried in 1.5 l water containing 10 cc concentrated aqueous ammonia and 0.5 g of ammonium chloride for 1.5 hours at 70°. After filtration this purification step was repeated. The yield of dried α-copper phthalocyanine was 77 per cent.

β-Copper phthalocyanine (26) is made by heating a mixture of 155 g phthalonitrile, 315 cc nitrobenzene, 40.6 g anhydrous copper sulfate, and 13 g ammonium sulfate to 105° while passing a stream of gaseous ammonia through the suspension until ammonia is no longer absorbed. The flow of ammonia is reduced and the mass is heated to 225–230° in 0.5 hr and is held at this temperature for 0.5 hr. The product is cooled, filtered, and washed with methanol. The β-modification thus obtained may be ground to a pigment by milling it with sodium chloride and tetrahydronaphthalene (32).

Copper 1,2-naphthalocyanine (10) has been prepared by heating 5 g of 1,2-dicyanonaphthalene and 1 g of reduced copper to 250–60° for 1 hour. The cold, powdered melt is extracted with boiling alcohol to remove the unreacted dinitrile. The residue is dissolved in cold concentrated sulfuric acid and is poured on ice. The green precipitate is filtered, and is washed with hot water, alcohol, and ether to give copper 1,2-naphthalocyanine in 46 per cent yield.

Copper chloro-1,2-naphthalocyanine is made by heating 10 g 1,2-dicyanonaphthalene and 2.1 g cupric chloride to 260–290° for 30 minutes. The green product is extracted with water and with boiling benzene to give copper chloro-1,2-naphthalocyanine in 87 per cent yield.

Silver phthalocyanine (4) is prepared by dissolving 2 g dilithium phthalocyanine in absolute alcohol and adding 50 per cent excess of a solution of silver nitrate in absolute alcohol. The silver complex precipitates as a blue pigment. It is also prepared by refluxing 3 g lead phthalocyanine and 3 g silver sulfate in 30 cc chloronaphthalene for 3 hours. It separates as fine needles with a red luster. Inorganic impurities are removed by flotation in ether. It is not certain whether the product is silver phthalocyanine or silver hydrogen phthalocyanine. Metallic silver is deposited when an attempt is made to recrystallize the product from chloronaphthalene. On treatment with sulfuric acid phthalocyanine is formed.

Group II

Beryllium phthalocyanine (35) is prepared by boiling 20 g of phthalonitrile with 3 g of etched beryllium in a nitrate bath. The melt is semisolid in 30 minutes and after one hour the product is cooled. The excess metal is removed and the powdered residue is washed with alcohol yielding 5.8 g. On sublimation at 5 mm Hg the blue vapor deposits long flat needles. The larger opposite faces have a bluish reflex and the two smaller faces have a bronze reflex. The crystals break up in moist air due to hydration. The long crystals of beryllium phthalocyanine curve and then become hook-shaped before fracturing to a blue powder. The blue powder is the dihydrate. Beryllium phthalocyanine is soluble to the extent of 2.8 per cent in boiling quinoline and almost 1 per cent in boiling pyridine. The crystals obtained from these solutions are solvated. Solution in concentrated sulfuric acid removes the beryllium to form phthalocyanine on dilution with ice water.

"Anhydrous beryllium phthalocyanine is difficult to handle on account of its hygroscopic nature" (53).

Calcium phthalocyanine is formed as a dull green precipitate upon the reaction of dilithium phthalocyanine and calcium chloride in absolute alcohol (4).

Phthalonitrile, 10 g, and 10 g calcium oxide are heated slowly with mechanical stirring to 275–280° for 15 minutes (2,35). The solid mass is powdered and is extracted exhaustively with boiling alcohol. It is freed from lime with ice-cold hydrochloric acid. A 70 per cent yield of calcium phthalocyanine is obtained as a dull green pigment with almost no luster. The calcium content is not lowered by treatment with dilute hydrochloric acid at 0°. The metal is eliminated by solution in concentrated sulfuric acid and pouring the solution into ice water. Phthalocyanine is also formed by boiling the calcium complex with 2 volumes of 15 per cent hydrochloric acid.

A similar method using formamide was used on a commercial scale in

Germany to make calcium phthalocyanine for conversion to phthalocyanine (60). It is described in Chapter 4.

Calcium phthalocyanine has also been prepared by boiling a mixture of 10 g phthalonitrile and 0.5 g calcium turnings in 30 cc amyl alcohol for five hours (34,35,51). Color development is slow and the yield is 2.2 g of a dark blue impure calcium complex.

Calcium phthalocyanine is of interest for its ready convertibility into other metallic phthalocyanines, but it is second to lithium phthalocyanine for this use especially in the laboratory.

Magnesium phthalocyanine (16) can be prepared by heating 3.8 g phthalocyanine and 0.15 g magnesium turnings in boiling benzophenone at 307° for 2 hours. The purified and recrystallized product contains 3.5 per cent magnesium. After boiling one more day with more magnesium and recrystallization a beautiful crystalline product containing the theoretical amount of magnesium is obtained.

Magnesium phthalocyanine can be prepared in a 79 per cent yield from phthalonitrile and etched magnesium turnings (2,25,35). A mixture of 32 g phthalonitrile and 2 g magnesium are boiled for 5 hours (51). The unchanged nitrile is removed by extraction with benzene and the residue is washed with hydrochloric acid, water, alcohol, and ether. The yield is 12.6 g. The complex is dried at 100° for 10 hours and 10 g are boiled with 150 cc quinoline. The solution is filtered from 4.5 g undissolved pigment. It is allowed to crystallize over phosphoric oxide in a dessicator depositing pure magnesium phthalocyanine dihydrate crystals. On treatment of the magnesium complex with concentrated sulfuric acid and dilution of the solution by pouring it onto ice water, phthalocyanine is formed.

When the dihydrate is heated to 116° for 358 hours it loses one molecule of water. Heating the partially dehydrated complex with quinoline, filtering hot and allowing the filtrate to cool gives 50 per cent yield of a magnesium complex containing one molecule of quinoline and one molecule of water (51). A similar complex is formed with pyridine. The anhydrous magnesium complex can be made from phthalonitrile and etched magnesium turnings. It is washed free of nitrile with anhydrous alcohol. Upon sublimation for 5 minutes, the complex is obtained as lustrous blue needles. It forms the dihydrate in moist air in one hour. It was shown that water and not oxygen is the addition compound (2).

Magnesium phthalocyanine can be prepared from o-cyanobenzamide and magnesium at 250° in a stream of ammonia (46,54), or from phthalimide and magnesium at 260-270° in a stream of ammonia (75), or from phthalonitrile, sodium cyanamide and magnesium powder at 250° for one hour (39).

Magnesium phthalocyanine has been prepared by the reaction of phthalamide and magnesium imide at 240–280° for 3 hours (61).

Magnesium phthalocyanine (12) has also been prepared by heating 10.5 g phthalic anhydride, 12.6 g urea, 0.91 g magnesium oxide, 0.25 g ammonium molybdate, 5.4 g ethane sulfonic acid and 40 g trichlorobenzene with agitation to 200° for four hours. After filtration the product is slurried with hot aqueous alkali. It is filtered hot and washed with water until neutral to obtain a high yield of bright blue magnesium phthalocyanine dihydrate. In a similar method, 5.4 g sodium tripolyphosphate (13), or 5.4 g sodium sulfate (14) replaces the ethane sulfonic acid.

α-Magnesium 1,2-naphthalocyanine (10) is prepared by heating 40 g of 1,2-dicyanonaphthalene and 2.1 g of etched magnesium turnings at 365–370° for 80 minutes. The unreacted dinitrile is removed with benzene and the residue is ground with water to convert the β-magnesium complex to the monohydrate, which is insoluble in ether, whereas the anhydrous β-complex appears to be slightly soluble. The dried product is exhaustively extracted with ether. Evaporation of the ether solution gives in 62 per cent yield α-magnesium 1,2-naphthalocyanine which is bright green with a purple luster. A small amount of 1,2-dicyanonaphthalene present could be sublimed out at 230–240° under reduced pressure in a stream of carbon dioxide.

β-Magnesium 1,2-naphthalocyanine left in the extractor was sifted from excess magnesium and boiled again with benzene. The yield was 24 per cent. The β-complex can be purified by crystallization from chloronaphthalene.

α-Magnesium 1,2-naphthalocyanine is soluble in ethanol, acetone, ethyl acetate, chloroform, and is extremely soluble in ether.

Magnesium may be removed from either complex by solution in concentrated sulfuric acid and pouring the acid solution onto ice. α-1,2-Naphthalocyanine is a green solid with a purple luster. The β-complex is a darker green.

Zinc phthalocyanine is formed as a blue precipitate upon the reaction of dilithium phthalocyanine and zinc chloride in absolute alcohol (4). It is insoluble in quinoline and chloronaphthalene.

A mixture of 10 g phthalonitrile and 1.3 g zinc dust is slowly heated to 245° by which time the melt has solidified (2). It is heated at 260–70° for 20 minutes. The product is cooled, ground and washed with alcohol to obtain 9.1 g of a blue lustrous mass. Zinc phthalocyanine sublimes in good yield and resembles copper phthalocyanine in appearance. Reprecipitation of the zinc complex from the concentrated sulfuric acid solution, followed by filtration and washing with aqueous ammonia, boiling water, and alcohol give substantially pure zinc phthalocyanine.

Zinc phthalocyanine is readily formed from 20 g phthalonitrile and 10 g fused zinc chloride at reflux for 30 minutes. The mass is extracted with boiling alcohol and with boiling water (35,51). A yield of 14.2 g of a dark blue powder is obtained. Treatment with sulfuric acid does not eliminate the metal.

Barrett, Linstead, and Dent (2) found an appreciable amount (4.6 per cent) of chlorine in the zinc phthalocyanine made from phthalonitrile and zinc chloride.

Zinc phthalocyanine (17) has also been made by heating 512 g phthalonitrile, 88 g zinc dust, and 3500 g α-chloronaphthalene to 200°. Then 9 g powdered potassium hydroxide are added and the mass is heated to 240° for 5 hours. It is filtered, washed with ethanol and water, reslurried with dilute hydrochloric acid, filtered again, reslurried with dilute sodium hydroxide, filtered, washed and dried. It is then converted to a pigment form by salt grinding. A beautiful blue pigment, soft in texture is obtained which is a mixture of the α- and β-zinc forms.

Zinc phthalocyanine (72) is obtained by heating 45 g phthalic anhydride, 120 g urea, 6.2 g zinc dust, 18 g titanium tetrachloride, 3 g boric acid, and 200 g nitrobenzene to 190–200° for 3 hr. After separating the product it is slurried in 5 per cent sulfuric acid, and drowned in ice water to obtain a 21 per cent yield of the zinc complex.

Zinc phthalocyanine has also been made by the phthalic anhydride-urea process by supplying the metal as zinc phthalate (73).

α-Zinc phthalocyanine (26) is made by heating 128 g phthalonitrile, 18 g zinc powder and 450 cc trichlorobenzene to 200° during 1 hour and holding the mass at that temperature for 12 hours. It is cooled to 100°, filtered, washed with trichlorobenzene, and then with warm ethanol. The product is then treated twice with 1.5 l water, containing 42 cc concentrated hydrochloric acid, at 70° for 1.5 hours to remove excess zinc metal and zinc oxide. The dried β-pigment is pure; yield 25 per cent. It is ball milled with dry sodium chloride and tetrahydronaphthalene (32) to obtain α-zinc phthalocyanine.

β-Zinc phthalocyanine (26) is obtained by heating the α-complex in boiling acetone for 8 hours.

Zinc naphthalocyanine (10) may be prepared by heating 10 g 1,2-dicyanonaphthalene and 1 g zinc dust at 275° for 20 minutes and at 310–320° for 45 minutes. The excess dinitrile is removed with boiling benzene. A yield of 7.3 g of green powder with a purple reflex is obtained. It is slightly soluble in ether, ethyl acetate. chlorobenzene and toluene, more soluble in quinoline, aniline and chloronaphthalene. The solution in sulfuric acid is purple. It may be recovered almost quantitatively on dilution.

Zinc phthalocyanine can be chlorinated in carbon tetrachloride under pressure to form zinc polychlorophthalocyanine containing 14–15 chlorine atoms (60).

Zinc chlorophthalocyanine has also been prepared from chlorophthalonitrile and zinc in trichlorobenzene at 235° (70), and by heating 500 g zinc phthalocyanine, 10 g zinc chloride and 1700 g chlorine in a pressure-tight vessel for 6 hours at 100° (58).

Cadmium phthalocyanine (2,35) is formed by heating 10 g phthalonitrile and 2.5 g cadmium filings for 2 hours at 290°. The product is drowned and boiled with alcohol which removes nitrile and a pink impurity. The excess of cadmium is removed by repeated flotation in alcohol. Cadmium phthalocyanine is a dull green color with a purple reflex which is more noticeable when the substance is moist with organic liquids. It appears soluble in all solvents and cannot be sublimed. Solution in concentrated sulfuric acid and precipitation yields 3 g phthalocyanine.

Cadmium phthalocyanine (76) has also been prepared by heating phthalonitrile, cadmium powder, and ethylene glycol to 137–140° for two hours.

Cadmium hexadecachlorophthalocyanine (41,56) is prepared by heating 72 g tetrachlorophthalic anhydride, 100 g urea, 9.8 g cadmium powder (99 per cent-300 mesh), 20 g zirconium tetrachloride, 4.25 g ammonium perchlorate and 945 g trichlorobenzene to 175° during 3 hours and holding at 175–180° for 1.5 hours. The product is filtered, washed with trichlorobenzene, isopropanol, water, sodium hydroxide, and again with water to give a good yield of the cadmium chloro-complex.

Barium phthalocyanine (2,35) is prepared by heating a mixture of 15 g phthalonitrile and 7.5 g of anhydrous baryta at 290° for 2 hours. The reaction is not so vigorous as in the case of calcium oxide. The excess of nitrile is removed with boiling alcohol. Since barium phthalocyanine is decomposed by ice cold dilute hydrochloric acid, the excess baryta can not be removed. The yield of crude barium compound is 16.5 g. It is insoluble and can not be sublimed. Boiling the barium complex with dilute hydrochloric acid yields free phthalocyanine.

Mercury phthalocyanine (4) is formed from 2 g dilithium phthalocyanine dissolved in absolute alcohol and a 50 per cent excess of mercuric chloride dissolved in the same solvent. It precipitates as a dull green pigment, very difficult to filter. It is washed free of mercuric chloride with hot alcohol. Recrystallization from chloronaphthalene as well as solution in sulfuric acid produces phthalocyanine. Mercury phthalocyanine has been reported to be a bright green pigment (60).

Group III

Chloroaluminum phthalocyanine (2) is prepared by boiling 20 g phthalocyanine with 40 g aluminum chloride in 150 cc quinoline for 20 minutes. There is no reaction with metallic aluminum under the same conditions. The greenish-blue color rapidly changes to a pure blue. The mass is cooled, 150 cc alcohol are added, the mixture is boiled and filtered, and the residue is washed with alcohol. Upon extraction with boiling chloronaphthalene, chloroaluminum phthalocyanine is obtained in the form of blue octahedra. This product shows no tendency to form a hydrate in moist air.

Hydroxyaluminum phthalocyanine monohydrate (2) is formed when the chloro compound is dissolved in sulfuric acid and then diluted to yield a bluish-green precipitate. The precipitate is filtered, neutralized with an excess of aqueous ammonia, filtered again, and washed with boiling alcohol. The blue product is insoluble in the usual solvents. It contains no chlorine. In moist air the monohydrate took up two additional molecules of water which were again lost at $100°$.

Aluminum phthalocyanine oxide (2) is formed by the sublimation of the monohydrate. The blue vapor deposited needles of this product. It showed no tendency to combine with water.

Chloroaluminum chlorophthalocyanine can be prepared by heating a mixture of 20 g of phthalonitrile and 5 g of powdered anhydrous aluminum chloride in a bath to $250°$. A reaction then occurs which raises the internal temperature to $300°$, the melt solidifies and evolves hydrogen chloride. "In a controlled experiment this was led by a current of nitrogen into silver nitrate and was found to be equivalent to 0.8 g-atom of chlorine per g-mole of phthalocyanine formed. The product was cooled, ground, and washed with benzene. Yield, 20.3 g." When 8 g were crystallized from 400 cc of chloronaphthalene, 5.0 g of chloroaluminum chlorophthalocyanine deposited as a hygroscopic blue powder. The labile (nonnuclear) chlorine was determined by oxidation with ceric sulfate, filtration of the imides and estimation of the chlorine in the filtrate gravimetrically. Oxidation of the chlorophthalocyanine with nitric and sulfuric acids gave a mixture of phthalimide and a chlorophthalimide, melting point about $205°$.

Chloroaluminum chlorophthalocyanine (2) is soluble to the extent of 1.6 per cent in absolute alcohol at room temperature and it is also soluble in pyridine, chloronaphthalene, nitrobenzene, acetone, and methanol, but is insoluble in amyl alcohol, ethyl acetate, chlorobenzene, and hydrocarbons. The dihydrate form of the complex took up 1 additional molecule of water from moist air at room temperature, and lost this at $115°$. The dihydrate gained in weight over calcium chloride.

Hydroxyaluminum chlorophthalocyanine (2) is formed by the addition of ammonia or alkali to an alcoholic solution of chloroaluminum chlorophthalocyanine. This substance is best prepared, however, by dissolving 5 g of the chloro compound in sulfuric acid, diluting with water, filtering, and reslurrying the product in the presence of ammonia. The yield was 3.1 g of a blue product insoluble in the usual solvents and in hot concentrated alkali solution and it contains no labile chlorine.

Neither of the chloroaluminum phthalocyanines gave quantitative results on oxidation with ceric sulfate.

Aluminum phthalocyanine is formed on heating 100 g of phthalonitrile, 30 g anhydrous aluminum chloride, and 200 g anhydrous sodium sulfate to 250–270° for 20 min. A good yield of the complex is said to be formed (25,38). It has a blue-green color.

Aluminum phthalocyanine (84) has been prepared by heating 74 g phthalic anhydride, 74 g urea, and 16.7 g aluminum chloride to 210°. The powdered melt is extracted with hot dilute sodium hydroxide and then with hot dilute hydrochloric acid. On purification from concentrated sulfuric acid it gave a bright bluish-green color.

Chloroaluminum phthalocyanine can also be prepared by heating phthalamide, urea, aluminum chloride and methanol sulfonic acid (12) or diammonium phosphate (13) or sodium sulfate (14) in trichlorobenzene for 6 hours. It may be separated from the solvent and purified in the usual manner.

Aluminum phthalocyanine has also been prepared by heating phthalic anhydride, urea, titanium tetrachloride and aluminum metal in chloronaphthalene at 190–200° for 3 hours (87). The product was purified as above.

Bromoaluminum phthalocyanine (42) has value as a starting point for the synthesis of various substituted aluminum phthalocyanines because it is reported to be easy to prepare and purify.

Aluminum polychlorophthalocyanine (58,60) has been prepared by chlorinating 25 g of aluminum phthalocyanine in 100 g chloroform and 3 g iodine with 70 g chlorine in a closed vessel at 60° for 1 hour. The purified pigment has a pale green color. Aluminum phthalocyanine has also been chlorinated in a phthalic anhydride medium (23).

Aluminum hexadecachlorophthalocyanine (56) has been prepared by heating 100 g urea, 72 g tetrachlorophthalic anhydride, 3 g powdered aluminum, 20 g zirconium tetrachloride, and 4.25 g ammonium perchlorate in 945 g trichlorobenzene to 165° during 2 hours, then at 165–180° for 3 hours with agitation. The solvent is removed and the product is purified in the usual manner. A similar reaction uses tetramethyl zirconate as the catalyst (41).

Aluminum polychlorophthalocyanine (70) may be prepared by heating a chlorinated phthalodinitrile, aluminum, a vanadate and trichlorobenzene to 235° for 15 hours.

Chlorogallium phthalocyanine, chloroindium phthalocyanine and iodoindium phthalocyanine (18) have been prepared by heating 6 moles of o-cyanobenzamide with one mole of the corresponding halides until the reaction was complete. The reaction mass was powdered, extracted with boiling acetone to remove the excess starting material, and then formed microcrystalline products, blue-violet in color with a purple reflex.

Hydroxygallium phthalocyanine and hydroxyindium phthalocyanine were formed on the hydrolysis of the corresponding halogen products, by solution in concentrated sulfuric acid, dilution and neutralization with ammonia.

Gallium phthalocyanine (59) has been prepared by heating phthalonitrile with anhydrous gallium chloride. When the reaction was complete, the product was cooled, ground and the unreacted nitrile extracted with warm alcohol. The product was purified by solution in sulfuric acid, drowning on ice and recovery of the precipitate.

Sulfonated phthalocyanine derivatives of lanthanum, neodymium, gadolinium, dysprosium, samarium, holmium, erbium, thulium, lutecium and ytterbium (30) have been prepared by mixing the rare earth metal salt with a liquid Lewis-base organic compound such as dimethyl formamide or methyl sulfoxide and separating the complex thus formed. This complex is then mixed at room temperature with a tetrasulfonated lithium phthalocyanine. The phthalocyanine complex precipitates and is then converted to a soluble form by anion exchange with an anionic exchange resin or by removing the rare metal salt of the sulfonic acid with hydrogen sulfide. The phthalocyanine products have been suggested for use in the treatment of cancer.

Group IV

Titanium phthalocyanine (60) has been reported to form highly colored products upon reduction with hydrosulfite in dilute alkali.

Stannous phthalocyanine (2) has been made by heating a mixture of 10 g phthalonitrile and 4 g tin at 300° for 3 hours. Mechanical stirring is necessary to keep the molten metal in contact with the nitrile. The reaction is slow in starting. The mass is cooled, separated from the excess metal, and extracted with alcohol to obtain a 70 per cent yield of dark blue powder. The powder is extracted with boiling quinoline which first removes a dark impurity after which the stannous phthalocyanine is extracted rapidly. It crystallizes in dark blue micro-parallelepipeds with a dark violet reflex. Solution of the stannous complex in sulfuric acid and the addition of the brown acid solution to crushed ice gives a green precipitate. It turns blue on the addition of alkali. After filtration, washing, and drying, the product contains a mixture of phthalocyanine and the tin complex. If the sulfuric acid solution is allowed to stand for four days, a low yield of phthalocyanine only is obtained.   The reaction of phthalonitrile and tin may also take place in an ethylene glycol medium (76).

Dichlorotin phthalocyanine (2) is obtained by heating 10 g of phthalonitrile and 5 g of anhydrous stannous chloride to 210°.   The melt turns green and the reaction temperature rises 100°.   The product is cooled, ground, and thoroughly washed with alcohol and yields 90 per cent of a green powder with a purple reflex.   Upon extraction with boiling quinoline the first dark extraction is discarded and the final pure green solution deposits dichlorotin phthalocyanine as blue green plates with a faint purple reflex.

Diiodotin phthalocyanine (2) in admixture with stannous phthalocyanine is formed from the reaction of stannous iodide and phthalonitrile at 210°.   Some iodine is evolved as the temperature rises to 270°.   This complex loses iodine upon boiling with chloronaphthalene or when heated alone.

Dihydroxytin phthalocyanine (2) is formed when 4 g of the dichlorotin complex is refluxed for 20 hours with a solution of 20 g of potassium hydroxide in 100 cc water.   The product is filtered, washed free of alkali, and dried to obtain 3.4 g of blue powder.   The product is free of chlorine and consists mainly of potassium salt of dihydroxytin phthalocyanine.   The dihydroxytin complex can not be obtained in a pure condition.   Other attempts to hydrolyze the dichloro compound give phthalocyanine and certain attempts to reduce the compound give unidentified products, however, reduction of the dichloro complex in a current of hydrogen in boiling quinoline for 48 hours does produce stannous phthalocyanine.

Chlorination of stannous phthalocyanine by passing the dry chlorine over the powder intermittently for 3 days gives dichlorotin chlorophthalocyanine.

Stannic phthalocyanine (2,81) can be prepared by refluxing 0.5 g dichlorotin phthalocyanine and 0.4 g disodium phthalocyanine in chloronaphthalene for 90 minutes.   The color changes from green to blue.   The solution is allowed to stand overnight and is filtered to remove salt. The solution is allowed to stand 5 more days and deposits a blue crystalline solid containing solvent of crystallization.   Extraction of this product with boiling benzene for 4 days removes the solvent of crystallization and leaves stannic phthalocyanine as greenish blue crystals. It sublimes substantially unchanged to give a micro-crystalline deposit. It is sufficiently soluble in benzene, xylene, and pyridine to give a blue color in the cold, but is not soluble in ether, alcohol, acetone, ethyl acetate, and light petroleum.   Unlike the stannous complex, stannic phthalocyanine gives a normal purple color with nitrogen dioxide.   The stannic complex made by the above process has been purified chromatographically (81).

Stannic phthalocyanine is unique in having two phthalocyanine groups attached to a single metal atom. It has been shown that the two phthalocyanine groups lie parallel to each other.

Phthalocyanine reacts with stannous chloride in boiling quinoline to give stannous phthalocyanine hydrochloride or stannous chlorophthalocyanine. The method of preparation suggests the first constitution while the stability of the halogen in the compound suggests the latter constitution.

Dichlorotin chlorophthalocyanine is formed by heating 10 g phthalonitrile and 5 cc stannic chloride at 300° for 12 hours. The product is extracted for 5 days with boiling alcohol to remove a brown impurity. The remainder is purified from quinoline yielding the complex as green crystals with a purple reflex. Dichlorotin phthalocyanine is also formed on heating phthalocyanine and dimethyltin dichloride in chloronaphthalene at 300° for 12 hours.

Stannous phthalocyanine (85) has also been made by heating a mixture of 48 g urea, 15.2 g stannous chloride, 40 g phthalic anhydride, 0.8 g boric acid and 0.08 g ammonium molybdate at 200–205° until the reaction is complete. The product is washed with hot dilute aqueous alkali and with hot dilute hydrochloric acid. It may be converted to the pigment form by salt-grinding.

Tin polychlorophthalocyanine (56) has been prepared by heating 100 g powdered urea, 72 g tetrachlorophthalic anhydride, 9.8 g tin, 20 g zirconium tetrachloride and 4.25 g ammonium perchlorate in 945 g trichlorobenzene. The mass is agitated and heated to 165° during 2 hours, then at 165–180° during 3 hours. The solvent is removed and the product is purified with concentrated caustic solution and dilute hydrochloric acid. Tetramethyl zirconate has also been used as a catalyst in the above reaction (41).

Lead phthalocyanine (2,48) is prepared by adding 10 g of pure litharge in small portions to 20 g of phthalonitrile at 200°. Heating is continued for 10 minutes after which the mass is cooled, ground, and washed with alcohol. It can be purified by crystallization from quinoline or by sublimation which gives a green vapor. The crystals are fragmented parallelpipeds, pure green by transmitted light and with a slight dark red luster.

Treatment of lead phthalocyanine with concentrated sulfuric acid gives a mixture of phthalocyanine and lead sulfate. Crystalline lead phthalocyanine is apparently not affected by concentrated hydrochloric acid but the addition of an equal volume of water causes the crystals to turn blue immediately without altering their form. The metal is completely eliminated by warming. The lead chloride can be removed with boiling water.

Lead cyanamide with or without sodium chloride as a diluent may replace the litharge in the above reaction (39). The reaction of phthalonitrile and litharge or metallic lead may also take place in an ethylene glycol medium (76).

When chlorine is passed over lead phthalocyanine at room temperature for 44 hours, a brown viscous product is formed. It contains about 26 per cent chlorine. Treating this product with sodium hydroxide solution regenerates the original complex almost free of chlorine.

Lead polychlorophthalocyanine can be prepared from tetrachlorophthalic anhydride in a manner similar to that used to prepare aluminum polychlorophthalocyanine (56,41). Powdered lead (18 g) is used instead of 3.0 g of aluminum powder.

Lead naphthalocyanine (10) can be prepared by heating 18 g 1,2-naphthalonitrile mixed with 6.8 g litharge at 274–280° for 30 minutes. The excess nitrile is removed with benzene. A yield of 20.3 g pigment containing some litharge is obtained. The lead complex is yellowish green with a blue reflex. It is soluble in hot pyridine, quinoline, chlorobenzene, chloronaphthalene, and aniline. The lead is removed on solution of the complex in concentrated sulfuric acid. Lead sulfate is formed.

The sulfonated derivatives of hafnium phthalocyanine, lead phthalocyanine and thorium phthalocyanine have been prepared in a manner similar to that used to prepare the rare earth metal sulfonated phthalocyanines discussed under Group III (30).

Thorium phthalocyanine (82) is prepared by heating anhydrous thorium chloride and phthalonitrile to 260–280°. The complex is a deep green color.

Group V

Vanadyl phthalocyanine (2,20) can be made by heating 10 g of phthalonitrile and 2 g of vanadium pentoxide at 240–250° for 30 minutes. The product is cooled, powdered, and boiled with alcohol to yield 6 g of the complex. The product is extracted and crystallized twice from chloronaphthalene giving vanadyl phthalocyanine as a microcrystalline blue powder without luster. The crude product sublimes with a deep blue vapor to give a cubical mass of crystals. The complex dissolves in concentrated sulfuric acid giving an orange-brown solution from which it is precipitated unchanged upon dilution.

It may also be prepared by heating 37 g of phthalic anhydride, 37 g of urea, and 15 g of vanadium trichloride hexahydrate to 250° until the melt becomes nearly solid and no further color is formed. It is cooled, extracted with hot dilute sodium hydroxide and then with hot dilute hydrochloric acid (20). A dark blue crystalline powder is obtained which applied as a pigment gives bright greenish blue shades. The yield is 50 per cent based on the phthalic anhydride used.

The structure (31) of vanadyl phthalocyanine and its magnetic properties (71) are discussed in Chapter 2.

Diantimony phthalocyanine is prepared in the following manner. "Phthalonitrile (20 g) was mechanically stirred with 7 g of finely powdered antimony at 300°; the mixture slowly turned dark blue and after 4 hours was nearly solid. Boiling alcohol removed the excess of nitrile and left 22 g. (75 per cent) of a dull blue, amorphous powder with a dull green rubbing. The same reaction occurred when atmospheric oxygen was excluded by a current of nitrogen. The crude product was purified by repeated flotations in alcohol; the excess of antimony sank and the lighter phthalocyanine could be poured off with the supernatant liquid. Eventually a solid was obtained which microscopic examination showed to be almost entirely amorphous blue *diantimony phthalocyanine*, contaminated with a few lustrous needles of free phthalocyanine and a few particles of antimony" (4). Analysis indicated the formula to be $C_{32}H_{16}N_8Sb_2$.

"It is difficult to reconcile the formula $PcSb_2$ with ordinary valency requirements, and it is impossible to find room in the centre of the phthalocyanine ring for two antimony atoms (effective radii 1.45 Å.) or ions. The compound may have a complex structure such as $Pc:Sb \cdot Sb:Sb \cdot Sb:Pc$. In this the two terminal antimony atoms are located in the centre of phthalocyanine rings and are joined by a chain of two antimony atoms in the manner shown" (4).

The substance could not be further purified. It decomposed when heated under reduced pressure. When crystallized from chloronaphthalene it gave a good yield of free phthalocyanine. Solution in sulfuric acid and reprecipitation in water gave the expected amount of phthalocyanine as did boiling the product for 24 hours with concentrated hydrochloric acid.

Chloroantimony phthalocyanine (4) can be prepared by heating a mixture of 5 g of phthalocyanine, 5 g antimony chloride, and 5 cc chloronaphthalene in a sealed tube at 300° for 6 hours. The liquid was filtered and the dark green residue washed with ether, heated to the boil with water and allowed to settle. The crystalline phthalocyanine complex settled to the bottom and the basic antimony compounds remained in suspension. This was cleared by the addition of a few drops of hydrochloric acid. It was filtered and washed with water and alcohol to yield 5 g of product. This dissolved easily in hot chloronaphthalene containing a little antimony trichloride to give a pure green solution from which chloroantimony phthalocyanine was desposited in cigar shaped needles, with a blue green luster. It may also be prepared from the same reagents by refluxing. It sublimes unchanged upon heating under reduced pressure forming a deep green vapor which deposits green plates with a dark green luster. On crystallization from quinoline or treatment with sulfuric acid phthalocyanine is formed.

Group VI

Chromium phthalocyanine is not formed by the reaction of phthalocyanine and chromium metal or chromium compounds (2).

Chromium phthalocyanine is prepared by heating a mixture of 74 g phthalic anhydride, 74 g urea, and 13.6 g chromium fluoride at 200–220° until the reaction is complete (84). The cooled product is ground and treated with dilute alkali and dilute hydrochloric acid to remove by-products and starting materials. On purification from sulfuric acid an olive colored pigment is obtained.

Elvidge and Lever (27,28) have prepared a number of chromium phthalocyanines in a study of perpendicular conjugation. These are:

"Phthalocyanine Chromium (III) Hydroxide—An intimate mixture of chromic acetate (3 g.) and phthalonitrile (6 g., purified) was heated to 270°. After 15 min., the melt thickened and was allowed to cool. The solid was powdered and triturated in turn with benzene, methanol, water, methanol, and ether. The product (8 g.), mainly phthalocyanine chromium (II) and phthalocyanine chromium (III) acetate, was heated at $400°/10^{-6}$ mm., whereupon the chromous complex sublimed but underwent oxidation. Further sublimation afforded phthalocyanine chromium (III) hydroxide as long purple needles.... On quantitative oxidation the pigment consumed 1.03 atom-equiv. of 0."

"Phthalocyanine Chromium (III) Acetate—The preceding hydroxide (50 mg.) was kept with acetic anhydride for 24 hr. The product was washed with anhydrous ether and dried at 180°/15 mm. to give the acetate...."

"Phthalocyanine Dimethanolchromium (III) Hydroxide—Phthalocyanine chromium (III) hydroxide (50 mg.) was heated with methanol (7 c.c.) under reflux for 2 hr. The complex was washed with anhydrous ether and dried in a desiccator (yield, 54 mg.).... When heated at 180°/20 mm for several hr., this complex afforded phthalocyanine chromium (III) hydroxide, as indicated by the infrared absorption.

"Phthalocyanine Aquomethanolchromium (III) Hydroxide—Phthalocyanine chromium (III) hydroxide (100 mg.) was kept with acetic acid 4·5 c.c.), water (3 c.c.), and methanol (1 c.c.) at 90° for 5 hr. After being washed with water, methanol, and then ether, the complex was dried in in a desiccator (yield, 105 mg.).... At 180°/20 mm., this complex lost weight (4 per cent) and afforded phthalocyanine hydroxoaquochromium (III) with infrared absorption identical with that of authentic material (see below).

"Phthalocyanine Diaquochromium (III) Hydroxide and the 6-Co-ordinate Complex—Phthalocyanine chromium (III) hydroxide (50 mg.) was warmed with 3:1:4 aqueous-ethanolic acetic acid at 95° for 3 hr. Alternatively the hydroxoaquochromium (III) compound (80 mg.) was suspended in water (5 c.c.) at 95° for 4 hr. The *complex* was washed with water, methanol and ether, and dried in a desiccator (yield, 97 per cent).... Sublimation of the complex (36 mg.) at 400°/10⁻⁶ mm. afforded phthalocyanine chromium (III) hydroxide (20 mg.) identified by its infrared spectrum. At 180°/20 mm., however, the complex yielded *phthalocyanine hydroxoaquochromium* (III).... Sublimation of this at 400°/10⁻⁶ mm. afforded phthalocyanine chromium (III) hydroxide (correct infrared spectrum) in 60 per cent yield....

"Phthalocyanine Acetatoaquochromium (III)—Powdered phthalocyanine hydroxoaquochromium (III) (50 mg.) was kept with acetic anhydride (1 c.c.) for 24 hr. The green powder (100 per cent) was washed with ether and dried at 180°/20 mm., so affording the *complex*.... An identical product (infrared spectrum) resulted from treatment of phthalocyanine chromium (III) hydroxide with 70 per cent aqueous acetic acid at 90° for 2 hr.

"Phthalocyanine propionatoaquochromium (III)—formed by keeping phthalocyanine hydroxoaquochromium (III) with propionic anhydride for 1 week, was washed with ether and dried at 180°/15 mm....

"Phthalocyanine Acetato (acetic acid) chromium (III)—Phthalocyanine hydroxoaquochromium (III) (50 mg.), or phthalocyanine chromium (III) hydroxide was refluxed in acetic anhydride (10 c.c.) for 1.5 hr. The *complex* (96 per cent) was washed with methanol and ether and dried at 180°/15 mm....

"Phthalocyanine Acetatomethanolchromium (III)—Phthalocyanine chromium (III) hydroxide (30 mg.), methanol (5 c.c.), and acetic acid (3 c.c.) were refluxed together for 3 hr. The green *complex* (30 mg.) was washed with methanol and ether, and dried in a desiccator.... At 180°/20 mm., this complex was converted into phthalocyanine chromium (III) acetate (Found: C, 65·2; H, 3·1; Cr, 8·5 per cent).

"Hydrogen [Phthalocyanine Dichlorochromate (III)]—Dry hydrogen chloride was passed into a refluxing suspension of phthalocyanine chromium (III) hydroxide (180 mg.) in methanol (15 c.c.) for 3 hr. The very dark green *product* (180 mg.) was dried at 180°/20 mm....

"Potassium [Phthalocyanine Hydroxocyanochromate (III)]—Phthalocyanine chromium (III) hydroxide (80 mg.), methanol (5 c.c.), butanol (5 c.c), and potassium cyanide (80 mg.) were refluxed together for 8 hr., and the mixture was then filtered. During 1 week at 2°, the filtrate deposited elongated prisms of the *complex* (35 mg.) which was washed with cold water, methanol and ether, and dried at 180°/20 mm....

"Disodium [Phthalocyanine Oxohydroxochromate (III)]—Powdered phthalocyanine hydroxoaquochromium (III) (100 mg.) was shaken with 1 per cent sodium hydroxide in ethanol (5 c.c.) for 24 hr. The purple crystals of the complex *salt* were washed rapidly with ethanol and then with ether, and dried at 180°/20 mm. (yield, 90 mg.)...

"Diammonium [Phthalocyanine Oxohydroxochromate (III)]—Liquid ammonia (~10 c.c.) was filtered on to the hydroxoaquocomplex (50 mg.), cooled with liquid ammonia. After 5 hr., the ammonia had evaporated and the *salt* was then dried in a desiccator.... At room temperature, the salt slowly evolved ammonia.

"Dipyridinium [Phthalocyanine Oxohydroxochromate (III)]—The powdered hydroxoaquo-complex (100 mg.) was kept with pyridine (1 c.c.) for 24 hr. and the resulting jade-green crystals (125 mg.) of the *salt* were washed with ether and dried at 150°/20 mm.... Alternatively, phthalocyanine chromium (III) hydroxide (80 mg.) was shaken for 24 hr. with pyridine (4 c.c.), acetic acid (3 c.c.), and water (0·5 c.c.). The product (100 mg.), after being washed with ether and dried at 150°/15 mm., had an infrared spectrum indistinguishable from that given by the preceding salt.

"Phthalocyanine Dipyridinechromium (II)—Dried, powdered phthalocyanine chromium (III) hydroxide (135 mg.) was shaken under nitrogen with pyridine (2 c.c., freshly distilled from barium oxide). After 24 hr., the olive-green chromium (II) *complex* was washed with anhydrous ether and dried at 150°/15 mm. (yield, 146 mg.)....

"Phthalocyanine Chromium (II)—Sublimation of the preceding complex at 400° in nitrogen at 10^{-6} mm. afforded the chromium (II) *complex* as dark purple needles" (27).

Chromium hexadecachlorophthalocyanine and molybdenum phthalocyanine (56) have been prepared by the phthalic anhydride-urea process in a manner similar to that described for aluminum hexadecachlorophthalocyanine but by using 4.6 g powdered chromium or 8.5 g molybdenum powder instead of 3.0 g aluminum. Tetramethyl zirconate replaces zirconium tetrachloride as the catalyst in a similar reaction (41).

Molybdenum phthalocyanine has been reported to form highly colored products upon reduction with hydrosulfite in dilute alkali (60).

✕ Uranyl phthalocyanine (30) has been made by the reaction of a uranyl compound-dimethyl formamide complex with lithium phthalocyanine. Uranyl nitrate hexahydrate, 10.4 g, is dissolved in 8.8 g of boiling anhydrous dimethyl formamide. The mixture is cooled to 0° and yellow crystals precipitate. They are filtered, washed in anhydrous ether at

0° and dried at 200°. A yield of 9.2 g of uranyl nitrate-dimethyl form-amide complex is obtained, at 85 per cent of theory. It has a melting point of 178°.

Lithium phthalocyanine, 5.26 g, is dissolved in 40 cc anhydrous dimethyl formamide at 25° and 5.40 g of the uranyl nitrate-dimethyl formamide complex is dissolved in 40 cc of anhydrous dimethyl form-amide at 25°. The latter solution is stirred into the lithium phthalocya-nine solution forming a heavy deep blue precipitate. It is filtered, washed with boiling dimethyl formamide then with ether and dried. A yield of 7.8 g uranyl phthalocyanine is obtained, 100 per cent of theory.

Uranyl phthalocyanine sulfonic acid has been prepared in the follow-ing manner: Phthalocyanine tetrasulfonic acid, 8.38 g, is dissolved in 250 cc boiling water, and 42 g uranyl sulfate $UO_2SO_4 \cdot 3H_2O$ is added. The solution is refluxed for 3 hours and a precipitate is formed. Hydro-gen sulfide is passed through the suspension for 3 hours and the mixture is subsequently refluxed for one hour. The black precipitate formed is filtered and the deep blue filtrate is evaporated to dryness. The yield is 7.3 g (67 per cent of theory) of uranyl phthalocyanine sulfonic acid. The hydrogen sulfide removes the uranyl groups attached to the sulfonic acid groups. This can also be accomplished by an anion exchange resin in which case the sodium salt of the sulfonic acid is formed.

Group VII

Manganous phthalocyanine (2,43) is formed when 30 g of phthalo-nitrile and 6 g of manganese dioxide are heated for 6 hours at 270°. The black amorphous product is ground and washed with benzene to yield 24.3 g of complex. Extraction of 9.2 g with 110 cc of chlorona-phthalene gives a deep brown solution from which 5.3 g of amorphous black solid precipitates.

"Manganese metal reacted more readily with o-cyanobenzamide than with phthalonitrile." A mixture of 30 g of o-cyanobenzamide and 8 g manganese metal are heated for 5 hours at 270°. The product is drowned and washed with sodium hydroxide solution and alcohol giving 18.5 g of black product. It is also purified by extraction with chloronaphthalene.

"The constitution of these products is uncertain. Both gave on sub-limation a greenish-black vapour depositing a poor yield of *manganous phthalocyanine* in fine lustrous black needles giving a greenish-black powder.... Both crude products and the pure manganous compound gave free phthalocyanine on treatment with sulphuric acid, but the yield was comparatively low (25–40 per cent), apparently owing to fission"(2).

When the atomic radii of the metals, e.g., manganese and lead, are considerably smaller or larger than 1.35 Å, the metal atom is more read-ily removable from the complex (2).

Manganous phthalocyanine reacts with methanolic potassium cyanide to yield hydroxycyanomanganese (IV) phthalocyanine, in which the manganese is in the 6 coordinate quadrivalent state. In a similar way, methanolic sodium hydroxide yields dihydroxymanganese (IV) phthalocyanine, which, on dissolution in the saturated sodium hydroxide provides disodium dioxymanganese (IV) phthalocyanine (28).

Manganese (II) phthalocyanine has been shown to be an oxygen carrier (29). It catalyzes air oxidation efficiently, but is too rapidly destroyed to be of value in synthesis.

Group VIII

Iron phthalocyanine is the phthalocyanine first described in both the patent literature (19) and in Linstead's first article of the phthalocyanine series (46,47).

In the original patent, phthalic anhydride was mixed with iron filings, or phthalamide was mixed with ferrous sulfide and ammonia or an amine was passed into the melt while stirring and heating it to 240 °.

Ferrous phthalocyanine is best prepared, according to Barrett, Dent, and Linstead (2,4), by heating 20 g o-cyanobenzamide with 4 g pure iron wire at 250°, for 6 hours. The product is freed from phthalimide with concentrated sodium hydroxide, the excess wire removed with dilute hydrochloric acid, and the product filtered and washed with water and alcohol. This gives 2.2 g of lustrous crystals. Crystallization from quinoline or aniline gives additive products. Sublimation gives long needles of the pure ferrous complex, blue-green in color but duller in color and luster than those of the nickel complex. Sublimation of the product crystallized from quinoline, liberates the solvent and gives the pure ferrous phthalocyanine.

The hexaaniline addition compound of ferrous phthalocyanine is prepared (4) by boiling 1 g of the ferrous complex in 10 cc aniline. The hot solution is filtered and then cooled and a mass of purple prismatic needles, resembling potassium permanganate, formed. It is filtered, washed with benzene and dried under vacuum. It gradually loses aniline on standing. The aniline may be removed by cold acid or by heating to 180° in a stream of carbon dioxide.

The hexa-o-toluidine addition compound of ferrous phthalocyanine is made in a manner similar to the aniline compound. It forms small purple prisms. The dipyridine compound is best prepared in a Soxhlet apparatus with dry pyridine. It separates in very small, purple crystals with a bright green smear and can be washed with water or alcohol and dried at 100° without decomposition. It appears much more stable than the aniline or o-toluidine addition products. There are indications that similar additive compounds are formed with β-naphthylamine, p-toluidine, and phenylhydrazine, but in these cases no crystalline solid can be isolated.

Chloroferric phthalocyanine (4) may be made by decomposing hexaaniline ferrous phthalocyanine with hydrochloric acid. A better method is to warm ferrous phthalocyanine with a large excess of concentrated hydrochloric acid on a steam bath for 1 hour. After filtration the solid is washed acid free, washed with alcohol, and dried at 100°. It is a dull green solid with a yellowish green rubbing. It dissolves in sulfuric acid with the liberation of hydrogen chloride to give a purplish red solution. The addition of water yields a green solid. It appears impossible to get a hydroxyferric phthalocyanine giving a satisfactory analysis.

The effect of phosphates, tungstates, and molybdates on the formation of iron phthalocyanine under static conditions at 240° has been studied (68). Low concentrations catalyze the reaction while higher concentrations passivate it. The intensity of the effects is determined by the stability of the intermediate complexes formed.

Ferrous phthalocyanine forms a brown viscous product when exposed to chlorine for 90 hours at room temperature (1). Treatment of the viscous product with alkali solutions regenerates the original ferrous phthalocyanine almost free of chlorine.

A number of patented methods for the preparation of iron phthalocyanine can also be used for cobalt and nickel phthalocyanines and are covered in the following paragraphs.

Iron, cobalt, and nickel phthalocyanines have been prepared by heating the free metal or one of its compounds with phthalonitrile at 230–280° (36). These stable phthalocyanines are generally purified by boiling the powdered reaction mass with acetone, then with dilute alkali and finally with dilute hydrochloric acid. They may be converted to the pigment form by solution in concentrated sulfuric acid, drowning this solution on ice and recovering the precipitated color.

Iron and nickel phthalocyanines are formed on heating ammonium phthalate and ammonium sulfamate with an iron or nickel salt (83).

Iron, cobalt and nickel phthalocyanines can be prepared by heating urea, phthalic anhydride, the metal salt and boric acid to 220–230° for three hours (84). In a similar procedure ammonium phthalate and ammonium sulfamate replace phthalic anhydride and urea, respectively (86). Similarly the metal may be supplied by the iron, cobalt or nickel salt of phthalic acid, replacing part of the phthalic anhydride (73). Ammonium molybdate catalyzes the reaction (62). In addition ethane sulfonic acid (12), diammonium hydrogen phosphate (13) and sodium sulfate (14) are said to improve the yield in the above process when it is run in a medium such as trichlorobenzene.

Iron and nickel phthalocyanine have been converted to polychloro derivatives by direct chlorination in carbon tetrachloride in an autoclave (58,60). Polybromo derivatives have been prepared from the phthalocyanine and bromine in an autoclave at about 250° (50).

Iron, cobalt and nickel polychlorophthalocyanines have also been prepared from the metal powder or chloride and chlorinated phthalonitrile with a molybdate as a catalyst and trichlorobenzene as a solvent. The reaction takes place at 200–300° (70). Other solvent media such as organic acid chlorides (40) or chlorosulfonic acid (57) have been used for halogenations. With chlorosulfonic acid the halogenation temperature must be kept as low as possible.

Iron, cobalt, and nickel hexadecachlorophthalocyanines have been prepared from tetrachlorophthalic anhydride by the method described for the aluminum complex, but using instead of 3 g of aluminum powder, 5 g of iron, cobalt or nickel powder (56). Tetramethyl zirconate has been used in place of zirconium tetrachloride in the above reaction (41).

Cobalt phthalocyanine (2,36) was obtained in a 30 per cent yield upon heating 10 g of phthalonitrile and 3 g of cobalt metal at the reflux for 4 hours. The product was cooled, freed of metal, and boiled with alcohol to remove excess nitrile. Cobalt phthalocyanine is unusually soluble in quinoline and chloronaphthalene giving green-blue solutions. It crystallizes readily from pyridine in blue microcrystals containing combined pyridine which were washed with ether and dried at 100°. Cobalt phthalocyanine sublimes to form beautiful blue needles with a reddish-purple reflex. It precipitates unchanged from its dark green solution in sulfuric acid.

β-Cobalt phthalocyanine has been prepared by heating phthalonitrile with cobalt metal powder in ethylene glycol at 190° (26). The α-form was obtained when the β-product was ball milled with sodium chloride.

Cobalt chlorophthalocyanine (2,36) may be formed by heating 10.2 g of phthalonitrile with 2.6 g of anhydrous cobalt chloride to 200°. The temperature rose rapidly to 250° and hydrogen chloride was evolved. After cooling the melt was ground and boiled with alcohol to yield 85 per cent of a blue powder with a purple luster. Its solution in quinoline or chloronaphthalene was green-blue and in pyridine gave a deep blue color. It precipitated in long blue needles with purple reflex from chloronaphthalene solution.

Nickel phthalocyanine (2) is prepared by heating 30 g of o-cyanobenzamide with 6 g of nickel foil previously etched with hydrochloric acid at 270° for 3 hours. The cooled product is freed of excess metal and is then warmed with 20 per cent sodium hydroxide solution overnight to remove the phthalimide. After filtering the solid is washed with water and then with boiling alcohol. The yield is 6–8 g of complex. On sublimation, pure nickel phthalocyanine forms needles with an extremely bright red luster. When ground the resulting powder is a dull greenish-blue. Precipitation of the concentrated sulfuric acid solution by adding to water yields the unchanged nickel complex.

Nickel phthalocyanine was first prepared by heating 100 g phthalimide, 10 g nickel sulfide, and 10 g aniline under vigorous reflux for one hour (19). The product was cooled, crushed, and extracted with dilute alkali and with dilute hydrochloric acid. The product is an intense blue-green color.

α-Nickel phthalocyanine (26) is prepared by heating a mixture of 120 g phthalic anhydride, 180 g urea, 49.7 g nickel chloride hexahydrate, 0.5 g ammonium molybdate and 200 cc trichlorobenzene to 200° for 4.5 hours. The reaction mass is cooled to 100°, filtered, and the trichlorobenzene removed from the filter cake by steam distillation in the presence of 110 cc of 30 per cent sodium hydroxide. The crude β-form pigment is extracted with 1 per cent hydrochloric acid at 70° for 1.5 hours, filtered, washed, and dried. The dry product is extracted with acetone. The extracted powder, 20 g, is milled with 180 g dry sodium chloride and 1800 g 3/8" steel balls for 72 hours at 70 rpm. The salt is removed by extraction with 1 per cent hydrochloric acid at 70°. The yield of α-nickel phthalocyanine is 82 per cent.

β-Nickel phthalocyanine is prepared from the crude β-form pigment by milling with sodium chloride and tetrahydronaphthalene (32). A finely divided β-complex is obtained.

Rhodium phthalocyanine (37) is prepared by heating rhodium chloride with phthalonitrile.

Palladium monochlorophthalocyanine (4) is formed upon heating 5 g phthalonitrile with 1 g palladious chloride. The melt turns a deep blue and evolves hydrogen chloride. After 2 hours an 80 per cent yield of the complex is obtained. It dissolves in chloronaphthalene with a bluish-green color and deposits palladium monochlorophthalocyanine as an amorphous blue solid. It can not be sublimed.

Palladium phthalocyanine (59) is prepared by heating phthalonitrile with anhydrous palladium chloride. When the reaction is complete the solid is crushed and extracted with warm alcohol to remove the nitrile. The mass is then dissolved in concentrated sulfuric acid and poured onto ice to precipitate and recover the palladium complex.

Osmium phthalocyanine has been prepared by Herr (59).

Platinum phthalocyanine (2) is formed by heating a mixture of 20 g of phthalonitrile and 1.8 g of platinous chloride to 280° during 20 minutes. Some hydrogen chloride is evolved. The cooled product is ground and washed with alcohol. The crude yield is 4.2 g which yields 2.75 g of crystalline complex as blue needles with a bronze reflex from chloro-

naphthalene. It sublimes readily in small needles. "Platinum phthalocyanine is the most resistant member of the group toward oxidation
being comparatively stable to cold nitric acid."

REFERENCES

1. Barrett, P. A., Bradbrook, E. F., Dent, C. E., and Linstead, R. P., *J. Chem.
   Soc.*, **1939**, 1820–8.
2. Barrett, P. A., Dent, C. E., and Linstead, R. P., *J. Chem. Soc.*, **1936**,
   1719–36.
3. Anderson, J. S., Bradbrook, E. F., Cook, A. H., and Linstead, R. P., *J.
   Chem. Soc.*, 1938, 1151–56.
4. Barrett, P. A., Frye, D. A., and Linstead, R. P., *J. Chem. Soc.*, **1938**,
   1157–63.
5. Baumann, F., Bienert, B., and Rösch, G. (to Farbenfabriken Bayer A.-G.),
   U. S. Patent 2,683,643 (July 13, 1954); British Patent 698,039 (Oct. 7,
   1953); German Patent 888,837 (Sept. 3, 1953); French Patent 1,023,765
   (Mar. 24, 1953).
6. *Ibid.*, U. S. Patent 2,778,819 (Jan. 22, 1957); British Patent 698,070 (Oct.
   7, 1953).
7. Bigelow, N. M., and Perkins, M. A., in Lubs, ed., "The Chemistry of
   Synthetic Dyes and Pigments," pp. 577–606, New York, Reinhold Publishing Corp., 1955.
8. Borodkin, V. F., *Zhur. Priklad. Khim.*, **31**, 813–16 (1958); Translation by
   Associated Technical Services, Inc., East Orange, N.J.
9. Borodkin, V. F., and Smirnov, R. P., *Izvest. Vysshikh Ucheb Zavedenii
   Khim. i Khim. Tekhnol.*, 4, 287–290 (1961).
10. Bradbrook, E. F., and Linstead, R. P., *J. Chem. Soc.*, **1936**, 1744–48.
11. Braun, A., and Tcherniac, J., *Ber.*, **40**, 2709–14 (1907).
12. Brouillard, R. E. (to General Aniline & Film Corp.), U. S. Patent 2,647,127
    (July 28, 1953); British Patent 729,124 (May 4, 1955).
13. *Ibid.*, U. S. Patent 2,647,128 (July 28, 1953); British Patent 714,083 (Aug.
    25, 1954).
14. *Ibid.*, U. S. Patent 2,673,854 (Mar. 30, 1954); British Patent 729,123 (May
    4, 1955).
15. Brumfield, S. N., Foltz, V. W., McGhee, C. M., and Thomas, A. L., *J. Org.
    Chem.*, 27, 2266–7 (1962).
16. Byrne, G. T., Linstead, R. P., and Lowe, A. R., *J. Chem. Soc.*, **1934**,
    1017–22.
17. Ciba Ltd., Swiss Patent 280,478 (May 1, 1952); British Patent 679,773
    (Sept. 24, 1952).
18. Colaitis, D., *Compt. rend.*, 242, 1026–7 (1956).
19. Dandridge, A. G., Drescher, H. A. E., Thomas, J., and Scottish Dyes Ltd.,
    British Patent 322,169 (Nov. 18, 1929).
20. Davies, J. S. H., Wyler, M., Barrett, P. A., and Linstead, R. P. (to Imperial
    Chemical Industries Ltd.), U. S. Patent 2,155,038 (Apr. 18, 1939).
21. Dent, C. E. (to Imperial Chemical Industries Ltd.), U. S. Patent 2,214,454
    (Sept. 10, 1940).

22. Dent, C. E., and Linstead, R. P., *J. Chem. Soc.*, **1934**, 1027–31.
23. Dent, C. E., and Silvester, W. A. (to Imperial Chemical Industries Ltd.), U. S. Patent 2,195,984 (Apr. 2, 1940).
24. de Diesbach, H., and von der Weid, E., *Helv. Chim. Acta*, **10**, 886–8 (1927).
25. Du Pont de Nemours & Co., British Patent 552,124 (Mar. 24, 1943).
26. Ebert, Jr., A. A., and Gottlieb, H. B., *J. Am. Chem. Soc.*, **74**, 2807–10 (1952).
27. Elvidge, J. A., and Lever, A. B. P., *J. Chem. Soc.*, **1961**, 1257–65.
28. Elvidge, J. A., and Lever, A. B. P., *Proc. Chem. Soc.*, **1959**, 123–4.
29. *Ibid.*, 195.
30. Frigerio, N. A., (to U. S. A. as represented by the U. S. Atomic Energy Commission), U. S. Patent 3,027,391 (Mar. 27, 1962).
31. George, P., and Irvine, D. H., *Nature*, **173**, 1148–9 (1954).
32. Graham, D. P. (to E. I. du Pont de Nemours & Co.), U. S. Patent 2,556,730 (June 12, 1951).
33. Haddock, N. H.. and Linstead, R. P., "Thorpe's Dictionary of Applied Chemistry," Vol. 9, pp. 617–20, ed. by M. A. Whitely, London, Longmans, Green & Co., 1949.
34. Heilbron, I. M., Irving, F., and Linstead, R. P., (to Imperial Chemical Industries Ltd.), U. S. Patent 2,116,602 (May 10, 1939); British Patent 410,814 (May 16, 1934).
35. *Ibid.*, U. S. Patent 2,202,632 (May 28, 1940).
36. Heilbron, I. M., and Linstead, R. P. (to Imperial Chemical Industries Ltd.), U. S. Patent 2,124,419 (July 19, 1938).
37. Herr, W., *Z. Naturforsch.*, **9a**, 180–1 (1954).
38. Holzach, K., and Niemann, G. (to I. G. Farbenindustrie A.-G.), German Patent 658,019 (Mar. 19, 1938); French Patent 799,901 (June 23, 1936); British Patent 453,767 (Sept. 14, 1936).
39. I. G. Farbenindustrie A.-G., British Patent 468,292 (July 2, 1937).
40. *Ibid.*, British Patent 500,471 (Feb. 6, 1937); German Patent 741,969 (Nov. 20, 1943).
41. Kehe, H. J., and Horne, S. E. (to The B. F. Goodrich Co.), U. S. Patent 2,825,733 (Mar. 4, 1958).
42. Kenney, M. E., *J. Inorg. & Nuclear Chem.*, **11**, 167–9 (1959).
43. Klemm, L., and Klemm, W., *J. Prakt. Chem.*, **143**, 82–89 (1935).
44. Lecher, H. Z., Lacey, H. T., and Orem, H. P., *J. Am. Chem. Soc.*, **63**, 1326–30 (1941).
45. Lich, H., and Schoniger, W., *Mikrochemie ver. Mikrochim. Acta*, **34**, 336–46 (1949).
46. Linstead, R. P., *British Assn. Advancement of Science Report*, **1933**, 465–6.
47. *Ibid.*, *J. Chem. Soc.*, **1934**, 1016–17.
48. Linstead, R. P., and Dent, C. E. (to Imperial Chemical Industries Ltd.), U. S. Patent 2,056,944 (Oct. 13, 1936); British Patent 441,332 (Jan. 13, 1936); French Patent 791,086 (Dec. 2, 1935).
49. *Ibid.*, U. S. Patent 2,124,742 (July 26, 1938).
50. *Ibid.*, U. S. Patent 2,214,469 (Sept. 10, 1940); French Patent 806,616 (Mar. 8, 1937).
51. Linstead, R. P., and Lowe, A. R., *J. Chem. Soc.*, **1934**, 1022–27.
52. *Ibid.*, 1031–3.
53. Linstead, R. P., and Robertson, J. M., *J. Chem. Soc.*, **1936**, 1736–8.

54. Linstead, R. P., Thorpe, J. F., and Thomas, J. (to Imperial Chemical Industries Ltd.), U. S. Patent 2,025,791 (Dec. 31, 1935).

55. Moser, F. H. (to Standard Ultramarine & Color Co.), U. S. Patent 2,469,66 (May 10, 1949).

56. *Ibid.*, U. S. Patent 2,569,842 (Apr. 24, 1951).

57. Mühlbauer, F. (to Badische Anilin- & Soda-Fabrik A.-G.), German Paten 929,081 (June 20, 1955).

58. Niemann, G., Schmidt, W., Mühlbauer, F., and Weist, G. (to General Anilin & Film Corp.), U. S. Patent 2,276,860 (Mar. 17, 1942); French Pater 815,088 (July 5, 1937); British Patent 474,740 (Nov. 5, 1937); Germa Patents 717,164 (Jan. 15, 1942) and 740,053 (Oct. 16, 1943); Canadia Patent 497,737 (Nov. 17, 1953).

59. Payne, B. R., Scargill, P., and Cook, G. B., in "Radioisotopes in Scientifi Research," Vol. 2, pp. 154–66, New York, Pergamon Press, Inc., 1958.

60. PB 85172, FIAT Final Report 1313, Feb. 1, 1948.

61. Porter, J. L. (to Kaiser Aluminum & Chemical Corp.), U. S. Patent 2,502,74 (Apr. 4, 1950).

62. Riley, A. (to Imperial Chemical Industries Ltd.), U. S. Patent 2,214,47 (Sept. 10, 1940); German Patent 870,150 (Mar. 12, 1953); British Pater 476,243 (Dec. 6, 1937); French Patent 48,515 (Mar. 8, 1938).

63. Rösch, G., Wolf, W., and Vollmann, H. (to Farbenfabriken Bayer A.-G.), U. Patent 2,727,043 (Dec. 13, 1955); British Patent 698,049 (Oct. 7, 1953

64. *Ibid.*, U. S. Patent 2,739,151 (Mar. 20, 1956).

65. *Ibid.*, U. S. Patent 2,739,154 (Mar. 20, 1956).

66. *Ibid.*, U. S. Patent 2,739,155 (Mar. 20, 1956).

67. *Ibid.*, U. S. Patent 2,752,346 (June 26, 1956).

68. Rudenko, A. P., and Dobrosel'skaya, N. P., *Zhur. Obshchei Khim.*, 3 3667–71 (1961).

69. Sander, A., *Die Chemie*, 55, 255–60 (1942).

70. Sato, S., and Haga, T. (to Sanko Chemical Co. Ltd.), Japan Patent 11039/ (Aug. 12, 1960).

71. Senff, H., and Klemm, W., *J. für prakt. Chemie*, 154, 73–81 (1940).

72. Shinabe, M. (to Sumitomo Chemical Industries Co.), Japan Patent 842/ (Feb. 18, 1954).

73. Sullivan, Jr., F. W. (to Standard Ultramarine & Color Co.), U. S. Pate 2,568,570 (Sept. 18, 1951).

74. Thorpe, J. F., and Thomas, J. (to Imperial Chemical Industries Ltd.), U. Patent 2,000,051 (May 7, 1935); Thorpe, J. F., Thomas, J., and Linstea R. P., British Patent 389,842 (Mar. 20, 1933).

75. Thorpe, J. F., and Linstead, R. P. (to Imperial Chemical Industries Ltd U. S. Patent 2,000,052 (May 7, 1935); British Patent 390,149 (Mar. 2 1933).

76. Turek, F. S. (to Interchemical Corp.), U. S. Patent 2,138,413 (Nov. 1938).

77. Venkataraman, K., "The Chemistry of Synthetic Dyes," pp. 1118–42, N York, Academic Press, Inc., 1952.

78. Vollmann, H., Baumann, F., and Bienert, B. (to Farbenfabriken Bay A.-G.), U. S. Patent 2,701,252 (Feb. 1, 1955).

79. Wettstein, W. (to Ciba Ltd.), U. S. Patent 2,699,441 (Jan. 11, 1955).

80. *Ibid.*, German Patent 933,047 (Sept. 15, 1955); Swiss Patent 297,412 (Ju 1, 1954); Swiss Patent 300,466 (Oct. 1, 1954).

81. Whalley, M., *J. Chem. Soc.,* **1961,** 866–69.

82. Wolf, L., and Jahn, H. J., *J. prakt. Chem.* [4], 1, 257–76 (1955).

83. Wyler, M. (to Imperial Chemical Industries Ltd.), British Patent 457,786 (Dec. 4, 1936).

84. *Ibid.,*, U. S. Patent 2,197,458 (Apr. 16, 1940); British Patent 464,126 (Apr. 12, 1937); Italian Patent 344,006 (Oct. 21, 1936).

85. *Ibid.,*, U. S. Patent 2,197,459 (Apr. 16, 1940); British Patent 486,782 (June 9, 1938); French Patent 830,595 (Aug. 3, 1938).

86. *Ibid.,*, U. S. Patent 2,216,868 (Oct. 8, 1940).

87. Yagi, H., and Hori, T. (to Sumitomo Chemical Industries Co.), Japan Patent 6686/55 (Sept. 20, 1955).

CHAPTER 4

MANUFACTURE

Three pigment types of phthalocyanines have attained commercial importance: Phthalocyanine (metal-free), copper phthalocyanine, and copper halophthalocyanines. A discussion of the manufacture of phthalocyanine and copper phthalocyanine is followed by a review of methods for converting these compounds to pigment forms. A discussion of the manufacture of copper polyhalophthalocyanine followed by a review of its conversion to pigment form completes this chapter.

The first phthalocyanine to be manufactured commercially was copper phthalocyanine. It was first made in England by Imperial Chemical Industries Limited (57,276) starting in 1934. This event was followed closely by start-up of production of the same pigment in Germany, where manufacture of phthalocyanine and copper polychlorophthalocyanine was also begun shortly afterwards. Production of these pigments was begun in the United States by the Du Pont Company about 1937 and copper phthalocyanine manufacture was started by several other pigment manufacturers within a few years.

Phthalocyanines have increased in commercial importance, as shown by the U.S. Tariff Commission Reports, from a reported 10,000 pounds of phthalocyanine blue in 1941 to about 2,400,000 pounds of both phthalocyanine blue and green in 1951, to 5,700,000 pounds of both products in 1960. Figure 4-1 illustrates the growth of phthalocyanine blue and green production.

Manufacturerers of phthalocyanine colors are listed in Appendix III.

The original commercial form of copper phthalocyanine was the metastable product (generally called the α-type) produced by the acid pasting process. In this process the pigment is dissolved in sulfuric acid and this solution is poured into water. The pigment precipitates on dilution with water and is recovered by filtration.

Because of the physical instability of the original phthalocyanine blue pigments a number of procedures intended to control the crystalline form of the pigment have been developed and described in the numerous patents on this subject. Mixtures of copper phthalocyanine with copper

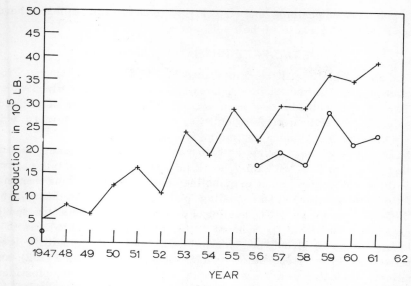

Figure 4–1. Phthalocyanine blue and green production, 1947–61; prepared from United States Tariff Commission Data.

x Phthalocyanine blue production
o Phthalocyanine green production

chlorophthalocyanine, tin phthalocyanine, aluminum phthalocyanine, mono- or disulfonated copper phthalocyanine and combinations of these have been suggested to improve the stability of the copper complex in commercial applications. These and other procedures are discussed later in this chapter. These procedures have resulted in the commercial production of several stable types of phthalocyanine blue. Experience has shown where the metastable types may be used to advantage.

The stable crystalline type of copper phthalocyanine (β-type) was developed as a pigment starting in 1949 and its use has been increasing since that time. The β-type is greener than the α-type. The β-type approximates the shade of fugitive Peacock Blue Lake C.I. 42090, and therefore has been called Peacock shade phthalocyanine blue.

α-Phthalocyanine is greener than α-copper phthalocyanine and β-phthalocyanine is greener than β-copper phthalocyanine. The commercial importance of α-phthalocyanine has diminished with the increasing importance of β-copper phthalocyanine.

Copper polyhalophthalocyanines are becoming of increasing importance. Copper pentadecachlorophthalocyanine has become the most important in number of pounds sold, of the halogenated derivatives. More recently the polybromopolychloro- and the highly brominated-complexes have aroused interest because of their yellower shades.

METAL-FREE PHTHALOCYANINE

Phthalocyanine is still being produced in England and Germany. Production in the United States apparently ceased in the early 1950's.

Two general methods have been used for the manufacture of phthalocyanine: (1) directly from phthalonitrile, and (2) indirectly from an acid and a metal phthalocyanine containing a replaceable metal.

Some methods for forming phthalocyanine directly include: heating phthalonitrile to 350–360° for 7 hours in a sealed tube, heating phthalonitrile in dimethylaniline or in quinoline solution while passing ammonia through the solution (116), heating phthalonitrile in triethanolamine to 170–180° for 4 hours (184), heating phthalonitrile with acetamide and/or formamide to the boil for 8 hours (210), heating phthalonitrile with a dihydroxybenzene, glycol, or glycerin (140), heating phthalonitrile in an inert solvent in the presence of cyclohexylamine or piperidine (232), and heating phthalonitrile in a solvent with potassium carbonate, piperidine and ethylene glycol (233).

Methods that include forming a metal phthalocyanine with a replaceable metal which is subsequently removed with an acid are: heating phthalonitrile with a sodium alcoholate (115,285), with sodium cyanamide (213), with sodium cyanamide and a solvent (209), with calcium metal in an alcohol, with calcium or barium oxides (118), with calcium oxide and methylglucamine (223), with an alcohol and sodium hydride (286), or with magnesium and a solvent under pressure (134).

Other methods for making labile metal phthalocyanines include those of Linstead's and Thorpe's early patents (181) using cyanobenzamide or phthalamide as the phthalocyanine forming intermediate and magnesium metal. A magnesium phthalocyanine is apparently formed by the action of a Grignard reagent such as methyl magnesium iodide with phthalonitrile (133). Tin phthalocyanine may be prepared by a urea-phthalic anhydride solvent process but without ammonium chloride (294). A fugitive antimony phthalocyanine can be formed also by the urea-phthalic anhydride solvent process (described later) with ammonium chloride and powdered antimony metal (80) whereby the ammonium chloride converts the product to metal-free phthalocyanine before isolation.

Methods of removing the metal from labile metal phthalocyanines include: solution of tin phthalocyanine in concentrated sulfuric acid, followed by drowning in water (294), boiling alkali or alkali earth metal phthalocyanine with hydrochloric acid (225), or stirring an alkali metal phthalocyanine with cold methyl alcohol, diluting with warm water and filtering (63). Heating an alkali metal phthalocyanine with the ammonium salt of a strong acid in a crystallizing solvent converts it to β-phthalocyanine (284).

Phthalocyanine had been made on a plant scale in Ludwigshaven prior to 1940. The process required an alcohol mixture with a boiling point of 145–155°, phthalonitrile, and sodium metal (224). In an attempt to develop a less expensive process, a method was developed in which phthalonitrile, calcium oxide and formamide were mixed in a wooden barrel (225). In this process no further agitation is needed. A highly exothermic reaction occurs and pigment formation is complete in 15 minutes. The product is ground, extracted with hot water and is then boiled with 6 to 15 per cent hydrochloric acid to remove the calcium.

COPPER PHTHALOCYANINE

Many processes for the manufacture of copper phthalocyanine have been patented, although it has not been possible to patent the compound itself because its preparation was disclosed by de Diesbach and von der Weid in 1927 (70).

Commercially two basic processes are used for the preparation of copper phthalocyanine: (1) from phthalonitrile and copper or a copper salt, and (2) from phthalic anhydride, urea, and copper or a copper salt. The phthalonitrile process was favored in Germany, at least prior to 1945. The urea process seems to be favored in England and in the United States.

The first patent on a method for the manufacture of copper phthalocyanine was issued to Dandridge, Drescher, Thomas and Scottish Dyes Limited in 1929. Their method was to heat cuprous chloride and phthalic anhydride in a stream of ammonia (61).

Phthalonitrile Process

Merely heating 4 moles phthalonitrile and 1 mole cupric chloride to 220–250° for 2–6 hours produces a 70–77 per cent yield of copper phthalocyanine (199). Methods for making copper phthalocyanine from phthalonitrile include: heating a mixture of o-phthalonitrile, pyridine and cuprous halide to 145° for 3 hours in an autoclave (136), with the addition of a solvent such as nitrobenzene (91), or with the addition of a solid diluent which may or may not be one of the reactants (86,127). In the latter case the reaction may be run in a ball mill. Copper phthalocyanine is also formed when a mixture of phthalonitrile and copper powder or cuprous chloride is gently heated under nitrogen (117,119) or in a ball mill to 240° (58), with or without a solvent (119). Other methods include: heating phthalonitrile with copper powder in an ethylene glycol medium (271), or similarly with a copper salt (230), heating phthalonitrile, copper powder, and a catalytic quantity of a chloride of copper, tin, antimony, aluminum or ammonia (65), heating phthalonitrile with cuprous chloride in nitrobenzene at 185° in the presence of catalytic quantities of sodium hydroxide, calcium oxide, or sodium carbonate (261), heating phthalonitrile with cupric acetate in a nitrobenzene medium and in the presence of ammonia (222,249), heating phthalonitrile with cupric chloride in a nitrobenzene medium in the presence of ammonia (165), or with cupric sulfate in the presence of sufficient ammonia to combine with the liberated sulfate anion (166), or similarly in an autoclave at 210° under ammonia pressure (157).

The use of phthalonitrile for the manufacture of copper phthalocyanine was technically well developed in Germany before 1940. Five processes were described (224,225) which were thoroughly tested in either a pilot or plant scale. Three of the processes used pyridine as a reaction medium and the other two were "dry" or "bake" processes. The yields based on phthalonitrile consumed varied from 90 to 93 per cent.

The process used in the plant was as follows: "A closed tray drier similar to a vacuum oven in which the shelves are heated to 140°C. with steam of five atmospheres pressure was used successfully in the manufacture of CPC. The mixture of phthalonitrile and anhydrous cuprous chloride was placed on black iron trays and heated in the closed baker from which the air was partially withdrawn, to 140°C. at which temperature a highly exothermic reaction takes place under formation of CPC. The use of a heat transfer agent such as sodium sulfate to achieve proper heat dissipation has been discontinued and is believed unnecessary in this equipment. No attempt was made to control the reaction temperature which was allowed to rise to approximately 300°C. The oven was then permitted to cool overnight and the crude pigment was discharged from the drier. It was reported to be essential to cool the reaction mass prior to discharge from the drier to avoid firing of the material. The sublimate and fumes formed during the reaction were run through a water spray vented trap."

Another "bake" process similar to the above was run in a kettle with a tin sheet metal insert and a strong anchor type agitator. A larger amount of cuprous chloride was used. The charge was heated to 160° to initiate the reaction after which the temperature rose to 280°. The yield was 90 per cent and the time cycle was 8 hours.

The other three processes used phthalonitrile, pyridine and either nitrobenzene, trichlorobenzene or monochlorobenzene under pressure. The nitrobenzene method is, for all practical purposes, quantitative and it is described at the end of this section as an assay method for the determination of the amount of phthalonitrile in the commercially produced product.

The "pan bake" process described above could also be accomplished in a continuous apparatus contained in a cylindrical shell twenty feet long shown in Figure 4-2. The baking was done on a continuous, copper mesh, flexible belt enclosed in the cylinder. The section receiving the mixture of phthalonitrile, cuprous chloride, and anhydrous sodium sulfate was heated electrically to initiate the reaction. The temperature then rose to approximately 320°. The cylinder was kept under a slight nitrogen pressure and vapors were suitably vented. Stirrup hammers knocked the finished material from the belt to a receiver. A second continuous process involves the reaction of phthalonitrile vapors with a copper revolving drum (272,273). Copper phthalocyanine is scraped from the drum as a powder. A rotating screw has also been suggested as a continuous reactor for this process (160).

One of the processes involving pyridine is now used only for analytical purposes. It is used to convert phthalonitrile to copper phthalocyanine

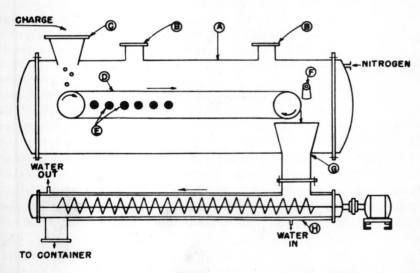

Figure 4-2. Continuous melt process for copper phthalocyanine in use in Ludwigshafen prior to 1940.

A. Cylindrical steel shell with bolted on dished heads 1.3 meters dia. × 5 meters long
B. Nozzles connected to scrubbing towers for sublimate
C. Charging hopper for phthalonitrile and $CuCl_2$
D. Belt conveyor, copper belt, variable speed drive, operating speed 3 meters/ minute
E. Electric heating elements (only on 1/3 to 1/2 length)-operating temp. 320°C.
F. Stirrup hammer for removal of finished product
G. Discharge hopper to screw conveyor
H. Jacketed screw conveyor, water cooled

I. G. Ludwigshafen Plant

quantitatively and therefore to determine the purity of commercial phthalo-nitrile.

"One hundred cc. of nitrobenzene, 20 g. of cuprous chloride, and 16 g. of pyridine are heated to 100°C. At this temperature 250 cc. more nitrobenzene are added, followed by the addition of 51.2 g. technical phthalonitrile. The charge is heated with an oil bath to 190–200° and kept at this temperature for one and one-half hours; 200 cc. of the nitro-benzene is then distilled off, and the charge is filtered hot. The cake is washed with a small amount of hot nitrobenzene and then with methanol until the filtrate is colorless. The cake is extracted twice with hot 5 per cent hydrochloric acid; the final filter cake is washed acid-free with water, then with methanol and acetone, and dried at 100°C. The yield is 99–100 per cent of theory from technical (approximately 95 per cent) phthalonitrile, based on the true phthalonitrile content of this intermediate. After finishing, the product was reported to show somewhat higher tint-ing strength than CPC made by the baking method. The method was demonstrated only on a 20 kg. scale, and was recommended solely for analytical control. The purity of technical phthalonitrile is calculated according to the formula:

$$\% \text{ Purity} = \frac{\text{Yield} \times 100}{57.5}." \qquad (225)$$

Phthalic Anhydride-Urea Process

The phthalic anhydride-urea process appears to be the process used to produce the major portion of copper phthalocyanine. Although the theo-retical yields in the manufacture of copper phthalocyanine from phthal-onitrile are better than from phthalic anhydride, the cost of manufacture of phthalonitrile may be difficult to justify economically, because of the low cost of phthalic anhydride and urea.

There are two methods of making copper phthalocyanine from phthalic anhydride and urea: (1) a dry or "melt" process and (2) a solvent process utilizing a high boiling organic liquid as the reaction medium. The melt process is discussed first because it was the first to be developed.

Wyler (293,298) disclosed the first melt process. A mixture of 130 g urea and 5 g boric acid was melted at 150° to which a mixture of 100 g phthalic anhydride and 20 g anhydrous cupric chloride was added. The reaction mass was heated at 200° until color formation was complete. The product was cooled, ground, slurried with dilute sodium hydroxide, filtered, slurried again with 5 per cent sulfuric acid, filtered, and dried. The product was not in a suitable pigment form but could be converted to that form by an "acid-pasting" process which is described on page 153. Riley (231) improved the above procedure by replacing the boric acid with 0.2 g of ammonium molybdate. Other compounds of group 6 metals may also be used as catalysts. The use of cuprous chloride (258) has generally replaced cupric chloride for several reasons: (1) it is easier to obtain and keep in the anhydrous form, (2) it is less expensive, especially in relation to its copper content, and (3) it has less tendency to produce chlorination in the phthalocyanine ring. A number of papers by Mori (197,198,200,201,202,203), have given the results of the investigation of a number of variables in the Wyler process. Borodkin (20) also studied copper phthalocyanine formation from phthalic anhydride, urea, and cuprous chloride and he isolated a diiminoisoindoline containing copper and determined its properties.

In Germany (224,225) a phthalic anhydride, urea, cupric chloride melt process was reported to give an 80 per cent yield in the laboratory, but only 70 per cent on a plant scale. It was considered to be uneconomical. Infrared heat has been used for processes of this type and may be used for continuous processes (84). It is reported that this type of fusion may be carried out in a continuous manner in a heated screw conveyor type of apparatus with a yield of 70 per cent in 12 minutes (160).

A number of variations of the Wyler process have been proposed. Urea may be substituted by biuret (221), aminosulfonic acid (295), and ammonium sulfamate (296,297). The copper chloride may be replaced by powdered copper and an oxidizing agent (204) or it may be added as copper phthalate (143,266).

The addition of a little potassium iodide to the Riley process reaction mixture affects the crystalline stability (304). If it is desired to avoid hardening of the reaction mass aromatic sulfonic acids such as naphthalene sulfonic acid may be used as the reaction medium or diluent (147). Mixtures of phthalic anhydride and phthalic anhydride substituted with sulfonic, carboxy or other groups have been used to make substituted copper phthalocyanines (139). Foaming in the above reaction is reduced by the addition of benzoic or benzene sulfonic acid to the reaction mixture (130). The reaction has also been run in the presence of a cyanamide derivative and an aromatic sulfonamide (194).

The use of an organic liquid as the reaction medium for the phthalic anhydride urea process is well known and widely used (22,204,225,236, 295,297). It is very similar to the Riley (231) process with the addition of trichlorobenzene as the reaction medium. The German (225) procedure is to mix 500 g phthalic anhydride, 1050 g urea, 100 g cuprous chloride, and 1500 g trichlorobenzene. After heating the mix to 130°, a mixture of 125 g anhydrous aluminum chloride and 50 g anhydrous ferric chloride is added in small portions and the reaction is then heated to 180–200° for seven hours. Removal of the solvent and isolation of the copper phthalocyanine results in a yield of 98 per cent of theoretical. Average laboratory yields are 94–96 per cent and the maximum yield obtained in the plant is 86–88 per cent.

Barnhart (8) indicates that a reaction mixture of 100 g phthalic anhydride, 23 g cupric chloride, 150 g urea, 2.5 g boric acid and 0.25 g ammonium molybdate in 400 g trichlorobenzene can be used to make copper phthalocyanine commercially. The reaction takes place at 195–200° during 4 to 6 hours. The copper phthalocyanine is recovered from the above product by adding 120 g of 98 per cent sulfuric acid, at 140–150°. Stirring is continued at 150° for 2 hours. The copper phthalocyanine tetrasulfate is filtered and washed with 200 g isopropanol. The filter cake is slurried in 500 g water, neutrallized with sodium hydroxide, filtered and dried. It is then finished by any of the known finishing methods.

Other methods for solvent recovery have been tried. For example, the the entire reaction mass can be drowned in a 9 per cent sodium hydroxide solution and heated to 100° for an hour. After standing the aqueous caustic layer is decanted and the wash is repeated four times with water. Finally the trichlorobenzene is removed by steam distillation. The caustic treatment is said to eliminate foaming and corrosion during the removal of trichlorobenzene by steam distillation (53). The product may still require a dilute acid slurry before being converted to the pigment form by finishing processes. In a somewhat similar process 1 part of the reaction mass at 140° is fed to a hammermill along with 4 parts of water to effect the drowning (40). The removal of the solvent medium is said to be aided by the addition of a surfactant to the steam distillation (235). Foaming is reduced by the proper selection of surfactant e.g. Span 85, Triton K-60, Daxol 23, Triton B 1956, Neutronyx, Duponol WA, Tamol.

Borodkin and Usacheva (22) have studied the phthalic anhydride-urea-solvent process for the synthesis of copper phthalocyanine. Some of their results are illustrated in Tables 4-1 and 4-2.

They also found that when the reaction was catalysed with 0.6 per cent ammonium molybdate for 10 hours at 170° the theoretical yield was 77.5 per cent in a polychlorobenzene solvent while in nitrobenzene the yield was 85.5 per cent. When the reaction took place in xylene at the boil the yield was 30 per cent. The yield in the presence of solvents is 10 to 15 per cent higher than in a fusion or melt process. A higher temperature is required by the fusion process. The use of cupric chloride instead of cuprous chloride results in a lower yield.

The addition of a lower boiling solvent, such as monochlorobenzene (71) to a trichlorobenzene reaction medium causes more refluxing and helps to prevent the solvent condensers from plugging with the vaporiza-

TABLE 4-1. EFFECT OF CATALYST ON YIELD OF COPPER
PHTHALOCYANINE (22).

Catalyst	% Yield
boric acid	26.3
ammonium chromate	27.3
chromic oxide	41.0
selenic acid	48.0
ammonium chloride	51.2
ferric chloride	60.0
potassium vanadate	40.0
vanadic acid	63.0
lead monoxide	65.0
lead dioxide	66.5
zinc oxide	51.2
arsenous oxide	65.0
arsenic oxide	66.5
antimony oxide	75.0
molybdic oxide	78.0
phosphomolybdic acid	92.0
molybdic acid	94.5
ammonium molybdate	96.0

ble by-products—phthalimide and ammonium carbonates. In addition to aromatic chlorohydrocarbons, nitrobenzene (22,235) and diethyl phthalate have been used as reaction media (236).

Most copper salts have been tried as a source of copper. Finely powdered copper with an oxidizing agent is an effective source of the metal (204).

In addition to the catalysts listed by Borodkin and Usacheva (22) zirconium tetrachloride and titanium tetrachloride are effective (204). Sulfuric acid digested titanium dioxide (218), titanium dioxide gel (153), titanate or zirconate esters (152), a mixture of titanium tetrachloride and monoethanolamine (301), and a mixture of aluminum chloride and ammonium chloride have been used as catalysts (299). The addition of alkyl sulfonic acids containing up to five carbon atoms in the alkyl chain (29), of ammonium, alkali or alkali earth phosphates (27), of

TABLE 4-2. EFFECT OF AMMONIUM MOLYBDATE ON YIELD OF
COPPER PHTHALOCYANINE (22)

% Ammonium molybdate based on phthalic anhydride	% Yield at Reaction Temperature 150°	170°
0.6	49.4	85.5
1.6	74.0	88.0
3.0	71.7	87.0

sodium or ammonium sulfates (28), or sodium xylene sulfonate (31) is said to aid the reaction.

It is of interest to note that the copper salt of cyanuric acid has been used in the preparation of copper phthalocyanine from phthalic anhydride (101). Among the products in the vapors from the synthesis of copper phthalocyanine from phthalic anhydride, urea, and cuprous chloride are phthalimide, ammonia, carbon dioxide, ammonium carbonate, and water. The weight of the gaseous products is about equal to the weight of the solid reaction product which consists of copper phthalocyanine (50–60 per cent), phthalimide and cyanuric acid.

Other Processes

In addition to the Dandridge, Drescher and Thomas (61) process mentioned earlier, a number of processes using starting materials other than phthalic anhydride and phthalonitrile have appeared.

Copper phthalocyanine has been made from o-cyanobenzamide and copper or a copper compound (181), and from o-chlorobenzonitrile or o-chlorobenzamide and cuprous cyanide in pyridine in a sealed tube (180,196). Heating o-dihalobenzenes with potassium copper cyanide is said to produce copper phthalocyanine (265). A method using pyridine or quinoline as a solvent medium for the reaction of o-dichlorobenzene with cuprous cyanide (19,137) is similar to the de Diesbach and von der Weid method (70).

Heating phthalyl chloride, urea, and cupric chloride to 195–200° forms copper phthalocyanine in excellent yield (267). Heating ω-chloro-o-tolunitrile (33) or $\omega,\omega,\omega,\omega',\omega'$-pentachloro-o-xylene (174), with urea, and cupric chloride in nitrobenzene also yields copper phthalocyanine.

Metal-free phthalocyanine may also be converted to the copper complex by heating it with copper powder in quinoline, chloronaphthalene or pyridine (177). Calcium phthalocyanine may be converted directly to the β-copper phthalocyanine pigment by ball milling it with salt, cuprous chloride, and a small amount of xylene (215).

FINISHING PROCESSES

Products of the phthalonitrile, or the phthalic anhydride-urea processes are usually ground and slurried with dilute mineral acid, or dilute alkali, or both to remove soluble by-products, and unreacted starting materials. Usually the products of such treatment contain 85 to 98 per cent of copper phthalocyanine, depending on the process of synthesis and number and type of washes used for this partial purification. When a solvent process is used the partial purification step may be combined with the solvent recovery. In either case the resulting products are not in a suitable form for pigment use and must be processed further to convert them into useful pigments.

Acid Treatment Methods

One method used since the process was first patented is the procedure used to prepare vat dyestuffs in a finely divided form. The compound is slurried or dissolved in concentrated sulfuric acid and precipitated by pouring the solution into ice or water. This technique is known as "acid pasting." A number of factors affecting the process have been studied and have resulted in patented procedures.

One early patent (195) relates to copper phthalocyanine slurries in sulfuric acid of 45 to 90 per cent concentration. The slurry becomes thick as the sulfate of copper phthalocyanine forms. After stirring two to four hours at room temperature the slurry is poured into cold water, maintained by adding ice, and then diluted to give a sulfuric acid concentration of 10 per cent or less. It is washed by decantation until neutral, rosin or dispersers are added, followed by filtration, drying and grinding.

Coprecipitation of a phthalocyanine with 5 per cent or less of a different phthalocyanine is said to improve the jetness of masstone and brightness of print tone of the phthalocyanine present to the extent of 95 per cent markedly when tested in a printing ink formulation (59). Dilution of a solution of copper phthalocyanine in concentrated sulfuric acid with 50 per cent sulfuric acid at 5° until the copper phthalocyanine precipitates, and pouring this into four times its weight of cold water is said to give a cleaner, stronger, easier grinding product than can be obtained by pouring the original solution into cold water (114). In a similar study copper phthalocyanine was dissolved in 92.4 per cent sulfuric acid (162), the sulfate precipitated by adding water (161), and the homogeneous sulfate suspension drowned in boiling water (163). Borodkin found that precipitation of copper phthalocyanine sulfate with water prior to drowning the sulfuric acid solution did not improve the purity of tint of the pigment (24).

In the study of the acid pasting process Borodkin also found that the product of the phthalic anhydride-urea-solvent process contained a higher proportion of copper phthalocyanine than did a phthalic anhydride-urea-melt process. A small percentage of impurities was found to remain with copper phthalocyanine after acid pasting (19). These impurities were soluble in organic bases such as pyridine, quinoline, aniline and dimethylaniline. Copper phthalocyanine is insoluble in as much as fifteen times its weight of 85 per cent sulfuric acid at 20° on prolonged stirring but forms a microsuspension of the sulfate (24). In 96 per cent sulfuric acid it is soluble in twelve times its weight at 20°. At 100° it is soluble in seven times its weight of 85 per cent acid or five times its weight of 96 per cent acid. An unsatisfactory pigment is obtained with any concentration of sulfuric acid at temperatures above 100°. The addition of a sulfonated castor oil to the drowning water does not give consistent results. From 5 to 10 per cent of a triethanolamine soap in the drowning water gives a pigment with improved dispersion properties.

Acid-pasted pigments are improved in strength and dispersibility if they are precipitated in the presence of an emulsion of water immiscible alkali soluble material, preferably an organic film forming acid, liquid at the precipitation temperature, such as a fatty acid, and then washing out the excess alkaline material. The pigment appears to retain a monomolecular layer of the soap (100). A purification method is described in which an acid stable phthalocyanine is slurried in sulfuric acid of 40–90 per cent concentration, sufficient to form the phthalocyanine sulfate, but not to dissolve it. The sulfate is filtered on glass cloth or porous stone. The sulfate is then placed in a large excess of water to recover the purified color or dissolved in 98–100 per cent acid before precipitation (67).

The addition of certain substances to a pigment often enhances its properties for certain uses. An example of this is the coprecipitation of 5 to 20 per cent of a higher fatty acid, such as lauric or stearic acid from a sulfuric acid solution by the acid pasting procedure (60). This results in a pigment more readily dispersible in rubber and similar plastics.

Acids other than sulfuric acid have been suggested for the acid pasting. These include oleum (61), chlorosulfonic acid (59), phosphoric acid (145), p-toluenesulfonic acid (146), fused napthalene-beta-sulfonic acid (144), and mixtures of organic sulfonic acids (146). A process for instantaneous dilution of the acid solution of copper phthalocyanine with turbulent flow in a special mixing nozzle forms the pigment in an extremely fine state of subdivision (66). This is said to reduce or prevent crystallization of the product when it is subjected to crystallizing solvents. Precipitation of copper phthalocyanine in the presence of a water immiscible organic liquid is said to enhance the softness and strength of the pigment (168,186).

The sulfate of copper phthalocyanine may be made by stirring crude copper phthalocyanine with a sufficient amount of fairly strong sulfuric acid in an inert organic liquid, especially nitrobenzene (186,173). The sulfate is hydrolyzed with an alcohol, filtered, washed with alcohol and dried. It is claimed that a good nonflocculating copper phthalocyanine pigment results.

An acid pasting procedure that gives higher strength and at the same time improves pigment stability is suggested in a recent patent (176). Two hundred grams of hexylene glycol are dissolved in a thousand grams of sulfuric acid at 20–30°. A slurry of 250 grams copper phthalocyanine in 125 grams of o-dichlorobenzene is added at 20–40°. After stirring at

40° for three hours the mixture is allowed to stand overnight. It is stirred and poured into fifteen liters of water at 60° with vigorous agitation. The o-dichlorobenzene is removed by steam stripping, and the slurry is filtered and dried. The product is solvent stable and disperses readily in plastics and inks.

Control of crystal size and form may be attained by causing precipitation of copper phthalocyanine from 90 per cent sulfuric acid by means of a change in temperature. Solution is attained at 70–110° and precipitation by rapidly cooling the solution to −10° to +30° (109). A detailed study of conditions for the acid pasting of copper phthalocyanine to obtain maximum dispersion of the pigment has been described (220).

Solution in eight to eleven parts of 98 per cent sulfuric acid per part of copper phthalocyanine is recommended along with dilution in ice water in the presence of surface active agents. Final dispersion is obtained by boiling the aqueous acid slurry.

The production of very soft pigments of the phthalocyanine type may be attained by diluting a sulfuric acid solution of the pigment containing a sulfonated monocyclic aromatic hydrocarbon having more than one alkyl side chain (183). The sulfonated hydrocarbon should be present to the extent of at least 25 per cent by weight of the pigment. Xylene is a favored hydrocarbon. Similarly acid pasting in the presence of water soluble carboxylic acid, such as five to ten times the pigment weight of acetic, chloroacetic, or propionic acids gives a readily dispersible pigment (2). Pigment made according to the above process (183) may be reslurried as an alkaline presscake containing 10 per cent of pigment with a liquid hydrocarbon or chlorohydrocarbon until the pigment transfers completely to the organic phase. The organic liquid is then removed by steam distillation and the product is filtered and dried to obtain a nonflocculating, strong, red-toned copper phthalocyanine (34).

A mechanism for drowning a sulfuric acid solution of copper phthalocyanine in water forces a very thin film of the solution 0.01 to 0.001 inches thick into water at a pressure up to 2500 psi (187). This is claimed to eliminate the formation of large particles which are said to form in drip or spray methods for introducing the sulfuric acid solution into water. Reduced amounts of sulfuric acid may be used in the acid pasting procedure by using a dough mixer to effect the mixing of the sulfuric acid and phthalocyanine pigment (30). An added advantage is claimed for the process as the pigment presscakes produced have high solids contents. The process also has an advantage in processing metal-free phthalocyanine because it gives less decomposition and, therefore, higher yields. A variation of the above process uses an acid stable, water-soluble, inorganic salt such as sodium sulfate in addition to the sulfuric acid (38). Copper phthalocyanine may be mixed with a small amount (25 per cent of its weight) of 17 per cent oleum. It is then drowned in water at 98°, cooled to 50°, and an emulsion of xylene and water is added. After stirring for half an hour the xylene is removed by steam distillation and a β-type phthalocyanine is recovered by filtration (155).

Another improvement in the process of acid milling a copper phthalocyanine is the addition of from 2 to 30 per cent of the pigment weight of a dicarboxylic acid or anhydride, such as phthalic anhydride, to the system (158). The resulting pigment is said to be lower in grit, stronger in masstone, and undertone effect, and cleaner and brighter than the color obtained when the dicarboxylic acid anhydride is omitted. Another variation of the acid milling process uses a monocyclic aryl sulfonic acid in place of sulfuric acid (150). Improved texture and other advantages are claimed.

Metal phthalocyanines that have been made by the phthalonitrile process in a saturated alicyclic hydrocarbon solvent in an autoclave apparently tend to give a pigment which is noncrystallizing when processed by acid pasting and then subjected to a variety of treating agents including aliphatic isocyanates, alkyl amines and certain quaternary ammonium salts (74,77), octadecyl amine, lauryl amine (75) or alkyl substituted ureas (76). A similar noncrystallizing effect can be obtained from the same type of phthalocyanine by subjecting it to the process known as "permutoid swelling." In this process the copper phthalocyanine is slurried in sulfuric acid of 62.5 to 80 per cent concentration. This forms the acid salt and changes the crystalline form of the product to the γ form. Products of the above procedure show remarkable resistance to crystallization (73).

The permutoid swelling process of phthalocyanine finishing was used in Germany (225), especially for the polychlorophthalocyanines. The β-modification in which the pigment is generally obtained by synthesis from intermediates is changed to the tinctorially strong α-modification. The change to the α-modification can be observed by preparing X-ray diffraction diagrams. By this means a preferred slurrying condition for each pigment is developed. In general the pigment is treated with sufficiently strong sulfuric acid to bring about the change from the β- to the α-crystalline form, but insufficient in concentration to dissolve it. This method has several advantages over the conventional acid pasting method: (a) the method is applicable to pigments which are not stable in sulfuric acid of sufficiently high strength to dissolve the pigment, but stable in acid of moderate concentration; (b) the method is applied to presscake by the careful addition of stronger acid followed by adjustment of acid concentration of the slurry; (c) the change from β- to α-form can be controlled by means of the concentration of acid, the time of contact, and the type of agitation; (d) usually the amount of sulfuric acid used is less than that required by the conventional acid pasting process; (e) the quality of the resulting pigment is improved in regard to shade and strength; (f) when the pigment is processed to a dry powder, the pigment produced by permutoid swelling is softer in texture than the acid pasted product.

Disadvantages of the permutoid swelling process are that the sulfuric acid concentration must be controlled within narrow limits and that in some cases the concentration of sulfuric acid needed presents problems regarding materials of construction.

Specific conditions for permutoid swelling various types of phthalocyanines are given in the above reference.

Several acid pasting procedures were used in Germany (225). For dry colors, crude copper phthalocyanine was dissolved in about 10 times its weight of sulfuric acid and diluted with a relatively small amount of water at 85°, maintaining the drowning temperature at 135°. This gives a product with a relatively soft texture. For paper dyeing the sulfuric acid solution was sprayed into a mixture of ice and water. For general use as an aqueous dispersion the sulfuric acid solution was sprayed into water at 75-85°.

Another method for preparing a highly dispersed copper phthalocyanine requires drowning the 90-93 per cent sulfuric acid solution in an acidified saturated ferrous sulfate solution. It is then further diluted, filtered, and washed free of ferrous sulfate. The resulting presscake is readily redispersed (275).

Conventional methods of acid pasting metal-free phthalocyanine are said to damage its brilliance. Conducting the operation in an inert atmosphere (free from oxygen) is said to give a superior product (189).

Grinding Methods

The second general method for finishing phthalocyanine pigments involves a number of grinding procedures for particle size reduction by salt grinding or solvent grinding. These procedures have been developed principally in the past fifteen years, although the earliest references were in 1936 (132,210).

These methods include (1) the so-called salt grinding methods: grinding a phthalocyanine color with a large amount of a soluble salt or other solid substance and (2) solvent grinding in suitable equipment with small media, such as small shot, sand, and small pebbles. Either method may be used to prepare the β-type of phthalocyanine and for grinding phthalocyanines which do not form a β-type, as well as for grinding under conditions which do not favor formation of the β-type crystal (32).

The salt-grinding method was briefly mentioned by Mühlbauer in 1936

(132,210). Molliet and Todd (193) found that the addition of an aliphatic acid containing ten or more carbon atoms improved the salt grinding of phthalocyanine pigments and gave a product better in dispersion in oils, cleaner in tint, and stronger. Anhydrous sodium sulfate was used as the grinding aid and an edge runner mill or a ball mill was used for the grinding. Bucher found that the tinctorial properties of copper phthalocyanine (or of vat dyes) were improved by grinding them for 24 hours on a roller mill with anhydrous calcium chloride and a dispersing agent such as the sulfuric acid ester of dodecyl alcohol (42).

In another process crude phthalocyanine made by the phthalonitrile process was ball-milled with four times its weight of sodium chloride for forty hours (172). The salt was extracted with warm slightly acid water. The phthalocyanine manufacturing process may take place in the presence of the salt subsequently used for grinding. An electron microscope study of the pigment particles so produced shows them to be roughly rounded particles of less than 50 mμ in diameter. The grinding diluent must have the qualification of being harder than the substance being ground. Most water soluble crystalline substances seem to possess this qualification. Crude copper phthalocyanine may also be salt ground in an aqueous slurry using 3 to 10 times the pigment weight of borax, with sufficient water to give a stirrable mass (83). The water should contain a suitable dispersing agent. The mass is ground in a cylindrical vessel with a smooth agitator disc operating at peripheral speeds in excess of 2000 ft per minute. The milling time is 40 minutes, after which water is added and most of the borax settles and may be reused. The aqueous suspension of copper phthalocyanine is separated by decantation, and the color is recovered by flocculation. The dispersion may be used for some applications in its original form.

A strong nonflocculating α-type copper phthalocyanine results from ball milling a crude β-form copper phthalocyanine with small amounts of aluminum and tin phthalocyanines using solid grinding aids such as sodium sulfate, calcium chloride, potassium ferrocyanide, or sodium acetate (228). The α-type copper phthalocyanine obtained by precipitation from sulfuric acid solution may also be used in place of crude β-copper phthalocyanine and results in the same highly dispersed α-copper phthalocyanine of the desired reddish-blue shade. The aluminum phthalocyanine may be precipitated with the copper phthalocyanine from sulfuric acid, but the tin phthalocyanine must be added during the milling operation.

A strong α-copper phthalocyanine was obtained upon salt grinding crude β-copper phthalocyanine in a ball mill in the presence of a small amount of acetic acid or formic acid (85).

The development of grinding procedures led directly to the production of the β-type of phthalocyanine and copper phthalocyanine in a form commercially suitable for use as a pigment. Both the methods of salt grinding (182,290) and solvent grinding (170) may be used. The β-copper phthalocyanine is greener than the α-type, just as β-phthalocyanine is greener than the α-phthalocyanine. Wiswall (268,290), and Loukomsky (182) both developed methods for the production of the β-copper phthalocyanine pigment and Wiswall characterized the product by means of X-ray diffraction. Wiswall used acid pasted, halogen free copper phthalocyanine, converted it to the β-form by contact with an organic liquid capable of promoting the conversion and subsequently ground the dry β-crystals to pigment size with a solid grinding aid in a ball mill. Loukomsky used a Werner-Pfleiderer mixer to grind a mixture of dry, acid pasted copper phthalocyanine, dry micromilled salt or other solid grinding aid, and xylene. Mixing was continued for eight to twelve hours.

An improvement in the method of salt grinding copper phthalocyanine to the β-form in a ball mill was obtained when the grinding took place in the presence of from 5 to 50 per cent of the pigment weight of a low boiling, polychlorinated aliphatic hydrocarbon such as tetrachloroethylene (107). The particle size was generally less than 0.2 μ and was usually between 0.01 and 0.1 μ. Both of the above methods (107,170) may be applied to the preparation of β-type metal-free phthalocyanine. Grinding crude phthalocyanine or copper phthalocyanine to β-phthalocyanine or β-copper phthalocyanine gives it the property of crystal stability (257,290). Salt-grinding of crude copper phthalocyanine in the presence of 5 to 50 per cent of its weight of xylene results in a flocculation resistant as well as crystallization resistant pigment (108). Sodium ferrocyanide, barium chloride, aluminum sulfate (142), and other solids have been used as the grinding aid in place of sodium chloride (49,52,283). Copper phthalocyanine may be ground in a rod mill at 100–150° until maximum strength develops, usually from 20 to 24 hours. The addition of small amounts of an alcohol, aldehyde, hydrocarbon or ketone ensures conversion to the β-form (52).

According to Gottlieb (104) brightness or brilliance of a pigment is a function of the range of size of individual particles comprising the pigment. The more narrow the range in particle size, the brighter the color. To achieve this goal in a phthalocyanine pigment the phthalocyanine is ground with salt and with from 0.01 to 0.1 per cent of solvent active dispersant based on the pigment weight. The dispersant should have in its structure radicals of an aliphatic carboxylic acid containing 8 to 30 carbon atoms. Typical dispersants used are polytitanium stearate and sorbitan monooleate. Improvement in rate of strength development, strength, and jetness of masstone are claimed for the resultant pigment. A slight change in shade from blue to a greener blue or from green to a yellower shade of green often accompanies the other improvements.

Mutaffis has shown a relationship between the particle size (surface area) of the grinding aid and the speed of grinding (217). Microatomized salt having a surface area ranging from 0.14 to 1.38 sq meters per gram made it possible to grind acid pasted phthalocyanine blue to the β-type product in six hours, while grinding with micropulverized salt having surface area of 0.06 sq meters per gram required twelve hours and produced a weaker pigment.

Tarantino and Tullsen (269) suggested that it is possible to make copper phthalocyanine from phthalonitrile in a liquid organic medium, add micropulverized salt to the mixture, and agitate at a high rate of speed to grind the product to β-copper phthalocyanine without any intermediate isolation of the pigment. Similarly they were able to make copper phthalocyanine by the urea-phthalic anhydride-solvent process (231), filter the product, wash it with the reaction medium until the filtrate is colorless, add the filter cake and salt to a dough mixer, and grind to the β-copper phthalocyanine without intermediate separation of the solvent.

The dough mixer salt grinding procedure (182) was improved by the use of a crystallizing organic liquid that is either water soluble or which can be made water soluble by dilute acid or alkali (97,270). Alcohols, amines, and phenols are typical classes of organic compounds which may be used. Instead of a crystallizing organic liquid, an organic solid with a crystallizing effect has been used (227) but offers no practical advantage.

β-Copper phthalocyanine has been made from calcium phthalocyanine by grinding crude calcium phthalocyanine with salt, cuprous chloride and a small amount of xylene for 20 hours (215). The product was boiled in 10 per cent hydrochloric acid for 3 hours, filtered, and dried.

Quinoline has been used to convert copper phthalocyanine to the β-form (96). Grinding was accomplished in a ball mill with calcium chloride or sodium sulfate as the grinding aid and glycerolmonooleic acid ester as a surfactant. The product does not crystallize in boiling toluene.

Cooper (55) has found it advantageous to salt grind at 100–140° in the presence of a crystallizing solvent. Temperatures below 120° increase the grinding time beyond 24 hours. Not less than 15 per cent of the weight of the pigment of tetrachloroethylene was used as the preferred crystallizing solvent.

The use of heavy duty mixers can shorten the time of salt grinding appreciably (47). Thus a Baker-Perkins dispersion mixer or a Banbury mixer each is capable of exercising sufficient shearing action to reduce the grinding time from 10 to 12 hours to from 1.5 to 3 hours. The viscosity of the mix was adjusted by changing the solids to vehicle ratio to obtain a viscous granular mixture. A polyethylene glycol of a molecular weight of about 400 was a favored vehicle to help provide the necessary viscosity, although other polyols, their ethers or esters have been used. β-Copper phthalocyanine has been produced from crude copper phthalocyanine by this process. It is also applicable for grinding phthalocyanine green and vat pigments.

Metal-free phthalocyanines are converted from either the α- or β-form to the γ-form by salt grinding in a rubber-lined ball mill for 21 hours (306). In an almost identical manner the β-form of phthalocyanine is obtained from the α-form, if a relatively small amount of crystallizing liquid, such as xylene, is present during the grinding cycle (226).

A similar effect to salt grinding has been obtained by milling copper phthalocyanine in a ball mill with very small grinding media, steel shot two millimeters in diameter, in the presence of an organic solvent (170). Thus either α- or crude β-copper phthalocyanine has been ground with small steel shot in the presence of an organic liquid capable of changing copper phthalocyanine to the β-form. Acetone and isopropanol have been used. After grinding 48 to 110 hours the maximum pigment size was below 0.2 μ. The above procedure was applied to other phthalocyanines, and to metal-free phthalocyanines as well as to partially or completely chlorinated copper phthalocyanine (171). Particle size reduction takes place in each case, and due to the solvent, α to β transformations take place with phthalocyanines subject to such changes. Solvent grinding does not invariably produce conversion to the β-form pigments. It may also be used to reduce the particle size of noncrystallizing types of copper phthalocyanine, such as those containing chlorine atoms, sulfonic acid groups, or both of these groups (164). Crude copper phthalocyanine, its partially or fully chlorinated derivatives, or vat pigments have been converted to a suitable pigment form by ball-milling for a few hours in dry form, slurrying the product in an organic liquid such as acetone, dimethylformamide, or tetrachloroethylene, and then passing the slurry through an efficient homogenizer (54).

The organic liquid is recovered and the pigment is extracted with acid, filtered, washed, and dried.

The solvent grinding method has been applied directly to copper phthalocyanine made by the urea-solvent process, by ball milling the reaction mass before separating it from the trichlorobenzene reaction medium (248).

Crude β-copper phthalocyanine may be converted to pigment of either the α- or β-type by grinding it in a slurry with hexachloroethane and water. In the presence of paraformaldehyde, formaldehyde, or no additive, 26 hour grinding gives an α-product. In the presence of a crystallizing substance, such as xylene, phenol, or naphthalene, a 48 hour grind gives the β-form with excellent pigment qualities (50).

Conversion of crude β-copper phthalocyanine to the useful β-form pigment has also been accomplished in aqueous suspension (129). The use of a high speed disc agitator and sand accomplished the grinding in 5 to 10 hours while ball mill grinding required 48 to 110 hours for the same degree of fineness. A surfactant was used in the water and the optimum temperature for grinding was 60–80°.

Crude copper phthalocyanine is converted to a useful β-form pigment by grinding it in aqueous suspension in a ball mill at temperatures of 95–170° (92). Lower temperatures require a longer grinding time and produce a redder shade product. The product ground at 95° or higher has excellent stability in lacquers and solvents.

Copper polychlorophthalocyanine, partly chlorinated copper phthalocyanine, or substantially chlorine-free copper phthalocyanine may be ground in a ball mill in the dry state for 6 to 18 hours usually in the presence of a surface active agent. The product is then slurried in 14 to 20 parts of water containing 1.5 to 2.0 times its weight of a water insoluble crystallizing type of organic liquid. The organic liquid is steam distilled, and the pigment is filtered and dried to form a tinctorially strong pigment. When chlorine-free copper phthalocyanine is used as the starting material, the product is the β-type copper phthalocyanine (192).

Pigment Treatments

Many techniques for improving the strength development, as well as the ultimate strength of phthalocyanine pigments are included in the preceding sections on pigment finishing by acid pasting or by grinding. Others will be covered in the section on noncrystallizing and nonflocculating phthalocyanine pigments which follows. A few techniques of interest to the manufacture of phthalocyanines and not covered elsewhere are discussed here.

Presscakes of copper phthalocyanines have been milled with dispersing agents, such as the condensation product of oleyl alcohol and ethylene oxide to improve their dispersion (131). The dispersion of copper phthalocyanines in water is improved by incorporating the sodium salt of a sulfonated naphthaleneformaldehyde condensation product in the drowning water of the acid pasting step (62). Naphtha or other immiscible liquid of similar volatility is emulsified with water, an emulsifying agent, and a copper phthalocyanine presscake, and the emulsion is dried to obviate the formation of lumps and hard aggregates during the drying step (277). The process is improved by first emulsifying the organic liquid and water before introducing the presscake (278).

Subjecting a slurry of an acid pasted copper phthalocyanine to the mild action of a small amount of an alkaline, inorganic oxidizing agent such as sodium hypochlorite solution has been claimed as a means of reducing bronzing and drying inhibiting effects noticeable with pigments not treated in this manner in certain paint vehicles (88).

Copper phthalocyanines are among other pigments that may be more easily dispersed when dried if the pigment slurry in water is first mixed with a volatile, water immiscible, organic liquid and a cation-active agent such as an amine, or quaternary ammonium compound, containing an aliphatic radical of at least eight carbon atoms in chain length (256).

Treatment of a slurry of a copper phthalocyanine pigment presscake in water with the reaction product of a polyalkanolamine and a higher aliphatic acid, such as triethanolamine and lauric acid is said to give a pigment with improved oil-dispersibility and rate of strength development when the product is filtered and dried (69).

Soft-textured copper phthalocyanines have been prepared by slurrying pigment presscake with nitrobenzene or anisole, together with from 0.5 to 20 per cent of diisobutyl ester or sodium sulfosuccinic acid based on the pigment weight (262,263). The mass is agitated until it forms a foam and the foam is dried. Sodium lauryl sulfonate (246) has been used in a similar manner.

Zeisberger (305) states that phthalocyanine pigments are capable of absorbing about 30 per cent of their weight of oily, resinous vehicles without changing their consistency so as to become sticky. The resulting pigments are dried and ground to form pigments that are as readily dispersed as flushed colors.

The concentration of phthalocyanine blue or green presscakes may be increased by mixing the presscake with methyl cellulose or methyl starch in a dough mixer (7). The resulting slurry is immediately filtered through a preheated filter press. The solids content of the presscake is increased from 29 to 39 per cent by this means.

An ultrasonic generator producing a 500 kc/sec frequency is used to improve the dispersion of an aqueous slurry of copper phthalocyanine containing Eriphor A (103).

Copper phthalocyanine, metal-free phthalocyanine and especially copper polychlorophthalocyanine may be converted into an easily dispersible pigment form by heating a water slurry of the pigment to a temperature between 100 and 300° in a pressure vessel (44). The dispersing properties of the same pigments are greatly improved when the presscake resulting from acid pasting and filtering the phthalocyanine is reslurried with a water insoluble monohydric alkanol having 5 to 12 carbon atoms (159).

Phthalocyanine Lakes and Resinated Colors

Phthalocyanine pigments are marketed in the form of full strength products extended with the metallic salts of rosin or other resins, lakes, and extended colors, as well as in the form of full strength toners. These products have been developed to enable the user to obtain the maximum color value and ease of handling for these valuable pigments.

The hard texture of the first copper phthalocyanine produced was a factor in the development of the products extended with metallic resinates and of lakes. The earliest patents on this subject showed that copper phthalocyanine can be sulfonated (61,181) and this realization led to the preparation of barium and calcium lakes of these sulfonated products.

Holzach and Niemann (125,126) made lakes of copper phthalocyanine monosulfonic acid with barium, aluminum, calcium, magnesium, iron, cobalt, strontium, zirconium, manganese, and nickel for pigment use. The barium lake of the disulfonic acid has been found to prevent both bronzing and can fading due to crystallization in paints and lacquers (17). The tetrasulfonic acid lake with barium, calcium, aluminum, or zinc forms pigments suitable for use in printing inks and lacquers (135). Recently it has been found possible to reslurry the presscake of the barium salt of copper phthalocyanine tetrasulfonate in a low boiling alcohol, to obtain improved rheological properties for inks made with this pigment (148).

Lakes of phthalocyanine sulfonic acids did not achieve permanent success because sulfonation reduces the outstanding lightfastness of these products and because the same shades can be obtained from unsulfonated phthalocyanines.

In general pigments are resinated to improve their ease of wetting, dispersion, and rheological properties in various vehicles. Resination of copper phthalocyanine with metallic resinates improves the flow, length, and consistency of linseed varnish type printing inks made from resinated phthalocyanines over those made from nonresinated toners (253). This process is said to be improved, especially for copper hexadecachlorophthalocyanine, by adding from 0.1 to 10 per cent of an ammonium salt of a strong acid to the pigment dispersion before the alkali earth metal resinate is precipitated (36,37). A somewhat similar product is made by precipitating aluminum benzoate in a slurry of phthalocyanine pigment in water (279), giving a product containing about 50 per cent pigment. The aluminum benzoate "lake" of the phthalocyanine pigment shows much less tendency to flocculate than the same pigment in toner form in certain paint systems. An improved product is obtained with aluminum-*p*-tertiarybutyl benzoate (206,207). Aluminum benzoates, or alkali metal resinates have also been used in conjunction with from 5 to 25 per cent of an insoluble salt of copper phthalocyanine sulfonic acid to reduce flocculation in paint systems (190).

Phthalocyanine pigments have been dispersed in resins which are plastic at elevated temperatures, but friable at 20–30° (281). The dispersions are cooled and ground to a particle size between 40 and 200 mesh. The resulting powders can be incorporated into paint and enamel vehicles by hand stirring without the necessity for more powerful dispersion equipment.

Extended pigments are physical mixtures of pigments and extenders such as calcium carbonate, blanc fixe (126), aluminum benzoate, and dextrin.

Phthalocyanines extended with calcium carbonate or whiting have been used for years. A recent patent covers a method for improving the dispersion of these products by making them with a ball-milling procedure (260).

Copper phthalocyanine has been dispersed on bentonite by mixing with 90 per cent of bentonite by heating the mixture to 400–500° at 2–3 mm Hg (289).

Aqueous slurry mixtures of activated silica gel having a surface area of 100 sq m per g and pigments such as copper phthalocyanine have been made. The products resulting after filtering and drying the mixtures have improved dispersibility in polystyrene and cellulose acetate plastics (120,303).

Metal phthalocyanines have been made from phthalonitrile and a metal salt in the presence of a calcined anhydrous oxide or titanium or zirconium (254). No acid pasting is necessary or desirable. The mixtures are free from flocculation.

Barium and calcium lakes have been formed from the copper tetrasulfotetracarboxyphthalocyanine made from 5-sulfotrimellitic acid (16). Other pigments and pigment mixtures have been formed by coupling diazotized amines with copper phthalocyanine, from mixtures of copper phthalocyanine and azo reds (112,126), by making salts of copper phthalocyanine sulfonic acids with basic dyestuffs such as Rhodulen Blue 6G, Methylene Blue 2G, and Auramin (113), and by laking in combination with azo colors (128).

NONCRYSTALLIZING AND NONFLOCCULATING PHTHALOCYANINES

Copper phthalocyanine may exist in three crystal modifications α, β, and γ. The metastable α-form is obtained by the acid pasting process, the stable β-form is obtained by solvent grinding or by heat, and the γ-form is obtained by slurrying the compound in 60–65 per cent sulfuric acid followed by dilution in water and filtration. These crystal modifications have been discussed in Chapter 2.

"Crystallization" is defined as the tendency of copper phthalocyanine blue pigment particles to grow due to recrystallization in the presence of many solvents such as toluene, xylene, alcohols, esters, ketones, chlorinated aliphatic and aromatic solvents. The practical effect of crystallization is a loss in color strength as well as a shift in hue toward the red. With pure copper phthalocyanine, the loss in strength may be as great as 90 per cent. Methods used to determine the stability of copper phthalocyanine to crystallizing solvents are given in Appendix II.

It has been noted that a number of factors affect crystallization and that results obtained by the so-called solvent (toluene or xylene) test may not represent those obtained in a practical application because: (1) agitation affects the rate of crystal growth, (2) presence of a few crystals may obscure suitability for actual use, (3) resins and oils used with phthalocyanines often inhibit crystallization and (4) limits of resolution of the optical microscope make it impossible to observe particle size changes at the lower end of the pigment particle size range (39).

It has also been observed that shade and strength are not detrimentally affected when changes in crystal form take place if the resulting particles are still in the pigmentary range. Stabilizing agents inhibit crystal growth and help to maintain particle size within the pigmentary range.

Flocculation may be defined as the formation of clusters of pigment particles in a vehicle. These clusters can be separated by relatively weak mechanical forces or by a change in forces at the interface between the solid and the suspending medium (87). Flocculation results in a loss in color strength. With a flocculating type system, the flocs of pigment form rapidly in the vehicle when it is allowed to stand, but the turbulence produced in spraying is frequently sufficient to separate them and to produce the maximum color intensity. Flocculation as a property of a paint system is influenced by the resins as well as by the pigment, the extender, and the solvents.

Crystallization and flocculation in copper phthalocyanine pigments have been discussed in numerous articles (25,169,252,274).

Additional discussion on flocculation appears in Chapters 2 and 6.

The elimination of both crystallization and flocculation is necessary in order to produce a pigment which is stable in paint, lacquer, and other fluid systems. Chlorination of the phthalocyanine molecule reduces its tendency to crystallize in solvents. Sulfonation of phthalocyanine aids in reducing flocculation. A combination of the two techniques gives an even better effect than either technique. However, other methods contribute toward making noncrystallizing, nonflocculating copper phthalocyanine: (1) admixture of copper phthalocyanine with small amounts of other phthalocyanines, (2) grinding procedures, (3) reacting the phthalocyanine with other materials, and (4) other treatments or procedures.

Mixtures of Phthalocyanines

Mixtures of phthalocyanines were first made by mixing the phthalocyanines in the acid pasting step and "coprecipitating" them. The objective of this early work was to improve copper phthalocyanine as a printing ink pigment. Five per cent of another phthalocyanine was coprecipitated with 95 per cent of copper phthalocyanine. The other phthalocyanines used were those of zinc, cobalt, nickel, lead, barium, and aluminum. The products were generally a little stronger and more jet in masstone than the original copper phthalocyanine (59).

It was found that tin, hydroxytin or chlorotin phthalocyanine reduces the tendency of copper phthalocyanine to flocculate and crystallize, especially in combination with monochlorophthalocyanine (13,14,15). From 1 to 10 per cent of the tin phthalocyanine was used and it was generally incorporated by salt grinding. Metal-free phthalocyanine may be stabilized in a similar manner. Magnesium phthalocyanine (2–6 per cent) also has the property of inhibiting the crystal growth of copper phthalocyanine especially when a small amount of an amine such as dodecylamine is present (12). The use of small amounts of both aluminum and tin phthalocyanines incorporated by grinding is covered in the section on copper phthalocyanine finishing by grinding (228). Aluminum phthalocyanine alone as an additive has also been used to provide stability in solvent systems (300). Similarly, acid pasting a mixed crude of 92 per cent copper phthalocyanine and 8 per cent aluminum phthalocyanine produces a phthalocyanine with improved crystal stability (238).

Copper phthalocyanine has been made nonflocculating by incorporating 2–5 per cent of vanadyl phthalocyanine either before or after acid pasting or grinding (1). Mixtures of copper phthalocyanine and its monochloro derivative have been made nonflocculating by the addition of 5 per cent each of tin and cobalt phthalocyanines (51).

Partially Chlorinated Phthalocyanines

It has been known for some time that copper phthalocyanine containing a small amount of chlorine is more crystal stable than the unchlorinated product after each product has been acid pasted or ground. Chlorine-containing copper phthalocyanines have been prepared by heating phthalonitrile with either anhydrous cuprous or anhydrous cupric chloride. The product from cuprous chloride contains about 2 per cent chlorine and the product from cupric chloride contains about 6 per cent chlorine (178,225). When the reaction is run in the presence of from 0.015 to 0.15 mole per cent of an aromatic tertiary nitrogen base such as pyridine and is finished by solvent grinding, the product is much more flocculation and crystallization resistant (141). With polytitanium distearate as an additive the final product has a slightly stronger, redder, and brighter tint (106).

Zirconium and titanium tetrachlorides have been used as catalysts in the urea-solvent process to produce partially chlorinated copper phthalocyanines that are resistant to crystallization (5,204). The 4-position for the chloro or other halogen atom is much more effective in reducing crystallization than the 3-position (30,79,105,164,214,216). From 5.5 to 17 per cent of halogen is effective in inhibiting crystallization (105). The process of chlorinating copper phthalocyanine that has first been acid pasted is effective in making a fully noncrystallizing product (208).

Copper phthalocyanine was made nonflocculating as well as noncrystallizing after the urea-solvent process by adding aluminum chloride and an excess of copper chloride to the solvent process reaction mixture and passing in a small amount of chlorine gas (18). Copper phthalocyanine made by another process has been slurried in trichlorobenzene, followed by addition of aluminum chloride and chlorination of the mass in a manner similar to the above process with a similar result (154). Copper phthalocyanine suspended in sulfuryl chloride has been chlorinated to a minor degree with thionyl chloride (302) or with chlorine (292) to improve its stability after acid pasting.

It has been found that small amounts of copper phthalocyanine substituted in the 4 position by a chloro, nitro or amino group is effective in stabilizing copper phthalocyanine (216). Stability was not attained when the substituent was in the 3 or 6 position (250).

A copper phthalocyanine pigment containing 2–15 mole per cent of a copper phthalocyanine which has as a substituent a carboxy, carbamide, or phosphono group was found to be nonflocculating (79). A similar product containing 60–70 mole per cent of copper monochlorophthalocyanine is noncrystallizing as well as nonflocculating. Solvent grinding is the preferred method of finishing the product.

The α- and γ-metal-free phthalocyanines have been stabilized by introducing chlorine by various methods (149,214), or by adding other substituents. Small amounts of metal phthalocyanines also have a stabilizing effect.

Sulfonated Phthalocyanines

This section treats sulfonated phthalocyanines only in relation to their use in preparing nonflocculating phthalocyanines. The barium salt of copper phthalocyanine disulfonic acid was first observed to be stable in lacquers (17) whereas copper phthalocyanine showed serious flocculation and crystallization. Giambalvo found that 10 per cent or more of copper phthalocyanine monosulfonic acid in copper phthalocyanine used to make lacquers gives a product which is nonflocculating (102).

Mixtures of copper phthalocyanine, copper monochlorophthalocyanine and copper phthalocyanine monosulfonic acid give excellent resistance to both flocculation and crystallization (78,164,208). They have been made from a mixture of phthalic anhydride, monochlorophthalic anhydride, and phthalic anhydride monosulfonic acid, or their equivalent phthalic acids by the urea-solvent process (78) by partially chlorinating copper phthalocyanine and adding the monosulfonic acid (208). They have been finished by solvent grinding (164) or by acid pasting (78). In place of copper phthalocyanine monosulfonic acid, zinc phthalocyanine sulfonic acid, containing 1.25 to 2.5 sulfonic acid groups per molecule, or its alkaline earth metal salts may be used to the extent of about 5 per cent to confer nonflocculating properties on copper phthalocyanine (35). From 3 to 10 per cent of barium, zinc, magnesium, tin, cadmium, manganese, aluminum or zirconium salts of sulfonated phthalocyanines containing about 2.5 sulfonic acid groups per molecule have been precipitated in a slurry of copper chlorophthalocyanine containing 4 per cent chlorine to obtain products highly resistant to flocculation (56). Copper phthalocyanines containing 3–5 per cent chlorine and in which less than 15 per cent of the molecules contain a sulfonamide or aryl or alkyl substituted sulfonamide group are resistant to flocculation and crystallization (255). Copper phthalocyanine has been mixed with 2–20 per cent of a number of metal phthalocyanines and the mixture sulfonated. The effects on crystallization in xylene, lightfastness and paint tinting strength were studied (6).

Carboxylic acid groups have an action similar to sulfonic acid groups. More than 2 per cent of pyromellitic anhydride with a mixture of phthalic anhydride and chlorophthalic anhydride has been used to make a nonflocculating and noncrystallizing copper phthalocyanine derivative (72).

Other Methods of Improving Noncrystallizing and Nonflocculating Properties

Amine salts of o-carboxybenzamide phthalocyanines have been successful in inhibiting flocculation of copper phthalocyanine in paint systems (167). Addition of the correct amount of methylolphthalimide to copper phthalocyanine (about 40 per cent of its weight) followed by condensation and formation of the ethylene diamine salt of that product gave a nonflocculating pigment. The use of a partially chlorinated copper phthalocyanine insured a noncrystallizing as well as nonflocculating pigment (188). Roberts (234) has found that the crystallizing type of copper phthalocyanine can be mixed in certain proportions with a methylolphthalimide-copper phthalocyanine condensation product which is also crystallizing in nature to produce a noncrystallizing pigment. A mixture of about 3 parts of copper phthalocyanine to 1 part of the methylol phthalimide derivative is fully noncrystallizing. In the range of from 2 to 75 per cent, the phthalimide derivative is effective in increasing crystallization resistance.

The acid salt of copper phthalocyanine has been prepared in an inert organic solvent using a relatively small amount of the strong acid. The salt was hydrolyzed with alcohol and washed with water to give a non-flocculating phthalocyanine pigment. Sulfuric acid, organic sulfonic or sulfuric acids, anhydrous hydrogen chloride, or phosphoric acid may be used as the salt forming acid (173). Hydrolysis may take place on the filter by washing the acid salt with alcohol and then with water until acid free. Other variations in the finishing process that may improve the flocculation and crystallization resistance of copper phthalocyanine are described in the section on phthalocyanine blue finishing (155,173, 176,227).

Flocculation resistance is greatly improved by slurrying a neutral copper phthalocyanine presscake obtained after acid pasting a copper phthalocyanine with an organic liquid such as toluene (34), or carbon tetrachloride (34,155). Stirring is continued until all the pigment is transferred to the organic phase. The product is changed to β-form crystals of less than 0.5 μ average length. The carbon tetrachloride is removed by steam distillation and the product is filtered and dried. Copper phthalocyanine has also been made crystallization resistant and non-flocculating by heating it in a eutectic mixture of sodium and aluminum chlorides to 140–180° for two hours (185), although the addition of a little chlorine apparently improved the noncrystallizing property (18).

Heating copper phthalocyanine with isophthalyl chloride in the presence of aluminum chloride in nitrobenzene and thereafter separating and acid pasting the product produced an α-type crystal-stable copper phthalocyanine (122). Acid chlorides other than isophthaloyl chloride may also be used (48). The addition of 1 to 50 per cent of formaldehyde, based on the weight of copper phthalocyanine, to a sulfuric acid solution of that pigment forms a flocculation and crystallization resistant α-form pigment upon its isolation in the usual manner (121).

Metal phthalocyanines made by the phthalonitrile process in an autoclave in a saturated alicyclic hydrocarbon solvent, and subsequently finished by acid pasting may be made noncrystallizing by a number of treatments as mentioned in the section of this chapter covering finishing methods (73–77).

Copper phthalocyanine made by the urea-phthalic anhydride-solvent process may be made noncrystallizing by adding 2 to 5 per cent of the weight of phthalic anhydride of phenylacetonitrile to the solvent reaction (191). The product may be converted to pigment form by acid pasting, or by grinding in a ball mill for 6 hours, followed by a permutoid swelling in 70 per cent sulfuric acid purification step.

Methods of reducing flocculation in the final lacquer, enamel, or paint have also been employed. They include adding benzylcellulose (259), or aluminum p-tertiary butyl benzoate (206,207) to the paint, as well as the method of passing the final ball milled enamel through a homogenizer (111).

POLYCHLORINATED PHTHALOCYANINES

Phthalocyanine and its metal derivatives have sixteen hydrogen atoms that may be replaced by chlorine, bromine or fluorine. Until recently, only the chloro derivatives were of commercial significance.

In 1959, a copper polychloropolybromophthalocyanine was promoted as a product with a slightly yellower shade than the copper polychlorophthalocyanines (41,287,288).

Copper phthalocyanine changes in shade from blue to green as the number of chlorine atoms in the molecule is increased. The effect of the first atoms on the change in shade is minor, and the effect increases rapidly from about ten to fourteen atoms and is less significant again for the final two atoms. Many commercial phthalocyanine greens contain 14–15 chlorine atoms. This pigment has excellent lightfastness, heat stability and resistance to acid, alkalies, and bleeding. Other properties are described in Chapter 6.

An early patent made use of a simultaneous halogenation and condensation to the color (245). The reaction took place in nitrobenzene or sulfuryl chloride and phthalonitrile or a phthalonitrile forming compound was the starting material. Copper polybromophthalocyanine or copper polychlorophthalocyanine containing up to 14 atoms of chlorine was obtained. The manufacture of highly chlorinated phthalonitrile (243,244) has been described as well as its conversion to copper polychlorophthalocyanine using ammonium molybdate as a catalyst (237).

The urea-phthalic anhydride process has also been tried for the manufacture of copper polychlorophthalocyanine using tetrachlorophthalic anhydride, cuprous chloride and urea with nitrobenzene as the reaction medium and ammonium molybdate as the catalyst (239). This procedure has been used to make the iron, cobalt, copper, and zinc polychlorophthalocyanines (241). The copper derivative was greenish-grey (241). A similar reaction was attempted with no solvent present. No green color could be isolated from the resulting black reaction product (175). Catalysts other than ammonium molybdate produce the brightest copper polychlorophthalocyanine with the urea process (205). These include zirconium and titanium tetrachlorides or other anhydrous chlorides such as those of tin, antimony, or arsenic. Other metal polychlorophthalocyanines have been similarly produced. The catalyst metals may be removed by an acid or alkaline wash. Copper polychlorophthalocyanines having up to the theoretical 50.3 per cent chlorine for the hexadeca-chloro-compound have been made by this process. Other catalysts such as sulfuric acid digested titanium dioxide (218), titanium dioxide gel (153), or a titanate ester (152) have been tried.

Other additives to the urea-tetrachlorophthalic anhydride-solvent process using a molybdate catalyst are an aliphatic monosulfonic acid(29), aromatic sulfonic acid (31), disodium hydrogen phosphate (27), or an alkali metal salt such as sodium sulfate (28). They are said to produce a good yield of brilliant green copper hexadecachlorophthalocyanine.

In a study of the synthesis of copper hexadecachlorophthalocyanine from tetrachlorophthalic anhydride it has been shown that in addition to the copper complex, copper-free polychlorophthalocyanine is formed and the mixture has a dull dark green color (21,22). The crude product cannot be converted into a pigment of a bright green color by purification or repurification and, therefore, the synthetic product is of no commercial value. The process using a slight excess of copper powder, an oxidizing agent, and a catalyst of the zirconium tetrachloride type has given superior results to other processes because much less of the metal-free complex is formed (205).

Less highly chlorinated products have been obtained more easily by the urea-solvent process (175). When the chlorine content of the copper phthalocyanine molecule averaged about 6 atoms per molecule the shade of the complex was close to that of fugitive Peacock Blue. Thus, when a mixture of mono- and dichlorophthalic anhydrides was used as the starting material, a product of this type resulted (3,247). The starting material consisted of equimolecular quantities of 4-chlorophthalic anhydride and a mixture of the 3,6-, 4,5- and 3,5-products The product was equal in shade and brightness to the fugitive type of Peacock Blue when both products were tested in printing ink formulations. Products made from mixed phthalic anhydrides with a greater difference in the number of chlorine atoms per molecule (from 0 to 3 or 4) give pigments that are less bright.

Halogenation Methods

The earliest method for the manufacture of copper polychlorophthalocyanine was by direct chlorination. Linstead and Dent (179) entered their patent application in England in August 1935, while Niemann, Schmidt, Mühlbauer, and Wiest (219) applied for a patent in Germany in December of the same year. Linstead and Dent describe the preparation of chloro- and bromo-derivatives of metal-free phthalocyanine with up to 12 or 13 atoms of halogen per molecule. Copper, nickel and zinc complexes were also prepared. Copper octachlorophthalocyanine prepared by the urea-phthalic anhydride process from 3,6-dichlorophthalic anhydride was brominated under pressure at 270° to make a copper chlorobromophthalocyanine. Apparently, some of the copper was removed during the bromination as the product was found to be a mixture of derivatives of phthalocyanine and copper phthalocyanine. The Niemann, Schmidt, Mühlbauer and Wiest (219) patent is basic for the production of copper polychlorophthalocyanine commercially known as phthalocyanine green. Various methods for chlorinating copper phthalocyanine are described. These include chlorinating (a) in a solvent medium such as trichloroacetic acid, (b) in an aluminum chloride-sodium chloride melt, (c) under pressure, (d) in a liquid such as carbon tetrachloride under pressure and (e) in a sulfur containing solvent such as thionyl chloride or sulfur dioxide under pressure. Catalysts for the reaction include zinc chloride, ferric chloride, antimony trichloride, iodine, antimony trisulfide, thionyl chloride, sulfur dioxide, copper chloride, and phosphorous oxychloride. The chlorination temperature ranges from 60 to 230°. Nickel, metal-free phthalocyanines and copper phthalocyanine trisulfonic acid are also chlorinated. Mixed halogenation using both chlorine and bromine is described. In each halogenation, the phthalocyanine shade shifts toward the green. The products are converted to the pigment form by acid pasting.

Barrett, Bradbrook, Dent and Linstead (11) found that the halogenation of phthalocyanine proceeds readily under conditions which will not effect the halogenation of phthalic anhydride or phthalonitrile. Under mild conditions, phthalocyanine forms addition compounds similar to those formed with aromatic compounds. They are easily converted by heat into substitution products in which the halogen atoms replace hydrogens in the benzene rings. They showed that most substitutions occurred in the 4 and 4,5 positions first. The most highly halogenated phthalocyanines obtained by them contained 12 to 13 atoms of halogen. Bromination at 300° under pressure gave a brown solid containing additive as well as substituted bromine. Heating the product under reduced pressure to 260° removed the additive bromine and left a green bromophthalocyanine containing 60 per cent (12.9 atoms) of bromine.

Phthalic anhydride and its chloro-derivatives were found to be satisfactory media for the chlorination of phthalocyanine or its copper complex (4,64,175,225,251), and chlorination to the extent of 12 to 16 atoms of chlorine per molecule was accomplished. The optimum temperature was 230–240° (175). Tri- or tetrachlorobenzene was also successfully used as a chlorination medium with antimony pentachloride, or trisulfide as catalysts (4,219,225,251). Acid chlorides such as phthalyl chloride, benzoyl chloride, chloroacetyl chloride, and benzenesulfonyl chloride, have also been used as the reaction media. The product was acid pasted in chlorosulfonic acid to convert it to a satisfactory pigment (211,225). Halogenation of the dry copper phthalocyanine takes place at 200–250°. Inorganic salts, such as anhydrous aluminum chloride, or anhydrous sodium sulfate may be used as diluents (138). Copper phthalocyanine has also been chlorinated in a sulfur dichloride liquid medium (90).

As Barrett (11) noted, it is difficult to halogenate phthalocyanines to contain more than 12 atoms of halogen. However, an aluminum chloride-sodium chloride eutectic mixture appears to provide both a solvent and a catalyst for the chlorination of copper phthalocyanine, resulting in the most widely-accepted technical means of chlorination (4,89,219,225,251). Iron, copper, nickel, or antimony chlorides have a catalytic effect. Phthalonitrile may be fused with a mixture of copper chloride and sodium chloride to form copper phthalocyanine. The reaction product may then be ground and fused with aluminum chloride to provide the chlorination melt (68).

Copper polychlorophthalocyanine was manufactured in Germany (224,225) by passing chlorine into a molten (180–200°) eutectic mixture of 900 kg of anhydrous aluminum chloride and 200 kg sodium chloride containing 200 kg of crude copper phthalocyanine and with ferric chloride as a catalyst, until 14.8 to 15.0 atoms of chlorine were introduced into the molecule. The chlorination required 24 hours. The steel vessel was 1 m in diameter and was equipped with a 20 cm turbine agitator operated at 940 RPM. The corrosion problem was severe, as the agitator and vessel needed replacement every 2–4 batches and every 30–40 batches respectively. It was essential to add the copper phthalocyanine slowly to avoid caking and with a minimum contact with the air to avoid firing. When the chlorination was completed, it was dropped into water, filtered, washed, and dried.

A study was made at Ludwigshaven to improve upon the above procedure. Four methods were studied: (1) chlorination in tri- or tetrachlorobenzene, (2) chlorination in phthalic anhydride, (3) chlorination under pressure in carbon tetrachloride and (4) chlorination in phthalyl chloride.

This cost study indicated that the trichlorobenzene process was the most costly, the phthalic anhydride process second most costly, the phthalyl chloride method about 8 per cent above the eutectic melt method in cost and the carbon tetrachloride process almost equivalent to the eutectic method in cost. These processes were described as follows:

"(1) Tri- or tetrachlorobenzene method:

In the search for a solvent which could be used as diluent at high temperatures for the chlorination of CPC (copper phthalocyanine), it was first attempted to use trichloro-acetic acid which, however, decomposed at 150 °C. Trichlorobenzene was used more successfully, but a considerable amount of this solvent was found to be chlorinated to give tetrachlorobenzene and higher chlorination products. The method was carried out according to the following process:

"One part of crude CPC is suspended in 4 parts of T.C.B. (trichlorobenzene) and 0.1 part of antimony trisulfide which must be free of iron and copper. The charge is heated in an autoclave at 160–170 °C. while chlorine is charged under pressure which is maintained at 5–10 atm. by regulating the amount of the hydrochloric acid gas which is allowed to escape through a release valve. This method gives polychloro CPC containing up to 14.5 atoms of chlorine. Two and one-half times the theoretical amount of chlorine was used. When the chlorination is completed, the mass is filtered and the cake is washed with benzene to remove the highly chlorinated solvent. A yield of 92 per cent of theory, based on copper phthalocyanine is obtained, but the shade of the pigment tends to be slightly duller than that obtained from the carbon tetrachloride method.

"(2) Phthalic anhydride method:

"Since this method is relatively expensive, information on it was obtained only as it applied to the chlorination of metal-free PC. This chlorination and the finishing of the chlorinated pigment were carried out according to the following processes:

"Fifty kg. of crude metal free PC (81–89 per cent purity), together with 7.5 kilograms of antimony pentachloride are added to 500 kg. of molten phthalic anhydride. The charge is heated to 155–160 °C. and 300 kg. of chlorine are introduced until the desired shade and chlorine content of the pigment is obtained. The charge is then drowned in cold water, and 890 kg. of a 34.5 per cent sodium hydroxide solution are slowly added. The charge is heated at the boil until all the phthalic anhydride is in solution, and the pigment is filtered off. The cake is first washed with water, then with dilute ammonia, and finally again with water. A yield of 85 kg. of crude Heliogen Green GG is obtained corresponding to 95 per cent of theory. The product contains close to 12 chlorine atoms.

"One hundred kilograms of the crude pigment thus obtained is dissolved in 300 kg. of chlorsulfonic acid at 25–30 °C. When a deep red colored clear solution has been obtained, the charge is diluted with 500 kg. of monohydrate and drowned at once in 2500 kg. of water and 2500 kg. of ice to which 7 kg. of xylene had been added. The temperature of the drowning slurry should not rise above 10 °C. The pigment is filtered off; the cake is washed and then ammonia slurried at 70 °C. in the presence of 1–2 per cent of 'Lorol' sulfate. The cake is dried at 70 °C.

"(3) CCl$_4$ pressure method:

"Two kilograms of CPC and 0.06 kg. of antimony trisulfide are suspended in 8 kg. of carbon tetrachloride in an autoclave. Chlorine is added and the charge is heated to 150–160 °C. under pressure allowing the temperature to rise finally to 180 °C. where it is kept for two hours. When the chlorination is completed, the charge is drowned in 30 l. of water at 80 °C. while allowing the carbon tetrachloride to distill off during the drowning operation. The carbon tetrachloride can be recovered in an anhydrous form, ready to be re-used in the next charge, by allowing the CCl$_4$ vapors to pass through a tower of soda lime and calcium chloride. When all CCl$_4$ has been removed, the pigment is filtered off and the cake is washed and dried. The yield is 3.6 kg. of crude polychloro CPC (or 3.6 kg. of polychloro metal-free PC) from 2 kg. of the crude pigments....

"The preferred apparatus for this high pressure chlorination was stated to be a nickel autoclave. The chlorine gas was pressed into the autoclave with nitrogen from a pressure measuring tank, with sightglass, allowing close control during the charging of the chlorine.

"The reaction in the early stages of the chlorination is highly exothermic, and the pressure might rise within a few minutes to 200, or even as high as 400 atm. pressure, if all the chlorine were charged at once in the beginning of the chlorination.

"The pressure range which appeared to have given the best results with respect to rate and consistency of chlorination, was 40 to 100 atm. During the last stage of the reaction, the HCl gas was not vented off in order to avoid loss of the diluent.

"Only 5–10 per cent excess over the theoretical amount of chlorine was stated to be necessary, and the chlorination was readily controlled by exactly measuring the amount of chlorine which was charged....

"(4) Phthalyl chloride method: Phthalyl chloride was reported to be a suitable solvent for the chlorination of CPC and metal free PC at normal pressure. It was stated that this solvent is very stable, but that its cost was believed to be too high to be practical. It was found, however, that a relatively small amount of phthalyl chloride, especially when formed in a nascent state, using phthalic anhydride as solvent, is sufficient to promote the chlorination. This modified method, involving the use of phthalic anhydride as the solvent and phthalyl chloride as chlorination promoter, was successfully demonstrated in Ludwigshafen on a semi-large scale. It was found that as little as four parts of phthalic anhydride per part of CPC are sufficient when the CPC is charged slowly within one hour into the molten phthalic anhydride. The following tentative process was obtained:

"Five kilograms of CPC are charged within one hour in four portions to 20 kg. of molten phthalic anhydride. Then 1.75 kg. of anhydrous zinc chloride (or aluminum chloride) are added and simultaneously chlorine is introduced at 175 °C. within three hours while adding simultaneously through the reflux condenser a total of 7.5 kg. of thionyl chloride. The rate of chlorine addition is adjusted so that 1.5 to 2 kg. of chlorine per hour is introduced. It requires 7–8 hours at 175 °C. to complete the chlorination under these conditions. The charge is then drowned in 80 l. of cold water. A total of 15.5 kg. of soda ash is carefully added to the pigment suspension while heating the charge to the boil. The pigment is filtered off, and the cake is washed with hot water. From the almost colorless filtrate, the phthalic acid may be recovered to the extent of 85 per cent of theory by adding 14 kg. of concentrated sulfuric acid and filtering off the precipitate. The phthalic anhydride recovered from this cake shows the same crystallizing point as the original material. The pigment press-cake is extracted with dilute hydrochloric acid to remove the zinc carbonate, and the product is finally washed free of acid and dried. A yield of 8.4 kg. of polychloro CPC is obtained, which corresponds to a yield of 98 per cent of theory, assuming that 14 atoms of chlorine have entered the molecule'' (225).

Copper phthalocyanine has been chlorinated to a chlorine content of 18 per cent (tetrachloro) in nitrobenzene using aluminum chloride as a catalyst (242). Solid copper phthalocyanine may be chlorinated in a fluid bed reactor, but must be ground with four times its weight of sodium chloride to provide a mixture which will fluidize in a satisfactory manner (10). The mass is fluidized with nitrogen and at 200° chlorine is added. The concentration of chlorine in the gas feed is gradually built up from 2 to 100 per cent during 3 hours and the temperature is gradually raised from 200° to 415° to complete the chlorination. After extracting the salt and acid pasting, a product containing 48.6 per cent chlorine (14–15 atoms per molecule) was obtained. Perchloroindan has been found to be a suitable solvent and chlorinating agent at 220–280° for copper phthalocyanine. Using this method 15 to 16 atoms of chlorine may be added to each copper phthalocyanine molecule (280).

Phthalocyanine or copper phthalocyanine has been chlorinated in a melt made from aluminum chloride and sulfur dioxide, thionyl chloride or sulfuryl chloride or their mixtures (229). Chlorine gas was passed into the melt at 65–70° and the temperature increased as the chlorination proceeded. Additional sulfur dioxide was added along with the chlorine from time to time. After drowning, washing, and filtering the product was obtained in a suitable pigment form without further treatment. Bromination has been accomplished by a similar procedure. A similar chlorination takes place in trichlorobenzene, with sulfur dioxide and chlorine in the presence of antimony trisulfide as a catalyst (98). Phthalocyanine (metal-free) chlorinated in this manner and acid pasted from a mixture of chlorosulfonic and sulfuric acids gives a product less lightfast but much yellower in undertone and tint than the usual shade of commercial phthalocyanine green.

Chlorination of copper phthalocyanine in sulfuric acid solutions generally results in decomposition. However, Holtzmann and Simon have found that solutions of copper phthalocyanine in chlorosulfonic acid react with chlorine gas at relatively low temperatures (25–100°) in the presence of catalysts such as sulfur monochloride, sulfur dichloride, iodine monochloride, and antimony trichloride to yield a copper polychlorophthalocyanine containing 12 to 15 atoms of chlorine (123). The yields range from 92 to 98 per cent of theoretical. They also found that benzene- and toluenesulfonic acids and their chloro- and nitro-derivatives, as well as naphthalenesulfonic acid were suitable as reaction media for this chlorination (124). In this case the chlorination also takes place at 110–120°.

Copper phthalocyanine has also been partially halogenated in chlorosulfonic acid solution to obtain products containing from 3 to 9 atoms of halogen (212). Chlorination has also been achieved in concentrated sulfuric acid or 20 per cent oleum at 0–5°. The products are obtained in a pigment form on drowning the acid solutions in water (93,94,95,240).

An unusual method for chlorinating copper phthalocyanine uses a melt of aluminum chloride, sodium chloride, and chlorosulfonic acid (45). This produces rapid chlorination of copper phthalocyanine at 140–160°. Consistent and good yields of high purity copper polychlorophthalocyanine (48 per cent chlorine) are obtained with little or no corrosion problem. The reaction is postulated as follows:

$$RSO_2Cl + AlCl_3 \longrightarrow [AlCl_3 \cdot RSO_2]^- \; Cl^+$$

$$[AlCl_3 \cdot RSO_2]^- \; Cl^+ + X-H \longrightarrow [AlCl_3 \cdot RSO_2]^- \; H^+ + X-Cl$$

The method has also been applied to the chlorination of other pigments (46).

In 1959, a copper polyhalophthalocyanine containing both bromine and chlorine was introduced commercially (41,287,288). This product contained about 4 to 5 atoms of bromine and 9 to 11 atoms of chlorine. Copper phthalocyanines containing both bromine and chlorine are known (179,219). Bromination and chlorination may take place simultaneously in an aluminum chloride, sodium chloride melt (156,219,291).

Cuprous cyanide and 3,4-dichlorobenzotrifluoride have been heated to 225° for 6–8 hours in quinoline to prepare a copper tetrokistrifluoromethylphthalocyanine (26). Copper phthalocyanine has been fluorinated in anhydrous hydrofluoric acid at a low temperature (43). The product is greener than the original compound but slightly bluer than an equivalent chlorine substituted derivative. A copper tetrafluorotetra-(trifluoromethyl) phthalocyanine has been made by heating copper phthalocyanine tetra-4-carboxylic acid with sulfur tetrachloride and hydrogen fluoride in an autoclave at 155° for six hours (282).

Borodkin and Usacheva have reviewed process variables in the chlorination of copper phthalocyanine (23).

Finishing Phthalocyanine Green

Some of the finishing procedures used to process phthalocyanine blue can be used with little change for phthalocyanine green, while others require modification. Acid pasting procedures during which the copper polychlorophthalocyanine is dissolved require chlorosulfonic acid or mixtures of chlorosulfonic and sulfuric acids to attain solution (64,68,123, 211). The permutoid swelling type of process requires stronger sulfuric acid for the polychloro compound than for the unchlorinated compound.

The method of slurrying copper polychlorophthalocyanine in concentrated sulfuric acid to convert the crude color to a pigment form is well known (64,68,89,219). This method may be improved by adding about 10 per cent of the acid weight of sodium sulfate to the slurry of the pigment in concentrated sulfuric acid (9). The addition of about 2 per cent of nitrobenzene to the slurry gives further improvement, the resulting product being more jet in masstone, yellower and brighter in undertone, and about 12 per cent stronger when evaluated in printing inks (110). When slurrying methods are performed in equipment such as a dough mixer or a Werner-Pfleiderer mill, much less sulfuric acid can be used (30). This process is also improved by the addition of 2 to 5 per cent of the pigment weight of a water insoluble benzenoid neutral liquid such as nitrobenzene, xylene, toluene, or dichlorobenzene, or from 10 to 30 per cent of the sulfonated form of such liquid, i.e., toluenesulfonic acid or xylenesulfonic acid (151).

Crude copper polychlorophthalocyanine has also been converted to a pigment form by grinding techniques. It has been ground in acetone with 1/8 inch steel shot (171). It was found that if water is present in the acetone, the pigment invariably becomes bluer and duller in shade as the grinding proceeds. The addition of oxidizing agents of a mildly alkaline reaction effectively prevents this change. Oxidizing agents such as sodium dichromate, sodium hypochlorite and sodium nitrite are effective.

Another method of converting copper polychlorophthalocyanine made by the eutectic method to the pigment form involves drowning the melt in water, adding an organic diluent capable of displacing water from the surface of the pigment particle, filtering and adding more liquid to completely wet the pigment surface, removing the organic liquid by steam distillation and recovering the pigment by filtration and drying (264). The product is yellower in hue and more jet in masstone than similar material which has been acid pasted.

The above procedure can be applied to copper polychlorophthalocyanine made by any other process or made by the eutectic process and drowned, filtered, and dried. In this case, the pigment is slurried in the organic liquid, o-dichlorobenzene, for 6 to 18 hours at room temperature, the liquid is steam distilled from the pigment, the resulting slurry filtered, and the pigment dried (82). The resulting pigment is more easily dispersed in organic vehicles and is jetter in masstone. The above procedure was also applied to the product of the sulfur dichloride-chlorine process. In addition, a metallic halide such as aluminum chloride, ferric chloride or cryolite was used as a catalyst in the sulfur dichloride chlorination (81). The product was slurried with o-dichlorobenzene as in the above two examples to give the pigment greater ease of dispersion and a jetter masstone.

When the copper polychlorophthalocyanine-aluminum chloride-sodium chloride-eutectic is drowned in water containing 50 per cent of the pigment weight of butylbenzylphthalate, the aqueous slurry filtered, the color washed and dried, the resulting pigment is stronger, yellower, and brighter when evaluated in floor coverings than the same pigment prepared in the usual manner and acid pasted (99).

Crude copper polychlorophthalocyanine may also be ground to the pigment form by the salt grinding procedure using a polyethylene glycol to provide an especially viscous mass and heavy duty dispersion equipment to effect the grinding rapidly (47).

REFERENCES

1. Badische Anilin- & Soda-Fabrik A.-G., British Patent 851,494 (Oct. 19, 1960); French Patent 1,186,701 (Aug. 31, 1959).
2. Badische Anilin- & Soda-Fabrik (I. G. Farbenindustrie A.-G. "In Auflösung"), French Patent 976,055 (Mar. 13, 1951).
3. Bansho, Y., Repts. Govt. Chem. Ind. Research Inst., Tokyo, 50, 353-60 (1955).
4. Bansho, Y. (to Industrial Technology Board Tokyo Industrial Experiment Station), Japanese Patent 7547/58 (Aug. 29, 1958).
5. Ibid. (to Bureau of Industrial Technics), Japanese Patent 1192/59 (Mar. 6, 1959).
6. Bansho, Y., Yagi, T., Suzuki, S., and Imura, G., Kôgyô Kagaku Zasshi, 61, 92-4 (1958).
7. Balassa, L. L. (to J. R. Geigy A.-G.), U. S. Patent 2,941,896 (June 21, 1960).
8. Barnhart, G. (to E. I. du Pont de Nemours & Co.), U. S. Patent 2,602,800 (July 8, 1952).
9. Ibid., U. S. Patent 2,765,319 (Oct. 2, 1956).

10. Barnhart, G., and Grimble, R. W. (to E. I. du Pont de Nemours & Co.), U. S. Patent 2,586,598 (Feb. 19, 1952).

11. Barrett, P. A., Bradbrook, E. F., Dent, C. E., and Linstead, R. P., *J. Chem. Soc.*, **1939**, 1820-8.

12. Baunsgaard, A. C., and Knudsen, B. I. (to Keminsk Vaerk Køge A/S), U. S. Patent 2,713,005 (July 12, 1955); German Patent 930,648 (July 21, 1955), 931,251 (Aug. 4, 1955).

13. Beard, E. E. (to E. I. du Pont de Nemours & Co.), U. S. Patent 2,476,950 (July 26, 1949).

14. *Ibid.*, U. S. Patent 2,476,951 (July 26, 1949).

15. *Ibid.*, U. S. Patent 2,476,952 (July 26, 1949).

16. Bienert, B., and Thielert, H. (to I. G. Farbenindustrie A.-G.), German Patent 739,050 (Sept. 10, 1943).

17. Black, C. K. (to E. I. du Pont de Nemours & Co.), U. S. Patent 2,238,243 (April 15, 1941).

18. Bluemmel, F. P., and Lytle, L. D. (to General Aniline & Film Corp.), U. S. Patent 2,615,027 (Oct. 21, 1952); British Patent 703,505 (Oct. 21, 1952).

19. Borodkin, V. F., *Izvest. Vysshikh Ucheb. Zavedenii, Khim. i Khim. Tekhnol.*, **1958**, No. 2, 147-51.

20. *Ibid.*, *Trudy Ivanovsk. Khim. Tekhnol. Inst.* **1958**, No. 8, 101-4.

21. Borodkin, V. F., Erykalov, Y. G., and Usacheva, K. V., *Zhur. Priklad. Khim.*, **29**, 1606-8 (1956).

22. Borodkin, V. F., and Usacheva, K. V., *Izvest. Vysshikh Ucheb. Zavedenii, Khim. i Khim. Tekhnol.*, **1958**, No. 3, 142-5.

23. *Ibid.*, *Zhur. Priklad. Khim.*, **29**, 1383-7 (1956).

24. Borodkin, V. F., Usacheva, K. V., and Dormidontova, A. I., *Izvest. Vysshikh Ucheb. Zavedenii, Khim. i Khim. Tekhnol.*, **1958**, No. 5, 131-5.

25. Botti, E. C., *Offic. Dig. Federation Paint and Varnish Production Clubs*, **305**, 408-17 (1950).

26. Braun, W., and Koberle, K. (to General Aniline & Film Corp.), U. S. Patent 2,225,441 (Dec. 17, 1940).

27. Brouillard, R. E. (to General Aniline & Film Corp.), U. S. Patent 2,647,128 (July 28, 1953); British Patent 714,083 (Aug. 25, 1954).

28. *Ibid.*, U. S. Patent 2,673,854 (Mar. 30, 1954); British Patent 711,376 (June 30, 1954); German Patent 924,764 (Mar. 7, 1955).

29. *Ibid.*, U. S. Patent 2,647,127 (July 28, 1953); British Patent 729,124 (May 4, 1955); German Patent 923,690 (Feb. 21, 1955).

30. *Ibid.*, U. S. Patent 2,716,649 (Aug. 30, 1955); British Patent 711,677 (July 7, 1954).

31. *Ibid.*, German Patent 913,217 (July 26, 1954); British Patent 729,123 (May 4, 1955).

32. Brouillard, R. E., *Am. Ink Maker*, **35**, No. 3, 36-40, 73 (1957).

33. Brouillard, R. E., and Baumgarten, E. (to American Cyanamid Co.), U. S. Patent 2,460,779 (Feb. 1, 1949).

34. Brouillard, R. E., and Giambalvo, V. A. (to American Cyanamid Co.), U. S. Patent 2,540,775 (Feb. 6, 1951).

35. Brouillard, R. E., and Katz, L. (to General Aniline & Film Corp.), U. S. Patent 2,867,539 (Jan. 6, 1959); British Patent 804,031 (Nov. 5, 1958); French Patent 1,166,510 (Nov. 12, 1958); Swiss Patent 347,927 (Sept. 15, 1960).

36. Brouillard, R. E., and Mutaffis, T. D. (to General Aniline & Film Corp.), U. S. Patent 2,774,677 (Dec. 18, 1956).
37. *Ibid.*, U. S. Patent 2,838,415 (June 10, 1958).
38. Brouillard, R. E., Mutaffis, T. D., and Shrader, M. O., U. S. Patent 2,840,568 (June 24, 1958); British Patent 795,414 (May 21, 1958).
39. Brouillard, R. E., and Mutaffis, T. D., *Paint and Varnish Production,* 44, No. 7, 30–1 (1954).
40. Brouillard, R. E., and Tarantino, T. R. (to General Aniline & Film Corp.), U. S. Patent 2,900,390 (Aug. 18, 1959); British Patent 819,457 (Sept. 2, 1959).
41. Brouillard, R. E., and Tullsen, V., *Am. Paint J.,* 42, 46, 48, 50 (Sept. 14, 1959).
42. Bucher, A. (to Ciba Ltd.), U. S. Patent 2,378,283 (June 12, 1945); Swiss Patent 239,214 (Dec. 17, 1945).
43. Calcott, W. S. (to E. I. du Pont de Nemours & Co.), U. S. Patent 2,227,628 (Jan 7, 1941).
44. Caliezi, A. (to Ciba Ltd.), U. S. Patent 3,016,384 (Jan. 9, 1962); Canadian Patent 603,575 (Aug. 16, 1960); British Patent 858,068 (Jan. 4, 1961).
45. Caliezi, A., Kern, W., and Holbro, T. (to Ciba Ltd.), U. S. Patent 2,862,929 (Dec. 2, 1958); British Patent 821,629 (Oct. 14, 1959).
46. *Ibid.*, U. S. Patent 2,862,930 (Dec. 2, 1958).
47. Chun, M., and Erskine, A. M. (to California Ink Co.), U. S. Patent 2,982,666 (May 2, 1961).
48. Ciba Ltd., Belgium Patent 564,881 (Aug. 18, 1958); Canadian Patent 602,076 (July 19, 1960); Swiss Patent 352,436 (Apr. 14, 1961).
49. *Ibid.*, British Patent 687,387 (Feb. 11, 1953).
50. *Ibid.*, French Patent 1,271,325 (Sept. 13, 1960).
51. *Ibid.*, French Patent 1,271,337 (Sept. 21, 1960).
52. *Ibid.*, Swiss Patent 279,293 (Mar. 1, 1952); British Patent 685,582 (Jan. 7, 1953).
53. Compton, J. D. (to E. I. du Pont de Nemours & Co.), U. S. Patent 2,668,171 (Feb. 2, 1954).
54. Cooper, J. H. (to E. I. du Pont de Nemours & Co.), U. S. Patent 2,857,400 (Oct. 21, 1958).
55. *Ibid.*, U. S. Patent 2,908,690 (Oct. 13, 1959).
56. Cooper, J. H., and Stratton, A. J. (to E. I. du Pont de Nemours & Co.), U. S. Patent 2,816,045 (Dec. 10, 1957).
57. Cronshaw, C. J. T., *Endeavour,* 1, No. 2, 79–83 (1942).
58. Dahlen, M. A., and Detrick, S. R. (to E. I. du Pont de Nemours & Co.), U. S. Patent 2,153,300) (Apr. 4, 1939).
59. *Ibid.*, U. S. Patent 2,192,704 (Mar. 5, 1940).
60. *Ibid.*, U. S. Patent 2,291,452 (July 28, 1942).
61. Dandridge, A. G., Drescher, H. A. E., and Thomas, J. (to Scottish Dyes Ltd.), British Patent 322,169 (Nov. 18, 1929).
62. Davies, J. S. H., Hailwood, A. J., and Todd, W. (to Imperial Chemical Industries Ltd.), U. S. Patent 2,213,693 (Sept. 3, 1940).
63. Dent, C. E. (to Imperial Chemical Industries Ltd.), U. S. Patent 2,214,454 (Sept. 10, 1940).
64. Dent, C. E., and Silvester, W. A. (to Imperial Chemical Industries Ltd.), U. S. Patent 2,195,984 (Apr. 2, 1940); British Patent 478,256 (Jan. 14, 1938); French Patent 48,638 (Apr. 19, 1938).

65. Detrick, S. R. (to E. I. du Pont de Nemours & Co.), U. S. Patent 2,160,837 (June 6, 1939).

66. Detrick, S. R., and Brandt, C. R. (to E. I. du Pont de Nemours & Co.), U. S. Patent 2,334,812 (Nov. 23, 1943).

67. Detrick, S. R., and Diver, R. T. (to E. I. du Pont de Nemours & Co.), U. S. Patent 2,284,685 (June 2, 1942).

68. Detrick, S. R., and Johnson, K. C. (to E. I. du Pont de Nemours & Co.), U. S. Patent 2,253,560 (Aug. 26, 1941).

69. Detrick, S. R., and Lang, J. W. (to E. I. du Pont de Nemours & Co.), U. S. Patent 2,305,379 (Dec. 15, 1942).

70. de Diesbach, H., and von der Weid, E., *Helv. Chim. Acta*, 10, 886–8 (1927).

71. Dudnikov, M. (to American Cyanamid Co.), U. S. Patent 2,657,213 (Oct. 27, 1953).

72. *Ibid.* (to Harshaw Chemical Co.), U. S. Patent 3,028,392 (Apr. 3, 1962).

73. Eastes, J. W. (to American Cyanamid Co.), U. S. Patent 2,770,629 (Nov. 13, 1956).

74. Eastes, J. W., and Cooke, T. F. (to American Cyanamid Co.), U. S. Patent 2,699,440 (Jan 11, 1955).

75. *Ibid.*, U. S. Patent 2,699,442 (Jan. 11, 1955).

76. *Ibid.*, U. S. Patent 2,699,443 (Jan. 11, 1955).

77. *Ibid.*, U. S. Patent 2,699,444 (Jan. 11, 1955).

78. Ehrich, F. F. (to E. I. du Pont de Nemours & Co.), U. S. Patent 2,799,594 (July 16, 1957).

79. *Ibid.*, U. S. Patent 2,805,957 (Sept. 10, 1957).

80. *Ibid.*, U. S. Patent 2,820,796 (Jan. 21, 1958).

81. *Ibid.*, U. S. Patent 2,833,784 (May 6, 1958).

82. Ehrich, F. F., and Gottlieb, H. B. (to E. I. du Pont de Nemours & Co.), U. S. Patent 2,833,783 (May 6, 1958).

83. Ehrich, F. F., and Stratton, A. J. (to E. I. du Pont de Nemours & Co.), U. S. Patent 2,816,114 (Dec. 10, 1957).

84. E. I. du Pont de Nemours & Co. (to Imperial Chemical Industries Ltd.), British Patent 552,124 (Mar. 24, 1943).

85. Farbenfabriken Bayer A.-G., French Patent 1,265,104 (Aug. 17, 1960).

86. *Ibid.*, French Patent 1,271,406 (July 31, 1961).

87. Fischer, E. K., "Colloidal Dispersions," p. 104, New York, John Wiley & Sons, Inc., 1950.

88. Fleysher, M. H., and Ogilvie, J. (to Allied Chemical & Dye Corp.), U. S. Patent 2,276,175 (Mar. 10, 1942).

89. Fox, A. L. (to E. I. du Pont de Nemours & Co.), U. S. Patent 2,247,752 (July 1, 1941).

90. Fox, A. L., and Johnson, K. C. (to E. I. du Pont de Nemours & Co.), U. S. Patent 2,377,685 (June 5, 1945).

91. Gassner, S., and Holzach, K. (to I. G. Farbenindustrie A.-G.), German Patent 698,218 (Oct. 3, 1940); British Patent 459,780 (Jan. 11, 1937).

92. Geiger, G. (to Sandoz Ltd.), U. S. Patent 2,999,862 (Sept. 12, 1961).

93. *Ibid.*, U. S. Patent 3,030,379 (Apr. 17, 1962).

94. Geiger, G., Geiger, A., and Pfister, X. (to Sandoz Ltd.), French Patent 1,256,794 (May 10, 1960); U. S. Patent 3,029,249 (Apr. 10, 1962).

95. Geiger, G., and Pfister, X. (to Sandoz Ltd.), French Patent 1,255,889 (Jan. 30, 1961).

96. Geigy A.-G., British Patent 872,659 (July 12, 1961).

97. *Ibid.*, British Patent 879,291 (Oct. 11, 1961).

98. General Aniline & Film Corp., British Patent 809,498 (Feb. 25, 1959).

99. *Ibid.*, British Patent 843,759 (Aug. 10, 1960).

100. Giambalvo, V. A. (to Interchemical Corp.), U. S. Patent 2,262,229 (Nov. 11, 1941).

101. *Ibid.*, U. S. Patent 2,375,780 (May 15, 1945).

102. *Ibid.*, U. S. Patent 2,526,345 (Oct. 17, 1950).

103. Górska, M., *Przemysł Chem.* **38**, 48–51 (1959).

104. Gottlieb, H. B. (to E. I. du Pont de Nemours & Co.), U. S. Patent 2,645,643 (July 14, 1953).

105. *Ibid.*, U. S. Patent 2,910,482 (Oct. 27, 1959); German Patent 1,020,138 (Nov. 28, 1957).

106. *Ibid.*, German Patent 1,030,486 (May 22, 1958).

107. Graham, D. P. (to E. I. du Pont de Nemours & Co.), U. S. Patent 2,556,728 (June 12, 1951).

108. *Ibid.*, U. S. Patent 2,556,730 (June 12, 1951).

109. Gross, P. F. (to E. I. du Pont de Nemours & Co.), U. S. Patent 2,365,464 (Dec. 19, 1944).

110. *Ibid.*, U. S. Patent 2,765,318 (Oct. 2, 1956).

111. Hanke, R., (to E. I. du Pont de Nemours & Co.), U. S. Patent 2,967,841 (Jan. 10, 1961).

112. Hartmann, E., and Moll, F. (to General Aniline Works, Inc.), U. S. Patent 2,187,816 (Jan. 23, 1940); German Patent 664,054 (Aug. 19, 1938); British Patent 460,152 (Jan. 22, 1937).

113. *Ibid.* (to I. G. Farbenindustrie A.-G.), German Patent 664,053 (Aug. 19, 1938); British Patent 460,147 (Jan. 18, 1937).

114. Hartwell, J. L. (to Interchemical Corp.), U. S. Patent 2,225,302 (Dec. 17, 1940).

115. Heilbron, I. M., Irving, F., and Linstead, R. P. (to Imperial Chemical Industries Ltd.), U. S. Patent 2,116,602 (May 10, 1938); British Patent 410,814 (May 16, 1934).

116. *Ibid.*, U. S. Patent 2,153,620 (Apr. 11, 1939).

117. *Ibid.*, U. S. Patent 2,166,213 (July 18, 1939).

118. *Ibid.*, U. S. Patent 2,202,632 (May 28, 1940).

119. *Ibid.*, U. S. Patent 2,242,301 (May 20, 1941).

120. Helfaer, B. M. (to Allied Chemical & Dye Corp.), U. S. Patent 2,772,984 (Dec. 4, 1956).

121. Hoelzle, K. (to Ciba Ltd.), U. S. Patent 3,002,845 (Oct. 3, 1961).

122. *Ibid.*, Swiss Patent 347,926 (Sept. 15, 1960); British Patent 855,098 (Nov. 30, 1960); German Patent 1,113,530 (Sept. 7, 1961).

123. Holtzman, H., and Simon, E. (to Ansbacher-Seigle Corp.), U. S. Patent 2,662,085 (Dec. 8, 1953).

124. *Ibid.*, U. S. Patent 2,793,214 (May 21, 1957).

125. Holzach, K., and Niemann, G., (to General Aniline & Film Corp.), U. S. Patent 2,099,689 (Nov. 23, 1937); German Patent 663,003 (July 27, 1938); British Patent 457,796 (Dec. 7, 1936).

126. *Ibid.* (to General Aniline Works, Inc.), U. S. Patent 2,099,690 (Nov. 23, 1937); British Patent 454,858 (Oct. 5, 1936).

127. *Ibid.* (to I. G. Farbenindustrie A.-G.), French Patent 799,901 (June 23, 1936); German Patent 658,019 (Mar. 19, 1938); British Patent 453,767 (Sept. 14, 1936).

128. *Ibid.*, German Patent 673,071 (Mar. 15, 1939).

129. Howell, E. T. (to E. I. du Pont de Nemours & Co.), U. S. Patent 2,816,115 (Dec. 10, 1957).

130. Hoyer, H., Colombara, H., and Bienert, B. (Leverkusen I. G. Werk, vested in Alien Property Custodian), Serial No. 403,866 (Apr. 20, 1943).

131. I. G. Farbenindustrie A.-G., British Patent 466,042 (May 21, 1937).

132. *Ibid.*, British Patent 470,079 (Aug. 9, 1937); French Patent 816,692 (Aug. 13, 1937); German Patent 692,977 (June 29, 1940).

133. *Ibid.*, British Patent 480,249 (Feb. 18, 1938); French Patent 823,037 (Jan. 12, 1938).

134. *Ibid.*, British Patent 482,387 (Mar. 29, 1938).

135. *Ibid.*, British Patent 501,681 (Mar. 3, 1939).

136. *Ibid.*, French Patent 806,835 (Oct. 5, 1936); British Patent 458,754 (Dec. 21, 1936).

137. *Ibid.*, French Patent 831,573 (Sept. 8, 1938).

138. *Ibid.*, French Patent 838,009 (Feb. 24, 1939).

139. *Ibid.*, French Patent 846,023 (Sept. 7, 1939).

140. *Ibid.*, German Patent 696,334 (Aug. 15, 1940).

141. Jackson, J. (to E. I. du Pont de Nemours & Co.), U. S. Patent 2,933,505 (Apr. 19, 1960).

142. *Ibid.*, U. S. Patent 3,030,370 (Apr. 17, 1962).

143. Jaffe, F., Belgium Patent 450,302 (May, 1943).

144. *Ibid.*, Belgium Patent 450,360 (May, 1943).

145. *Ibid.*, Belgium Patent 450,361 (May, 1943).

146. *Ibid.*, Belgium Patent 450,836 (June, 1943).

147. *Ibid.*, Belgium Patent 450,950 (July, 1943).

148. Jutz, E., and Mühlbauer, F. (to Badische Anilin-& Soda-Fabrik), German Patent 1,002,100 (Feb. 7, 1957).

149. Jutz, E., Mühlbauer, F., and Fischer, H., (to Badische Anilin- & Soda-Fabrik A.-G.), British Patent 805,514 (Dec. 10, 1958); Swiss Patent 348,223 (Sept. 30, 1960); German Patent 1,080,715 (Apr. 28, 1960).

150. Katz, L. (to General Aniline & Film Corp.), British Patent 843,051 (Aug. 4, 1960); Canadian Patent 619,133 (Apr. 25, 1961).

151. Katz, L., Gannon, J., and Brouillard, R. E. (to General Aniline & Film Corp.), U. S. Patent 2,930,796 (Mar. 29, 1960).

152. Kehe, H. J., and Horne, Jr., S. E. (to The B. F. Goodrich Co.), U. S. Patent 2,825,733 (Mar. 4, 1958); Canadian Patent 601,022 (July 5, 1960).

153. Kehe, H. J., and Newton, E. B. (to The B. F. Goodrich Co.), U. S. Patent 2,824,108 (Feb. 18, 1958); Canadian Patent 601,024 (July 5, 1960).

154. Keller, J. L., and Lytle, L. D. (to General Aniline & Film Corp.), U. S. Patent 2,618,642 (Nov. 18, 1952); British Patent 703,507 (Feb. 3, 1954).

155. Kemisk Vaerk Køge A/S, Denmark Patent 85,237 (July 7, 1958).

156. Kershaw, A., and Fazackerley, R. (to Imperial Chemical Industries Ltd.), British Patent 850,237 (Oct. 5, 1960).

157. King, V. L., and Foote, J. W. (to American Cyanamid Co.), U. S. Patent 2,318,783 (May 11, 1943).

158. Kirby, B. H., Bernard, D. P., and Milazzo, J. S. (to Standard Ultramarine & Color Co.), U. S. Patent 2,964,531 (Dec. 13, 1960).

159. Kirby, B. H., and Getty, S. E. (to Standard Ultramarine & Color Co.), U. S. Patent 3,004,986 (Oct. 17, 1961).

160. Klenke, Jr., E. F. (to E. I. du Pont de Nemours & Co.), U. S. Patent 2,964,532 (Dec. 13, 1960).

161. Koike, E., *Repts. Govt. Chem. Ind. Research Inst. Tokyo,* **50,** 16–18 (1955).

162. Koike, E., and Yagi, T., *J. Chem. Soc. Japan, Ind. Chem. Sect.,* **57,** 552–5 (1954).

163. *Ibid.,* 828–30 (1954).

164. Kudzin, S. F. (to E. I. du Pont de Nemours & Co.), U. S. Patent 2,799,595 (July 16, 1957).

165. Lacey, H. T. (to American Cyanamid Co.), U. S. Patent 2,302,612 (Nov. 17, 1942).

166. *Ibid.,* U. S. Patent 2,318,787 (May 11, 1943); British Patent 559,247 (Feb. 10, 1944).

167. *Ibid.,* U. S. Patent 2,761,868 (Sept. 4, 1956).

168. Lacey, H. T., and Lecher, H. Z. (to American Cyanamid Co.), U. S. Patent 2,359,737 (Oct. 10, 1944).

169. Lacey, H. T., Roberts, G. L., and Giambalvo, V. A., *Paint and Varnish Production,* **48,** No. 4, 33–38,92 (1958).

170. Lane, F. W. (to E. I. du Pont de Nemours & Co.), U. S. Patent 2,556,726 (June 12, 1951).

171. Lane, F. W., and Stratton, A. J. (to E. I. du Pont de Nemours & Co.), U. S. Patent 2,556,727 (June 12, 1951).

172. Lang, J. W., and Detrick, S. R. (to E. I. du Pont de Nemours & Co.), U. S. Patent 2,402,167 (June 18, 1946).

173. Lecher, H. Z., Brouillard, R. E., and Giambalvo, V. A. (to American Cyanamid Co.), U. S. Patent 2,524,672 (Oct. 3, 1950); British Patent 662,386 (Dec. 5, 1951).

174. Lecher, H. Z., Brouillard, R. E., and Baumgarten, E. (to American Cyanamid Co.), U. S. Patent 2,460,783 (Feb. 1, 1949).

175. Leibnitz, E., Theurer, H. J., and Keil, A., *Chem. Tech. (Berlin),* **5,** 179–86 (1953).

176. "LePont-du-Risse" Société nouvelle de chimie industrielle, British Patent 824,558 (Dec. 2, 1959).

177. Linstead, R. P., and Dent, C. E. (to Imperial Chemical Industries Ltd.), U. S. Patent 2,124,742 (July 26, 1938).

178. *Ibid.,* U. S. Patent 2,129,013 (Sept. 6, 1938).

179. *Ibid.,* U. S. Patent 2,214,469 (Sept. 10, 1940); British Patent 461,268 (Feb. 15, 1937); French Patent 809,616 (Dec. 12, 1936).

180. Linstead, R. P., Lowe, A. R., Heilbron, I. M., and Irving, F. (to Imperial Chemical Industries Ltd.), U. S. Patent 2,075,043 (Mar. 30, 1937); British Patent 418,367 (Oct. 22, 1934).

181. Linstead, R. P., Thorpe, J. F., and Thomas, J. (to Imperial Chemical Industries Ltd.), U. S. Patents 2,000,051-2 (May 7, 1935); British Patent 389,842 (Mar. 20, 1933).

182. Loukomsky, S. A. (to American Cyanamid Co.), U. S. Patent 2,486,304 (Oct. 25, 1949).

183. Loukomsky, S. A., and Lacey, H. T. (to American Cyanamid Co.), U. S. Patent 2,375,120 (May 1, 1945).

184. Lowe, A. R. (to Imperial Chemical Industries Ltd.), U. S. Patent 2,155,054 (Apr. 18, 1939); British Patent 460,594 (Feb. 1, 1937).

185. Lytle, L. D. (to General Aniline & Film Corp.), U. S. Patent 2,615,026 (Oct. 21, 1952); British Patent 707,601 (Apr. 21, 1954).

186. Manufactures de produits Chimiques du nord, Etablissements Kuhlmann, French Patent 966,774 (Oct. 18, 1950).

187. Marnon, D. E. (to General Aniline & Film Corp.), U. S. Patent 2,611,771 (Sept. 23, 1952).

188. McKellin, W. H., Lacey, H. T., and Giambalvo, V. A. (to American Cyanamid Co.), U. S. Patent 2,855,403 (Oct. 7, 1958); Canadian Patent 598,048 (May 17, 1960).

189. Merner, R. R. (to E. I. du Pont de Nemours & Co.), U. S. Patent 2,917,518 (Dec. 15, 1959).

190. Meyer, R. O. (to Chemetron Corp.), U. S. Patent 2,902,384 (Sept. 1, 1959); Canadian Patent 605,479 (Sept. 20, 1960).

191. Minnich, J. W. (to E. I. du Pont de Nemours & Co.), U. S. Patent 3,014,917 (Dec. 26, 1961).

192. Minnich, J. W., and Sweet, R. L. (to E. I. du Pont de Nemours & Co.), U. S. Patent 3,017,414 (Jan. 16, 1962).

193. Moilliet, J. L., and Todd, W. (to Imperial Chemical Industries Ltd.), British Patent 569,402 (May 22, 1945).

194. "Montecatini" Societa generale per l'industria, mineraria ed agricola, British Patent 503,029 (Mar. 30, 1939); French Patent 826,017 (Mar. 21, 1938); Austria Patent 157,098 (Sept. 25, 1939).

195. *Ibid.*, British Patent 502,623 (Mar. 22, 1939); French Patent 826,232 (Mar. 25, 1938); Austria Patent 157,099 (Sept. 25, 1939); Italian Patent 354,407 (Nov. 22, 1937).

196. *Ibid.*, Italian Patent 343,836 (Oct. 15, 1936).

197. Mori, M., *J. Chem. Soc. Japan, Ind. Chem. Sect.*, **56**, 37–9 (1953).

198. *Ibid.*, 116–8.

199. *Ibid.*, 512–14.

200. *Ibid.*, 595–6.

201. *Ibid.*, 679–81.

202. *Ibid.*, 681–3.

203. *Ibid.*, 768–9.

204. Moser, F. H. (to Standard Ultramarine & Color Co.), U. S. Patent 2,469,663 (May 10, 1949).

205. *Ibid.*, U. S. Patent 2,549,842 (Apr. 24, 1951).

206. *Ibid.*, U. S. Patent 2,965,511 (Dec. 20, 1960).

207. *Ibid.*, U. S. Patent 2,965,662 (Dec. 20, 1960).

208. Moser, F. H., and Stepp, J. D. (to Standard Ultramarine & Color Co.), U. S. Patent 3,024,247 (Mar. 6, 1962).

209. Mühlbauer, F. (to General Aniline Works, Inc.), U. S. Patent 2,182,763 (Dec. 5, 1939); French Patent 809,359 (Mar. 2, 1937); Italian Patent 342,439 (Aug. 1, 1936); British Patent 462,239 (Mar. 1, 1937).

210. *Ibid.* (to General Aniline & Film Corp.), U. S. Patent 2,212,924 (Aug. 27, 1940); British Patent 457,526 (Nov. 30, 1936); French Patent 805,879 (Dec. 2, 1936); German Patent 658,018 (Mar. 19, 1938).

211. Mühlbauer, F. (to I. G. Farbenindustrie A.-G.), British Patent 500,471 (Feb. 6, 1939); German Patent 741,969 (Nov. 23, 1943).

212. *Ibid.*, (to Badische Anilin- & Soda-Fabrik A.-G.), German Patent 929,081 (June 20, 1955).

213. Mühlbauer, F., and Niemann, G. (to General Aniline Works, Inc.), U. S. Patent 2,154,912 (Apr. 18, 1939); German Patent 679,988 (Aug. 18, 1939); French Patent 815,412 (July 12, 1937).

214. Mühlbauer, F., Plankenhorn, E., and Zell, R. (to Badische Anilin- & Soda-Fabrik A.-G.), U. S. Patent 2,826,589 (Mar. 11, 1958); British Patent 783,634 (Sept. 25, 1957); Swiss Patent 332,813 (Nov. 15, 1958).

215. *Ibid.*, German Patent 945,405 (July 5, 1956).
216. Mühlbauer, F., Zell, R., Plankenhorn, E., and Jutz, E. (to Badische Anilin, & Soda-Fabrik A.-G.), U. S. Patent 2,846,441 (Aug. 5, 1958); British Patent 761,718 (Nov. 21, 1956).
217. Mutaffis, T. D. (to American Cyanamid Co.), U. S. Patent 2,669,596 (Feb. 16, 1954); British Patent 712,378 (July 21, 1954).
218. Newton, E. B., and Kehe, H. J. (to The B. F. Goodrich Co.), U. S. Patent 2,824,107 (Feb. 18, 1958); Canadian Patent 601,023 (July 5, 1960).
219. Niemann, G., Schmidt, W., Mühlbauer, F., and Wiest, G. (to General Aniline & Film Corp.), U. S. Patent 2,276,860 (Mar. 17, 1942); British Patent 474,740 (Nov. 5, 1937); British Patent 499,415 (Jan. 24, 1939); French Patent 815,088 (July 5, 1937); Canadian Patent 497,737 (Nov. 17, 1953); German Patent 717,164 (Jan. 15, 1942); German Patent 740,053 (Oct. 16, 1943).
220. O'Neal, G. M. (to The Sherwin-Williams Co.), U. S. Patent 2,367,519 (Jan. 16, 1945); British Patent 649,911 (Feb. 7, 1951).
221. *Ibid.*, U. S. Patent 2,410,301 (Oct. 29, 1946); Reissue 23,304 (Dec. 12, 1950); British Patent 633,713 (Dec. 19, 1949).
222. *Ibid.*, British Patent 648,688 (Jan. 10, 1951).
223. Palmer, F. S., and Gross, P. F. (to E. I. du Pont de Nemours & Co.), U. S. Patent 2,413,191 (Dec. 24, 1946).
224. PB 65657 (BIOS Final Report No. 960, Item No. 22).
225. PB 85172 (FIAT Final Report No. 1313) (Feb. 1, 1948).
226. Plankenhorn, E., Mühlbauer, F., Zell, R., and Fischer, H. (to Badische Anilin- & Soda-Fabrik A.-G.), German Patent 950,799 (Oct. 18, 1956).
227. Pugin, A. (to J. R. Geigy A.-G.), U. S. Patent 2,791,589 (May 7, 1957); Canadian Patent 520,811 (Jan. 17, 1956).
228. *Ibid.*, U. S. Patent 2,823,137 (Feb. 11, 1958); British Patent 781,239 (Aug. 14, 1957); Swiss Patent 331,525 (Sept. 15, 1958); French Patent 1,145,176 (Oct. 23, 1957).
229. Randall, D. I., and Taras, J. (to General Aniline & Film Corp.), U. S. Patent 2,873,279 (Feb. 10, 1959); British Patent 818,831 (Aug. 26, 1959); Canadian Patent 620,933 (May 30, 1961).
230. Reynolds, W. B., and Scully, S. A. (to Interchemical Corp.), U. S. Patent 2,382,441 (Aug. 14, 1945).
231. Riley, A. (to Imperial Chemical Industries Ltd.), U. S. Patent 2,214,477 (Sept. 10, 1940); British Patent 476,243 (Dec. 6, 1937); German Patent 870,150 (Mar. 12, 1953); French Patent 48,515 (Mar. 8, 1938).
232. Ritelman, W. L. (to E. I. du Pont de Nemours & Co.), U. S. Patent 2,485,167 (Oct. 18, 1949).
233. *Ibid.*, U. S. Patent 2,485,168 (Oct. 18, 1949).
234. Roberts, Jr., G. L., (to American Cyanamid Co.), U. S. Patent 2,891,694 (June 23, 1959).
235. Roberts, Jr., G. L., McSheehy, J. A., and Soffer, H. (to American Cyanamid Co.), U. S. Patent 2,975,190 (Mar. 14, 1961).
236. Rodriguez, E. S., Spanish Patent 203,884 (Jan. 22, 1954).
237. Saito, S., and Haga, H. (to Sanko Chemical Co.), Japan Patent 11,039 (Aug. 12, 1960).
238. Sander, A., German Patent 1,095,430 (Dec. 22, 1960).
239. Sandoz Ltd., British Patent 585,727 (Feb. 21, 1947); Swiss Patent 238,337 (Oct. 15, 1945).

240. *Ibid.*, British Patent 878,753 (Oct. 4, 1961).

241. *Ibid.*, Swiss Patents 242,276-9 (Sept. 16, 1946).

242. *Ibid.*, Swiss Patent 258,299 (May 2, 1949).

243. Sanko Chemical Co., Ltd., Japan Patent 5716/61 (May 25, 1961).

244. Scalera, M., and Brouillard, R. E. (to American Cyanamid Co.), U. S. Patent 2,525,621 (Oct. 10, 1950).

245. Schmidt, W., Mühlbauer, F., Wiest, G., and Niemann, G. (to I. G. Farbenindustrie A.-G.), British Patent 470,079 (Aug. 9, 1937); French Patent 816,692 (Aug. 13, 1937); German Patent 692,977 (June 29, 1940).

246. Schmitt, B. (to I. G. Farbenindustrie A.-G.), German Patent 708,834 (July 30, 1941).

247. Scully, A., and Pizarello, A. (to Interchemical Corp.), British Patent 717,783 (Nov. 3, 1954); German Patent 1,060,529 (July 2, 1959).

248. Sekiguchi, Y., Japan Patent 7817 (June 24, 1960).

249. Sherwin-Williams Co., British Patent 640,576 (July 26, 1950).

250. Shigemitsu, M., *Bull. Chem. Soc. Japan*, **32**, 693-5 (1959).

251. *Ibid.* (to Toyo Ink Mfg. Co., Ltd.), Japan Patent 15786/60 (Oct. 20, 1960).

252. Shur, E. G., *Paint & Varnish Production*, **45**, No. 5, 30-3, No. 6, 30-9, 70 (1955).

253. Siegel, A. (to E. I. du Pont de Nemours & Co.), U. S. Patent 2,173,699 (Sept. 19, 1939).

254. *Ibid.*, U. S. Patent 2,452,606 (Nov. 2, 1948).

255. *Ibid.*, U. S. Patent 2,861,005 (Nov. 18, 1958).

256. Sloan, C. K. (to E. I. du Pont de Nemours & Co.), U. S. Patent 2,282,006 (May 5, 1942).

257. Stallman, O. (to E. I. du Pont de Nemours & Co.), U. S. Patent 2,556,729 (June 12, 1951); Canadian Patent 516,754 (Sept. 20, 1955).

258. Stefaniak, S. (to Wolskie Zakłady Przemysłu Barwników P. P.), Poland Patent 41,969 (June 2, 1959).

259. Stephens, B. T. (to Pittsburgh Plate Glass Co.), U. S. Patent 2,851,371 (Sept. 9, 1958).

260. Stepp, J. D. (to Standard Ultramarine & Color Co.), U. S. Patent 3,013,889 (Dec. 19, 1961).

261. Stocker, R., and Bucher, A. (to Ciba Ltd.), U. S. Patent 2,276,598 (Mar. 17, 1942); Swiss Patent 211,494 (Dec. 16, 1940); British Patent 538,957 (Aug. 22, 1941).

262. Strobel, A. F., and Marnon, D. E. (to General Aniline & Film Corp.), Canadian Patent 461,088 (Nov. 15, 1949).

263. *Ibid.*, Canadian Patent 461,089 (Nov. 15, 1949).

264. Stryker, H. I., Williamson, A. H., and Gross, P. F. (to E. I. du Pont de Nemours & Co.), U. S. Patent 2,833,782 (May 6, 1958); Swiss Patent 348,222 (Sept. 30, 1960); German Patent 1,114,462 (Oct. 5, 1961).

265. Sullivan, Jr., F. W. (to Standard Ultramarine & Color Co.), U. S. Patent 2,568,569 (Sept. 18, 1951).

266. *Ibid.*, U. S. Patent 2,568,570 (Sept. 18, 1951).

267. Sumner, R. J. (to Roberts Chemical Co.), U. S. Patent 2,471,794 (May 31, 1949).

268. Takahashi, T., and Susa, W. (to Dai Nippon Ink Manufacturing Co.), Japan Patent 4337 (June 24, 1955).

269. Tarantino, F. R., and Tullsen, V. (to American Cyanamid Co.), U. S. Patent 2,723,980 (Nov. 15, 1955); British Patent 712,380 (July 21, 1954).

270. Tullsen, V. (to American Cyanamid Co.), U. S. Patent 2,723,981 (Nov. 15, 1955); British Patent 712,379 (July 21, 1954).

271. Turek, F. S. (to Interchemical Corp.), U. S. Patent 2,138,413 (Nov. 29, 1938); French Patent 831,955 (Sept. 16, 1938); British Patent 508,583 (July 4, 1939).

272. *Ibid.*, U. S. Patent 2,194,250 (Mar. 19, 1940).

273. *Ibid.*, U. S. Patent 2,245,098 (June 10, 1941).

274. Turk, M. J. H., *Verfkroniek*, 32, 494 (1959).

275. Valík, J., and Slechta, J., British Patent 884,154 (Dec. 6, 1961); Poland Patent 94,180 (1960).

276. Venkataraman, K., "The Chemistry of Synthetic Dyes," pp. 1118–42, New York, Academic Press, Inc., 1952.

277. Vesce, V. C. (to Harmon Color Works, Inc.), U. S. Patent 2,138,049 (Nov. 29, 1938).

278. *Ibid.*, U. S. Patent 2,268,144 (Dec. 30, 1941).

279. Vesce, V. C., and Stalzer, F. M. (to Harmon Color Works, Inc.), U. S. Patent 2,327,472 (Aug. 24, 1943).

280. Vollmann, H. (to Farbenfabriken Bayer A.-G.), U. S. Patent 2,786,062 (Mar. 19, 1957); German Patent 928,344 (May 31, 1955); British Patent 736,436 (Sept. 7, 1955).

281. Walton, W. T., and Holton, A. B. (to Sherwin-Williams Co.), U. S. Patent 2,613,158-9-60 (Oct. 7, 1952).

282. Weinmayr, V. (to E. I. du Pont de Nemours & Co.), U. S. Patent 3,006,921 (Oct. 31, 1961).

283. Wettstein, W. (to Ciba Ltd.), U. S. Patent 2,686,010 (Aug. 10, 1954); British Patent 715,763 (Sept. 22, 1954); Swiss Patent 290,892 (Aug. 17, 1953).

284. Wettstein, W. (to Ciba Ltd.), U. S. Patent 2,686,184 (Aug. 10, 1954); British Patent 708,040 (Apr. 28, 1954); German Patent 913,216 (June 10, 1954).

285. *Ibid.*, U. S. Patent 2,699,441 (Jan. 11, 1955); Swiss Patent 292,413 (Nov. 2, 1953); British Patent 708,039 (Apr. 28, 1954).

286. *Ibid.*, Swiss Patent 297,412 (June 1, 1954); German Patent 933,047 (Sept. 15, 1955).

287. Wich, E. A., *Am. Ink Maker*, 37, No. 8, 26–7, 63 (1959).

288. Wich, E. A., *Am. Dyestuff Reptr.*, 48, No. 18, 42–3 (1959).

289. Wintersberger, K., Schwab, W., and Ebel, F. (to Badische Anilin- & Soda-Fabrik A.-G.), German Patent 935,389 (Nov. 17, 1955).

290. Wiswall, Jr., R. H. (to American Cyanamid Co.), U. S. Patent 2,486,351 (Oct. 25, 1949).

291. Woerth, L., and Chabrier, G., (to Compagnie Française des Matières Color-antes), French Patent 1,263,272 (Apr. 25, 1960).

292. Woerth, L., and Haquin, P. (to Compagnie Française des Matières Colorantes), French Patent 1,094,451 (May 20, 1955).

293. Wyler, M. (to Imperial Chemical Industries Ltd.), U. S. Patent 2,197,458 (Apr. 16, 1940); British Patent 464,126 (Apr. 12, 1937); French Patent 808,845 (Feb. 16, 1937); Italian Patent 344,006 (Oct. 21, 1936).

294. *Ibid.*, U. S. Patent 2,197,459 (Apr. 16, 1940); British Patent 486,782 (June 9, 1938).

295. *Ibid.*, U. S. Patent 2,216,761 (Oct. 8, 1940); British Patent 457,786 (Dec. 4, 1936).

296. *Ibid.*, U. S. Patent 2,216,867 (Oct. 8, 1940).

297. *Ibid.*, U. S. Patent 2,216,868 (Oct. 8, 1940).

298. *Ibid.*, British Patent 464,673 (Apr. 22, 1937); U. S. Patent 2,213,726 (Sept. 3, 1940).

299. Yagi, H. (to Sumitomo Chemical Industries Co.), Japan Patent 843 (Feb. 18, 1954).

300. *Ibid.*, Japan Patent 6128 (July 14, 1959).

301. Yagi, H., and Hori, T. (to Sumitomo Chemical Industries Co.), Japan Patent 6127 (Aug. 31, 1955).

302. *Ibid.*, Japan Patent 6,530 (Aug. 4, 1956).

303. Yoshii, T., and Itahara, K. (to Oriental High Pressure Industries Co.), Japan Patent 4439 (June 5, 1958).

304. Zeisberger, R. (to G. Seigle & Co. G. m. b. H.), German Patent 943,789 (June 1, 1956).

305. *Ibid.*, German Patent 1,044,027 (Nov. 20, 1958).

306. Zell, R., Plankenhorn, E., and Mühlbauer, F. (to Badische Anilin- & Soda-Fabrik A.-G), German Patent 948,002 (Aug. 23, 1956).

CHAPTER 5

DYES

The first phthalocyanine dye was a phthalocyanine polysulfonic acid prepared by Dandridge, Drescher, and Thomas in 1929. Example 14 of their British Patent 322,169 states:

> "10 parts of the product of Example 6 [copper phthalocyanine are added to 200 parts of 23 per cent oleum, stirred for some time and poured into water, and a bright green precipitate which when filtered off and washed may be used as a dyestuff for animal fibers."

Since this first synthesis, several hundred patents have appeared describing the preparation and color properties of several thousand phthalocyanine dyes.

Phthalocyanine compounds that are soluble in water and in organic media have been synthesized. Direct dyes, and dyes that develop their color form after reduction or oxidation, for application on materials of animal, vegetable, or synthetic origin immersed in solutions of the dyes, have been developed. Also, formation of the dye compound within the pores of the material to be colored has been accomplished by impregnation of the material with phthalocyanine precursors followed by heat treatments.

A variety of combinations of wash-, light-, heat-, and chemical-fastness is represented by the phthalocyanine dyes which account for perhaps from 5 to 10 per cent of the total poundage of phthalocyanine compounds produced per year. United States production of Colour Index Direct Blue 86, copper phthalocyanine disulfonate, was one-half million pounds in 1959.

Although a dye compound may be soluble in both inorganic and organic media, may be used as a direct dye or as a dye intermediate, and may contain more than one type of functional group imparting either solubility or reactive dye properties, dyes in this chapter are treated for convenience in the following sections: Sulfonic acid dyes, sulfonic acid chlorides, water soluble dyes that do not as a whole contain sulfonic acid groups, quaternary and ternary dyes, solvent soluble dyes, sulfur dyes, azo dyes, vat dyes, leuco dyes, chrome dyes, precursor dyes, and s-triazine dyes.

Appendix III provides a list of phthalocyanine dyes and dye manufacturers from the Colour Index of 1956. A list of review articles relating to phthalocyanine dyes is included in Appendix I.

SULFONIC ACID DYES

Bienert and Holzach (31) have obtained water soluble phthalocyanine and naphthalocyanine sulfonic acid direct dyes by the action of fuming sulfuric acid on phthalocyanine and naphthalocyanine pigments.

For example, a mixture of copper phthalocyanine and 30 per cent fuming sulfuric acid is stirred for 1 hour at room temperature. The mixture is poured onto ice and filtered. The precipitated sulfonic acid filter cake is neutralized with sodium carbonate. A mixture of copper phthalocyanine sulfonic acid, sodium carbonate, and sodium sulfate in water is heated to 80–90° and cotton is dyed therein for 1 hour, rinsed, and dried. "Clear shades of excellent fastness to light are thus obtained which in case of applying a copper-containing phthalocyanine sulfonic acid show a sky-blue shade, in case of applying a nickel-containing phthalocyanine sulfonic acid show a more greenish shade and in case of applying a cobalt-containing dyestuff show a more reddish tint."

The authors point out the unusual nature of these results since "... most of the sulfonic acids of other dyestuffs show affinity towards vegetable fibers only in case diphenyl groups or similar groups are present. By the term 'cellulosic materials' we mean vegetable fibers, such as cotton, cuprammonium or viscose silk, furthermore, paper or raw materials for the preparation thereof, such as paper pulp, pasteboard, straw, cellulose, jute, linters, cotton, wool, sponges, and so on. For the dyeing of textiles such compounds are preferred, as contain about 1 to 2 sulfonic acid groups in the molecule, whereas in case of paper or raw materials for the preparation thereof higher sulfonated compounds, which contain about 3 sulfonic acid groups in the molecule are preferably employed."

Tetrasulfonated phthalocyanines (158) are prepared from monosulfonic phthalic derivatives, the salts of which are water soluble, being useful dyes for natural and synthetic textile fibers.

Wiest and Niemann (247) produced water soluble phthalocyanine sulfonic acids containing halogen atoms, by halogenation of the phthalocyanine sulfonic acids with chlorine, bromine, or sulfuryl chloride.

"The new water-soluble phthalocyanine sulfonic acids containing halogen have affinity for different kinds of goods of vegetable or animal fibers. They yield clear, brilliant, generally speaking blue-green to green dyeings."

Bienert and Thielert (32) prepared water soluble phthalocyanine dyes of the formula

$$CuPc \begin{bmatrix} -SO_3X \\ -Y \end{bmatrix}_4$$

where $-SO_3X$ group is substituted at 4 or 5 position
X = H, NH_4, or salt forming metal atom
Y = halogen atom at 5 or 4 position

Cellulose and artificial silk are readily dyed in greenish blue shades of excellent lightfastness with these dyes.

A process (131) for the production of phthalocyanines that contain one sulfonic acid group and one carboxylic acid group in each of the four phenylene groups of the phthalocyanine molecule involves heating benzene-5-sulfonic-1,2,4-tricarboxylic (5-sulfotrimellitic) acid with the salt of a heavy metal in the presence of urea. The tetracarboxy tetrasulfonic acid derivatives may be used to dye textiles from aqueous media in a greener shade than from the corresponding tetrasulfonic acid derivatives.

Bienert (18) prepared acylaminophthalocyanines in order to obtain green shade phthalocyanines which may be sulfonated.

Copper tetra-4-acetylaminophthalocyanine is prepared by the reaction of 4-acetylaminophthalonitrile and copper chloride in quinoline. The mixture is diluted with pyridine; the precipitate is filtered and is washed with pyridine and alcohol. 4-Acetylaminophthalonitrile is made from 4-nitrophthalonitrile by reduction and acetylation.

Sulfonation of the copper tetra-4-acetylaminophthalocyanine by sulfuric acid monohydrate and 20 per cent oleum for 1 hour at 85–90° is followed by saponification of the acetylamino group in aqueous potassium hydroxide. In order to reintroduce the acyl radicals that have been split off during sulfonation the product is heated with acetic acid anhydride with agitation for 1 hour at 50°. The reaction mass is precipitated out in aqueous sodium chloride solution and ice. The precipitate is filtered and washed to neutrality with sodium chloride solution.

Gassner and Bienert (84) found that the presence of acyl groups in the phenylene nuclei of phthalocyanines changes the shade from blue to greenish blue or green. These dyes are soluble in some organic solvents. They are prepared by effecting the formation of phthalocyanine from o-dinitriles of the benzene series that have acyl groups as substituents. "The acyl-phthalocyanines obtained by the said processes show greenish-blue to green shades. Owing to their fastness to light, water and spirit they represent excellent pigment dyestuffs, for instance, for graphic wall paper printing and for the coloring of artificial silk."

For example, the acylphthalocyanine prepared from 4-phenyl-3′,4′-di-cyanobenzophenone dissolves in sulfuric acid monohydrate with sulfonation occurring in the phenyl radicals.

Holzach and Mühlbauer (123) prepared a new series of phthalocyanine compounds with blue-green to green shades by the reaction of halogen-bearing phthalocyanines with organic hydroxyl compounds giving oxy or ether phthalocyanine derivatives of the general formula:

$$Pc\!-\!\!\left[OX\right]_n$$

where Pc = phthalocyanine radical
    X = organic radical
    n = integer from 1 to 4

For example, a mixture of copper tetrachlorophthalocyanine, α-naphthol, potassium hydroxide, naphthalene, and copper meal is heated for 10 hours at 350° with agitation. After cooling the reaction mass is freed from naphthalene by hot toluene or alcohol, followed by boiling with dilute hydrochloric acid, water wash, and drying. "When sulphonating it the dyestuff forms green sulphonic acids."

Eisele, Federkiel, and Tartter (64) have made sulfonated hydroxymethylphthalocyanines that are useful to dye cotton materials.

For example, cotton is immersed in a solution of a dye produced from oleum and copper tetrachloromethylphthalocyanine, sodium chloride, and sodium hydroxide, squeezed, dried, heated at 180–200°, boiled, and soaped. Very good light, wash, and rubbing resistance is obtained on the cotton which is dyed turquoise blue.

Pugin (192) has prepared halogenated phthalocyanine disulfonic acids "...which are distinguished from similar known compounds by an increased affinity to cellulose fibres" by reacting copper or nickel phthalocyanine disulfonic acid with a halogenating agent at a temperature between 120° and 220° in a melt containing aluminum chloride until from 2 to 7 halogen atoms have entered the phthalocyanine molecule.

"A process is already known for halogenating metal-containing phthalocyanin sulphonic acids by means of halogenating agents in an alkali chloride-aluminium chloride melt which however, is expressly limited to such phthalocyanin sulphonic acids as contain at least 3, and preferably 4, sulphonic acid groups in the molecule... chlorination must take place to such a degree in these higher sulphonated starting materials that when a good cellulose affinity and a high halogen content are obtained an alteration of the shade towards green has already taken place.... As a result of the new process there is only slight alteration in the shade with no loss of brilliance but with considerably improved affinity to cellulose fibres."

"While the higher sulphonated products have no practical significance for the dyeing of textiles according to the usual methods, the disulphonic acids particularly possess the quality of dyeing cellulose fibres directly, and the alkali metal salts have sufficient water solubility for dyeing purposes. However, the copper phthalocyanindisulphonic acid for example, in comparison with the generally used direct cellulose dyestuffs shows only a limited affinity, poor take-up and very bad wet fastness properties... There has been no lack of endeavor to improve the bad take-up of these interesting metal-containing phthalocyanin sulphonic acids. These include, for example, the conversion of the sulphonic acid groups into sulphonamide groups, their complete or partial substitution by carboxyl groups, or the use of diphenyl for building up the phthalocyanin sulphonic acids. However, none of these suggestions has been of practical significance, because either the small degree of improvement did not justify the greater expense or because undesirable changes, particularly as undesired alteration in the shade towards green, became apparent."

Dent (58) found that the sulfonic acid derivatives of tetrabenzotriazaporphin "... are soluble in water and their aqueous solutions dye cotton, wool and acetate rayon in bright green shades."

For example, a mixture of copper tetrabenzotriazaporphin and 5 per cent oleum is heated at 100° for 1 hour with agitation. The mixture is poured into cold water, precipitating the sulfonic acid. The precipitate is filtered off and the residue is washed with cold water, followed by dissolution in water and addition of ammonia, followed by filtration and evaporation to dryness. "The ammonium salt of the sulphonic acid is thus obtained as a dark green powder readily soluble in water to give a green solution.

"This sulphonic acid dyes cotton, wool and acetate rayon a bright green shade. It is also useful for dyeing paper."

Gassner and Bienert (85) have prepared clear yellow-green to green phthalocyanine dyes in the form of sulfonated thiazolyl-, oxazolyl-, or imidazolylphthalocyanines. The sulfonated compounds have "... a certain solubility in water and in some cases some affinity towards cellulosic materials such as cotton and viscose or copper silk."

Pugin and Keller (194) have prepared yellow-green to green triazolylphthalocyanine pigments of the formula:

$$Pc \left[N \underset{N}{\overset{N}{\diagup}} A \right]_4$$

where A = phenylene, naphthalene, or 1,2,3-triazolylphenyl radical.

These pigments are discussed in Chapter 7. They may be converted into water soluble dyes by sulfonation or into sulfamide compounds by sulfohalogenation and reaction with amines.

Pyrazine-phthalocyanine sulfonic acid dyes, prepared by Eckert and Quint (61), are water soluble and dye vegetable fibers in green to yellowgreen tints.

Bienert and Gassner (29) attempted to produce phthalocyanine dyes of clear green shades with the fastness properties of copper phthalocyanine by introducing phenyl groups into the molecule and imparting water solubility with sulfonic acid groups. The phenyl groups are introduced by preparing phthalocyanines from o-dinitriles of the diphenyl series. They are sulfonated by dissolution in sulfuric acid monohydrate, pouring the solution into dilute sodium chloride solution, and washing the precipitate with water until neutral.

"It contains 4 sulfonic acid groups in the average it being assumed that each of the external phenyl groups contains one of the sulfonic acid groups. In case a higher number of sulfonic acid groups is desired we prefer to work with oleum at a somewhat higher temperature of say about 60-70°C. With the tetraphenyl-copper phthalocyanine the best result has been obtained in case 5 or at the most 6 sulfonic acid groups have been introduced whereas in the case of the other products the optimum properties are already reached with about 4 sulfonic acid groups. An increase of the number of sulfonic acid groups over six generally results in a loss of brightness so that nothing is gained by the introduction of 7 or more such groups."

Bienert and Gassner (28) extended the range of clean green shade phthalocyanines by introducing phenyl groups into the phthalocyanine phenylene nuclei by preparing phthalocyanines from o-dinitriles of the diphenyl, fluorenone, or diphenylene oxide series. "Among the substitution products of our new phthalocyanines particular importance is attached to the sulfonic acids which can easily be obtained by the action of sulfuric acid monohydrate or fuming sulfuric acid."

Bienert and Hansen (30) prepared polyphenylsulfonylphthalocyanines the alkali salts of which are water soluble.

For example, a mixture of diphenylsulfon-3,4-dicarboxyimide, anhydrous copper chloride, ammonium chloride, ammonium molybdate, and urea is added to nitrobenzene at 140-150°. The temperature is increased slowly to 185°; the mixture is stirred for 12 hours at 185°, cooled to 80-90°, diluted with methanol, filtered off, and washed with methanol. The filter cake is further purified with dilute hydrochloric acid, boiled with dilute sodium hydroxide solution, washed with hot water and dried. Copper tetra-4-phenylsulfonylphthalocyanine is obtained which dissolves in concentrated sulfuric acid with a green color. The copper tetraphenylsulfonylphthalocyanine is stirred in oleum at 20-30° until water soluble. The sulfonation mixture is stirred in a mixture of ice and sodium chloride, filtered, and washed to neutrality. It can be dried immediately or dissolved in water, made slightly alkaline, and again salted out. A sulfonic acid soluble in water is thus obtained.

Bienert and Thielert (34) obtained a series of phthalocyanine dyes that are green in shade by incorporation of a sulfonic acid group and an alkoxy or aryloxy group in the 4 and 5 positions of each phenylene group of the phthalocyanine molecule. "These new dyestuffs are capable of directly dyeing cellulose materials such as cotton, viscose or cuprammonium silk. The dyeings obtainable by means of our new dyestuffs combine excellently clear greenish shades with very good fastness properties." A method of preparation of these compounds is to start from phthalocyanine forming benzene derivatives that contain the sulfonic acid and o-alkoxy or aryloxy groups.

Bradbrook, Heilbron, Hey, and Haworth (36) condensed phthalic dinitriles containing a pyridyl radical to obtain pyridylphthalocyanines that react with acids to form salts that yield green shade phthalocyanine dyes. "Some of these salts dissolve readily in water, and the aqueous solutions so obtained dye cellulose directly . . . dry compositions suitable for dissolving in water for preparing dye-baths or for other coloring purposes are made by mixing together in the dry state the new phthalocyanines and a suitable proportion of sulphamic acid."

Rösch, Bayer, and Hoyer (204) have prepared a group of phthalocyanine sulfonic acids by the reaction of a benzene-o-dicarboxylic acid, urea, and a copper compound, at elevated temperature. The benzene-o-dicarboxylic acid contains in the 4-position a sulfonic acid radical of the form $-SO_3H$, $-SO_2Cl$, or $-SO_2NH_2$.

"These products are distinguished by a better fastness to light than the prior known phthalocyanine sulphonic acids which have been prepared by sulphonating the ready-made phthalocyanine and contain the sulphonic acid groups mostly in 3-position.

"Depending on the amount of the sulphonic acid groups which are present in the molecule the resulting products are more or less soluble in water. The di- and tri-sulphonic acids represent blue to greenish-blue substantive dyestuffs for cotton, viscose and cuprammonium silk."

Fox (76) found that attaching 3 or 4 sulfonamidopyridine or 2-sulfonamidopyridine groups to the phenylene nuclei of copper phthalocyanine confers water solubility to the pigment. "The new phthalocyanine colors are of a brilliant blue to greenish-blue shade and are capable of dyeing various textile fibers such as cotton, wool and silk."

Gutzwiller (92) developed a new type of water soluble phthalocyanines by treating phthalocyanine arylthioethers with sulfonating agents. The new dyes ". . . are easily soluble in water and can be used for the dyeing of paper, cotton, silk and the like and are intermediates for the manufacture of pigments. The shades obtained with these dyestuffs are bluish-green to yellow-green and possess generally a great brilliancy and an extraordinary fastness to light."

"As sulfonating agents one can use concentrated sulfuric acid, sulfuric acid monohydrate, fuming sulfuric acid of various concentrations, chlorosulphonic acid and mixtures of these agents alone or in presence of dilating and suspending media, such as dichlorobenzene, nitrobenzene, tetrachloroethane and the like. The temperature at which the sulfonation is carried out can be varied within wide limits, whereby according to the constitution of the starting product used the operation can be carried out at a temperature ranging from 0°C. up to 150°C., the time of the sulfonation depending upon the concentration of the sulphonation agents used and upon the temperature."

Bucher (47) prepared phthalocyanine dyes in which the phthalocyanine phenylene nuclei are joined together by a —SO$_2$— or —CO— group in the 4 position of a phenylene nucleus of each phthalocyanine molecule or in which two—CO—or—SO$_2$—groups are each attached to adjacent phenylene groups in the 4 position in one phthalocyanine molecule. The resulting pigment is greener than the individual parent phthalocyanine monomer and is sulfonated for the substantive dyeing of cellulose fibers.

For example, tetra-3,3',4,4'-cyanobenzophenone is heated in nitrobenzene at 80° with stirring, and cuprous chloride and sodium hydroxide are then added, followed by heating to 200–210° and stirring for 15 hours at 200°, followed by cooling, filtration, and extraction of the dye by boiling with dilute hydrochloric acid, dilute sodium hydroxide solution, and alcohol, yielding a black powder insoluble in organic solvents. Purification in concentrated sulfuric acid followed by precipitation in water yields a blue-green dye, corresponding to the formula:

"By heating the dyestuff so obtained in oleum of 25 per cent strength for 2 hours at 160°C. a sulfonation product is obtained which dyes cotton pale green tints."

The tetra-3,4,3′,4′-cyanobenzophenone is made by tetraazotizing di-4,4′-aminobenzophenone-di-3,3′-carboxylic acid, reacting the tetraazo compound with cuprous cyanide to the corresponding di-4,4′-cyanobenzo-phenone-di-3,3′-carboxylic acid, forming its ammonium salt, and treating the ammonium salt with phosphorous oxychloride in pyridine to split off water and give tetra-3,4,3′,4′-cyanobenzophenone.

Mayhew (153,155,156) synthesized a series of substituted and unsubstituted phthalocyanine sulfonamides from the corresponding sulfonyl-chlorides treated with ammonia, or a primary or secondary amine to yield blue to bluish green dyes that are soluble in dilute aqueous sodium hydroxide.   The phenylene nuclei in the substituted sulfonamides may carry substituents such as halogen atoms or amino or carboxy groups.

Because of the stability of these dyes in caustic solutions, they are useful colorants in quick drying inks which employ caustic media, since they penetrate rapidly into paper.

Sayler (217) makes use of the copper phthalocyanine sulfonamide dyes in writing inks in alkaline media with the inclusion of copper inhibitors such as disalicylal ethylene diamine.

Seibert, Triebeneck, Bienert, and Baumann (219) have prepared a series of dyes for writing inks and polymers by the reaction of salts of carboxylic acids with phthalocyanine sulfonamides.

"Substances which have proved particularly suitable for the manufacture of ball-point pen pastes, printing and stamp inks and typewriter ribbon inks are the reaction products of basic phthalocyanine dyestuffs with carboxylic acids, sulfonic acids or acid esters of dibasic or poly-basic acids which are of relatively high molecular weight and which contain an alkyl or aryl radical of relatively high molecular weight."

"Inks which are prepared by using a water-soluble salt such as, for example the hydrochloride or acetate of a blue or green basic copper phthalocyanine dyestuff have a high degree of fastness to light and do not produce deposits either as a result of oxidation agents or reduction agents, and impressions produced with these inks cannot be removed by chemical agents."

Chechak and Allen (50) have prepared copper phthalocyanine sulfonic acids having an absorption maximum at 668 mμ.   The authors state that previous oleum sulfonation procedures have produced a mixture of at least two dyes, "... one having a maximum absorption at 615 mμ and the other a maximum absorption at 668 mμ.   These fractions can be separated by means of a tedious alcohol precipitation."   Further, the sulfonated copper phthalocyanine dye that has an absorption maximum at

668 mμ is useful in the imbibition process in photography whereas the dye with the absorption maximum at 615 mμ is not as useful.

It is conjectured that copper phthalocyanine tetra-4-sulfonic acid has an absorption peak at 615 mμ and copper phthalocyanine tetra-3-sulfonic acid has an absorption peak at 668 mμ because "When tetrasulfonated copper phthalocyanine is prepared by condensing 4-sulfophthalimide the 615 mμ dye is produced exclusively."

Thus, the authors apparently produce copper phthalocyanine tetra-3-sulfonic acid with 15 per cent oleum as follows: "copper phthalocyanine is added to about 10 times its weight of 15 per cent oleum at 170°C. to 175°C. and about 4 per cent of the weight of copper phthalocyanine of mercuric sulfate is then added to the mixture. The mixture is heated at 170°C. to 175°C. for about two hours, cooled and diluted with 15 to 20 times its volume of water. It is then brought to about pH 8 with 40 per cent sodium hydroxide solution after which it is brought to pH 5 with glacial acetic acid and cooled to about 30°C. An excess of triphenyl guanidine in solution in hot ethyl alcohol, glacial acetic acid and water is then added to precipitate the dye as the guanidine salt and this is stirred for 10 or 15 minutes and filtered. The guanidine salt of the dye is washed on the filter with a large amount of cool water at 20 to 30°C., pressed as dry as possible and redissolved in boiling ethyl alcohol. This solution is filtered to remove any impurities and heated to about 70°C. An excess of anhydrous sodium acetate is stirred into the solution and the dye is thrown down as the sodium salt from the alcohol solution of the guanidine salt. The dye is recovered from the solution as the sodium salt of the sulfonated copper phthalocyanine.

"The sulfonation temperature must be held within the limits of 170 to 175°C. Too low temperature results in incomplete sulfonation with a considerable amount of the 615 millimicron component appearing while too high a temperature results in excessive destruction of the dye, yielding a colorless material."

Mühlbauer (161) describes a process for the sulfonation of phthalocyanines "of any degree of sulfonation" by heating a phthalocyanine such that sulfonation takes place in the solid phase. "All phthalocyanines are suitable for this kind of sulfonation. It is especially remarkable that phthalocyanines which cannot be sulfonated in other ways without undergoing change, in particular metal phthalocyanines which when dissolved in sulfuric acid give up their metal, such as is the case for example with magnesium, lead, manganese or mercury phthalocyanines, may also be sulfonated to the point of water-solubility in this simple way... phthalocyanines of any degree of sulfonation can be obtained by heating a phthalocyanine dyestuff... with such amounts of a sulfonating agent that sulfonation takes place in the solid phase. This is especially the case when one mol of a phthalocyanine dyestuff is heated with from 0.5 to 8 mols of a sulfonating agent depending on the desired degree of sulfonation. Temperatures between 80° and 220° are used depending on the desired degree of sulfonation and the speed of sulfonation.... At temperatures of 125° to 130°C., all degrees of sulfonation are passed through within from ½ to 5 hours. At lower temperatures the process of sulfonation is more protracted, whereas at 220° to 250°C. a complete sulfonation is attained within 20 to 30 minutes.... The process takes place entirely in the solid phase. The dyestuff is charged into the reaction vessel in powder form, the powder form is retained throughout the whole treatment and the final product is present as a powder in the form of the free dyestuff sulfonic acid. The reaction proceeds at first by way of addition products, namely sulfuric acid salts, which are then converted at higher temperatures into the phthalocyanine sulfonic acids. The final products are very loose powders. They are from insoluble to almost completely soluble in water depending on the degree of sulfonation. Upon the addition of alkali metal hydroxide solutions in the case of the least attainable monosulfonation, deep colored solutions are obtained which dye vegetable fibres extremely pure turquoise blue, blue or blue-green to green shades which are very fast to light.... The process offers great advantages as compared with the prior 'wet' sulfonation. No precipitation, pressing, washing, drying, grinding or the like, is necessary; in practice only a single, extremely simple working operation has to be carried out, only a single vessel is necessary for the complete preparation of the dyestuff and products ready for use are immediately obtained.... The sulfonating products, depending on their degree of sulfonation, may be used as vat dyestuffs or, in the form of their alkali salts, as substantive dyestuffs or, in the form of their alkaline-earth metal or earth metal salts, as pigments.''

Heyna and Schumacher (120) have developed a sulfonic acid derivative of phthalocyanine that is water soluble and that can be fixed on the fiber by making it water insoluble in alkaline solution. The general formula of the new dye is:

$$Pc \left[SO_2CHC\substack{R_2 \\ |} - OSO_3H \right]_n$$
$$\substack{| \quad | \\ R \; R_1}$$

where R, R_1, and R_2 = hydrogen or hydrocarbon radical of low molecular weight.

n = from 1 to 3

Mühlbauer (167) has found that phthalocyanine dyes of the formula

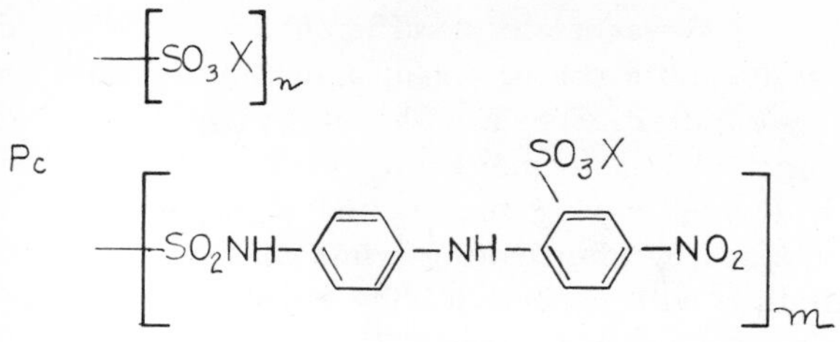

$$Pc \begin{cases} -\left[SO_3 X\right]_n \\ \left[-SO_2NH-\langle\bigcirc\rangle-NH-\langle\bigcirc\rangle-NO_2\right]_m \end{cases}$$

where Pc = phthalocyanine radical which may be metal-free, copper, cobalt, nickel, iron, chromium, zinc, aluminum, or tin

X = hydrogen, ammonium, diethyl ammonium, ethanol ammonium, sodium or potassium

n = 1 or 2

m = 1,2 or 3

$n + m$ = 2,3, or 4

re soluble in water and in organic solvents, and produce "... pale luish-green to deep yellowish-green dyestuffs."

An ammoniacal solution of 4-amino-4'-nitrodiphenylamine-2'-sulfonic cid is added to the copper phthalocyanine sulfonyl chloride paste. The emperature of the reaction mass rises to 15–20°. The paste is evapo- ated and dried. The dye that is obtained "dyes both leather and paper nd also varnish lacquer clear bluish-green shades of great color strength nd very good fastness."

Bluish green phthalocyanine sulfonamides with solubility in water and 1 organic solvents (129) were prepared by heating phthalic acid-4-sul- onamides, urea, and copper salts, in the presence of a suitable catalyst. he sulfonamides were made by the reaction of phthalic acid sulfonyl hloride with ammonia or amines. "The resulting phthalocyanines rep- esent valuable dyestuffs showing bluish to greenish-blue shades and eing characterised by excellent fastness properties."

Brentano, Grossmann, and Müller (39) have prepared a series of water oluble azo phthalocyanine dyes that are derived from a phthalocyanine etrasulfonic acid and contain at least (1) one —SO$_2$NH— group, (2) one zo linkage, and (3) one salicylic acid group.

"The dyestuffs yield green to olive tints which are in part distin- uished by remarkable properties of wet fastness and excellent fastness o light."

"The alkali metal salts of the azo-phthalocyanine dyestuffs of the in- ention are easily soluble in water, and are suitable for dyeing or print- ng vegetable, animal or wholly synthetic fibres, and also for dyeing xidic protective coatings on aluminum."

"Furthermore, if they contain a sufficient number of mordanting elements, the new dyestuffs can be fixed, according to known methods, on textile fibres by an aftertreatment with metal yielding substances, if desired together with high molecular basic substances. Thus, in particular, green to olive dyeings having good fastness properties to washing and to light are obtained by aftertreating prints on fibres of cellulose or regenerated cellulose with copper-yielding substances together with high molecular basic condensation products."

Thirty-eight amino azo dyestuffs are listed as examples of suitable intermediates leading to the phthalocyanine dyes of the general formula:

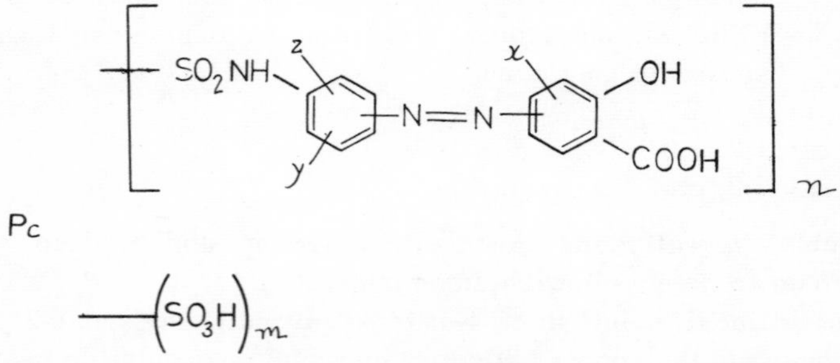

where —SO_2NH— or —SO_3H are in the 3 or 4 position, n = integer from 1 to 4, m = integer from 0 to 3, $m + n = 4$, X = hydrogen atom, halogen atom of a methyl, hydroxyl, nitro, or sulfonic acid group, Y = hydrogen atom, halogen atom or an alkyl, alkoxy, nitro, sulfonic acid or carboxycyclic acid group, and Z = a hydrogen atom, halogen atom, or an alkyl or alkoxy group, and the —SO_2NH— group is in a m- or p-position relative to the azo linkage.

Bienert, Baumann, and Vollmann (24) have prepared 4-amino-phthalimide-5-sulfonic acid as an intermediate in the preparation of phthalocyanine dyes presumably such as phthalocyanine 4-amino-5-sulfonic acid.

The new phthalic acid derivative is prepared by reacting 4-amino-phthalimide with a sulfonating agent and recovering the 4-amino-phthalimide-5-sulfonic acid.

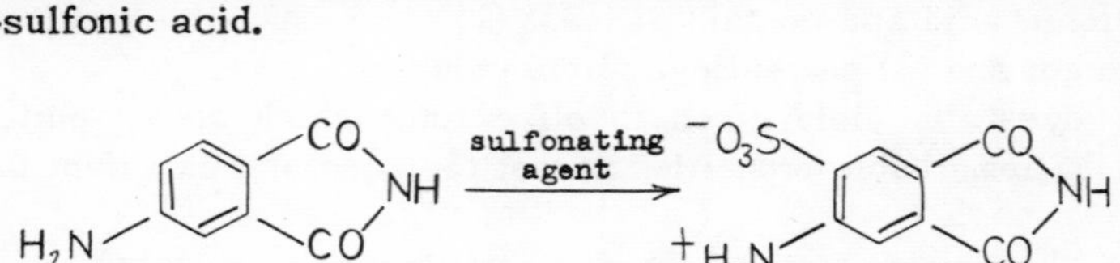

"This reaction is most surprising since phthalic acid and phthalic anhydride may be sulfonated only under severe reaction conditions and 4

amino-phthalic acid is very easily decarboxylated at higher temperatures."

The sulfonation agent may be concentrated sulfuric acid, 100 per cent
sulfuric acid, oleum, or chlorosulfonic acid at a temperature from 100°
to 200°.

Heslop, Legg, Mawson, Stephen, and Wardleworth (119) have prepared
a series of water soluble pyrimidine dyes that include phthalocyanine
sulfonic acids. They claim "Water-soluble colored phthalocyanine compounds substituted by a member selected from the group consisting of
the 2:6-dihalogeno-4-pyrimidylamino radical and the 4:6-dihalogeno-2-
pyrimidylamino radical" and "Copper phthalocyanine 3-(N-3'-dichloro-
pyrimidylamino-4'-sulfophenyl) sulfonamide sulfonic acid."

Jaeger, Huber, and Zollinger (138) have found that sulfonic acid
phthalocyanines containing epichlorohydrin are useful for dyeing animal,
vegetable, and synthetic fibers in two stages: application of the dye to
the fiber and fixation of the dye on the fiber. "The material to be dyed
is advantageously impregnated at room temperature or a slightly higher
temperature with an aqueous solution of the dyestuff and then subjected
to a heat treatment, advantageously in a current of air heated above
100°C. The impregnation can be carried out by the direct-dyeing method,
by printing or by the so-called pad-dyeing method.

"As bases capable of bringing about fixation of the dyestuff on the
fiber may be mentioned the hydroxides and carbonates of the alkali
metals, more especially sodium carbonate as well as sodium acetate or
trisodium phosphate or tertiary amines. As a rule it is immaterial whether
the dyestuff is first applied by padding and then the alkali added, or
whether the alkali is present in the dye bath from the start."

An epichlorohydrin phthalocyanine sulfonic acid may correspond to the
general formula:

$$Pc\left[X-NHCH_2CHCH_2 \atop OHCl\right]_m$$

$$-[SO_3H]_n$$

where   Pc = copper phthalocyanine radical
        X = $-CH_2-$, $-SO_2-$, $-NH\ C_2H_4-$, $-SO_2-NH-$phenylene, or
            $-SO_2-NH-$sulfophenylene
        m = from 1 to 2
        n = from 2 to 3
      $m + n = 4$

Poole and Wardleworth (190) have prepared copper phthalocyanine sulfonic acid water soluble dyes that dye cellulose material in greenish

blue shades in conjunction with an acid binding agent by the reaction of
an aqueous suspension of a copper phthalocyanine polysulfonyl chloride
which may or may not contain sulfonic acid groups with an amine of the
formula $NH_2CH_2CH_2X$, where X may be a chlorine or bromine atom, or
sulfate group. This new series of phthalocyanine sulfonamide reactive
dyes is stated to give higher washfastness than previously known sul-
fonamidophthalocyanines made by reacting chlorosulfonated phthalocyanines with an aqueous suspension of an amine, on cellulosic materials.

Price, Reece, and Wardleworth (191) have prepared water soluble
phthalocyanine sulfonethyleneimide reactive dyes for vegetable and
animal fibers, viscose rayon, regenerated cellulose, and nylon. Dyeing
preferably is carried out with an acid binding agent such as sodium
hydroxide or sodium carbonate. The new dyes contain at least one sulfonethyleneimide grouping and are formed by treating a water soluble
phthalocyanine that contains at least one sulfonyl chloride group with
ethyleneimine.

Koller (143) has prepared a water soluble copper phthalocyanine consisting of copper phthalocyanine 3,4′,4′′,4′′′-sulfonic acid and copper
phthalocyanine tetra-4-sulfonic acid of which two to three sulfonic acid
groups are free and at least one is a sulfonic acid ethylamide group, in
which the ethyl group bears in β-position a chlorine atom or a sulfonated hydroxyl group. With these dyes "... there are obtained on poly-
hydroxylated and especially cellulosic, materials very valuable strong
and generally very full dyeings and prints having excellent properties of
wet fastness and a very good fastness to light."

The sodium salt of copper phthalocyanine 3,4′,4′′,4′′′-sulfonic acid
is added to chlorosulfonic acid with cooling, followed by heating to 80°
Thionyl chloride is added over 1–1.5 hours and the reaction mass is
heated for 2–3 hours. The phthalocyanine sulfonyl chloride is precipitated over ice, washed free of acid with ice water, filtered, and dried. The
phthalocyanine sulfonyl chloride and β-chloroethylamine are stirred into
pyridine. The mixture is heated for 5 hours at 40–45°. The pyridine is
boiled off in vacuum and the reaction product is suspended in water and
adjusted to pH 8.0 by the addition of sodium hydroxide. The hydrolysis
of all sulfonyl chloride groups is assured by heating at 40–50° with addition of sodium carbonate. The dye is isolated by the addition of sodium
chloride, filtration, and drying at 70–80°. The dye is dissolved in water
and urea. Cotton fabric is immersed in the solution, dried, rinsed, and
soaped. "There is obtained a brilliant blue tint fixed fast to boiling."

Water soluble dyes (49) have been prepared of the formula

$$Pc\left[SO_2-N-R-N-Y\atopXX\right]_n$$

where Pc = phthalocyanine radicals that may contain water solubilizing
  groups

X = hydrogen, alkyl, aralkyl, cycloalkyl, or aryl residue

R = residue of a diamino compound of the aliphatic, aromatic, or
  heterocyclic series

Y = acyl residue of a halofatty acid

n = integer from 1 to 4

These dyes "...give to textile fibres of wool, silk, or polyamides fast and especially light fast blue dyeings. Furthermore, they possess the valuable property of giving dyeings or printings which are characterised not only by good wet stability but also by a very good fastness to light and clarity of shade when dyed or printed and subsequently steamed in the presence of acid-binding or alkaline-acting materials, such as alkali metal carbonates, bicarbonates or caustic alkalies, on vegetable textile fibres or fibres prepared from regenerated cellulose. In this case, the dyestuff apparently forms a chemical combination with the fibre which is stable to the soaping and washing processes."

Eisele, Federkiel, Tartter, Lange, Krehbiel, and Stein (65) prepare dyes of the formula

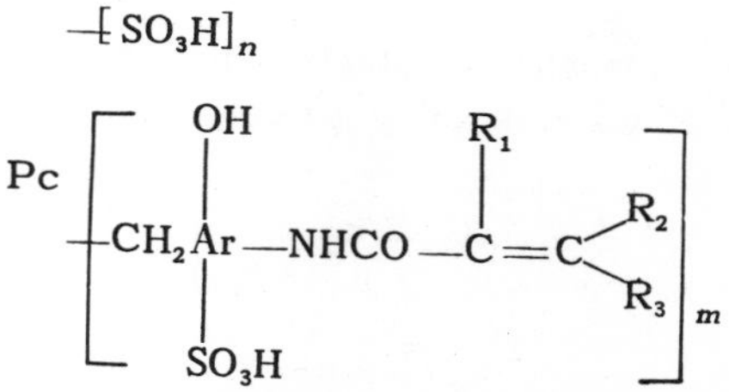

$$Pc \left[CH_2 Ar - NHCO - \underset{\underset{SO_3H}{|}}{\overset{\overset{OH}{|}}{C}} = C \overset{R_2}{\underset{R_3}{<}} \right]_m \quad (SO_3H)_n \quad \overset{R_1}{|}$$

here   Ar = aromatic radical that contains up to 2 benzene nuclei

R_1 and R_2 = hydrogen atom, alkyl group, hydroxyalkyl group, or halogen
  atom

R_3 = hydrogen atom, alkyl group, hydroxyalkyl group, halogen
  atom, or carboxyl group

m = 1 to 8

n = 0 to 4

which produce greenish blue dyeings.

Tartter, Graser, Rohland, Stöckl, Schuster, Gehm, Eisele, and Federkiel (239) have prepared water soluble dyes of the formula

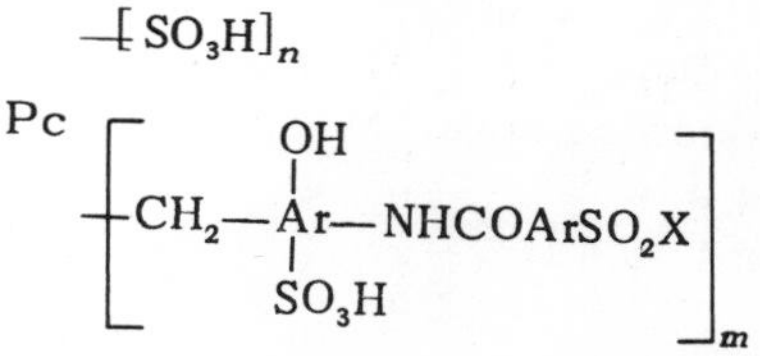

$$Pc \left[CH_2 - \underset{\underset{SO_3H}{|}}{\overset{\overset{OH}{|}}{Ar}} - NHCOArSO_2 X \right]_m \quad (SO_3H)_n$$

where Ar = aromatic radical that contains up to 2 benzene nuclei

    X = radical of a chloro- or bromoalkylamine that contains up to 4 carbon atoms connected to sulfur atom by means of the nitrogen atom.

    n = integer from 0 to 3

    m = integer from 1 to 4

    $m + n$ = integer from 1 to 4

These compounds dye cellulose and regenerated cellulose in greenish blue shades.

Water soluble dyes (87) that impart green and blue colors to animal, vegetable, and synthetic textile materials, with excellent washfastness are

$$Pc-[Ar_n-SO_2NH-X]_m$$

where Ar = aromatic or heterocyclic radical

    X = saturated hydrocarbon with an —OH group in the β-position with respect to the nitrogen atom

    m = integer

    n = 0 or 1

Tartter, Dohland, Mesch, Ludsteck, and Federkiel (238) have synthesized a series of water soluble phthalocyanine dyes of the general formula

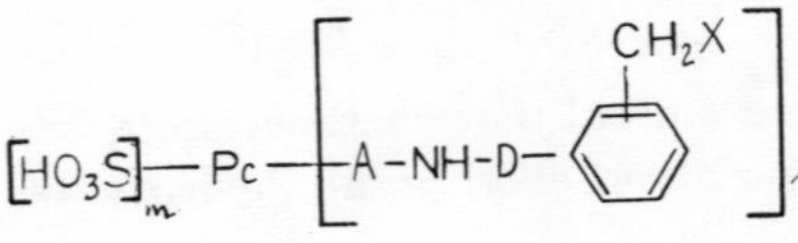

where A = —CH$_2$—, —SO$_2$—NH—R—, or —CH$_2$—(...)

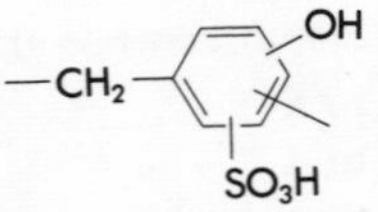

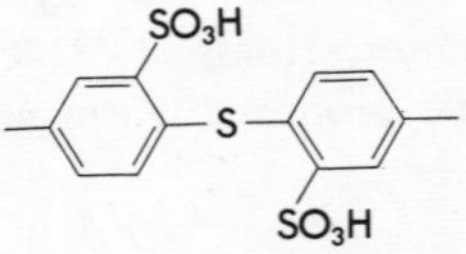

    D = —CO— or —SO$_2$—

    X = chlorine or bromine atom

    m = integer from 0 to 7

    n = integer from 1 to 4

   $n + m \leqslant 8$

The new dyes color animal, vegetable, and synthetic fibers blue to greenish blue with excellent fastness to light and moisture.

Tartter, Hensel, and Baumann (240) have synthesized water soluble dyes that color cotton fabrics in greenish blue shades of excellent fastness to light and humidity of the formula

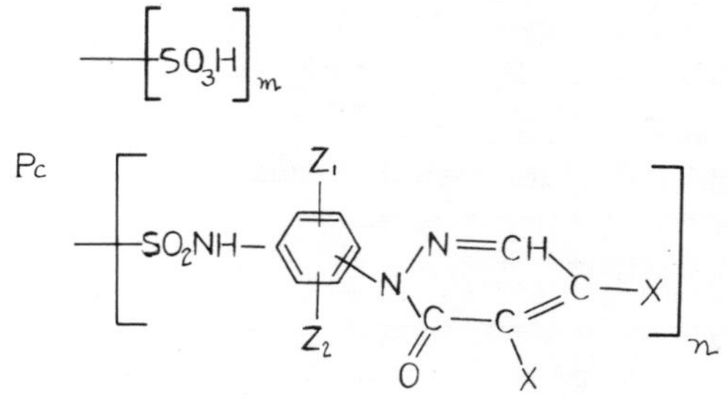

$$Pc \left[SO_3H \right]_m$$
$$Pc \left[SO_2NH-\underset{Z_2}{\overset{Z_1}{\bigcirc}}-N\overset{N=CH}{\underset{C-C}{\overset{|}{\underset{\underset{O}{\parallel}}{}}}}C-X \right]_n$$

where Z_1 = hydrogen or chlorine atom, methyl or methoxy group

Z_2 = hydrogen atom or sulfonic acid radical

X = chlorine or bromine atom

m = integer from 0 to 5

n = integer from 1 to 4

$m + n \leqslant 6$

Rümens, Federkiel, Schuster, and Maier (212) improve lightfastness and ironing properties of textile cellulose fabrics with mixtures of precondensates for aminoplasts, nitrate-containing curing agents, and aliphatic nitriles which contain at least one basic group. N,N-Dimethyl-β-aminopropionitrile, β-pyrrolidylisobutyronitrile, or the reaction product from 4,4'-diaminodicyclohexylmethane are suitable nitriles. They can be used as water soluble addition compounds with sodium bisulfite or formaldehyde, or as emulsions. Ammonium, zinc, and aluminum nitrates are preferred curing agents.

For example, a cellulosic fabric dyed with copper phthalocyanine disulfonic acid is immersed in a solution containing dimethylolurea, ammonium nitrate, and the reaction product of 4,4'-diaminodicyclohexylmethane and acrylonitrile. The fabric is dried at 70–80° and is finally heated for several minutes at 120°.

Eisele, Federkiel, Plankenhorn, and Zell (63) use copper phthalocyanine monosulfonic acid to dye polyamides and polyurethanes.

For example, a polyamide yarn is dyed over a period of 1 hour at 95–100° with an aqueous solution containing finely divided copper phthalocyanine monosulfonic acid and sulfuric acid. The yarn is dyed clear blue with very good light- and washfastness.

Phthalocyanine sulfonic acids (86) of the formula

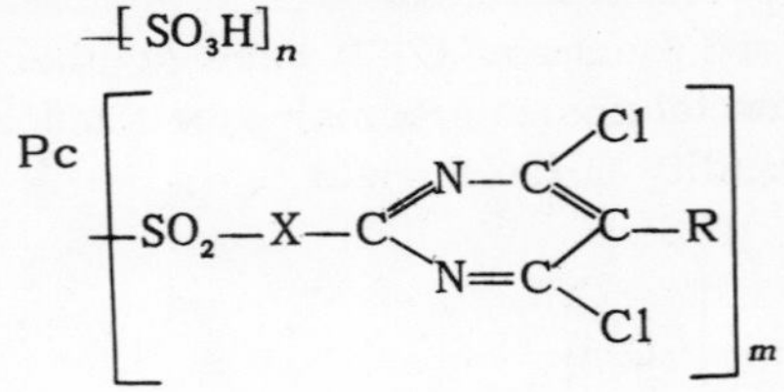

$$-[SO_3H]_n$$

where R = alkyl group

      X = organic polyamine residue bound to the SO_2 group and pyrimi-
         dine ring by nitrogen atoms

n and m = small integers

are prepared by reacting an organic polyamine containing at least 2
non-tertiary amine groups with a molecule of a sulfohalogenated phthalocyanine of the formula

$$[HO_3S]-Pc-[SO_2-\text{halogen atom}]_m$$

with m molecules of a trichloropyrimidine of the formula:

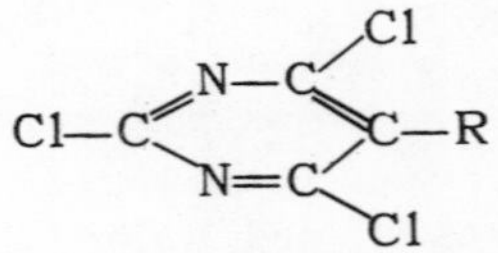

The dyes color animal and vegetable fibers in green to blue shades, with
outstanding washfastness.

    Water soluble dyes (51) have been prepared of the formula

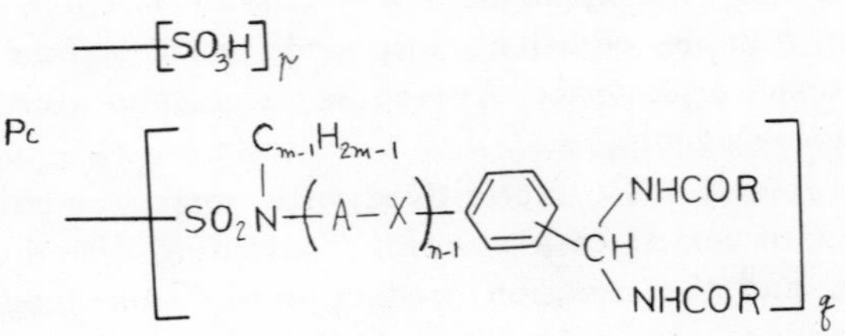

$$-[SO_3H]_p$$

where R = vinyl or β-haloethyl group

      A = 1-phenylpyrazolone-5, heterocyclic, aryl or acetylacetic residue

      X = azoic or imidogen group

      m = integer $\leqslant 5$

      n = integer $\leqslant 2$

      $p \geqslant 2$

      $q = 1$ or 2

These compounds dye polyhydroxy fibers such as cellulose, regenerated cellulose, as well as animal and synthetic fibers of good light- and washfastness. The dyes are prepared as illustrated by the following example.

Copper phthalocyanine is added to chlorosulfonic acid at 20–30° and the reaction mass is maintained at 130–133° for 4 hours. After cooling, the reaction product is poured into a mixture of water, sodium chloride, and ice such that the temperature does not exceed 3°. The product is separated by filtration and is washed on the filter with a mixture of a saturated solution of sodium chloride and ice. The sulfonyl chloride thus obtained is put into suspension with ice and the pH is adjusted to 6.5–7.0 by means of sodium hydroxide.

A compound of the formula

is dissolved in acetone. The solution is added to the suspension of sulfonyl chloride with good agitation. Pyridine is added and the mix is stirred for 24 hours. The dye is precipitated by the addition of concentrated hydrochloric acid and is separated by filtration. The product is pasted with water, the pH is increased to 7.5 by means of sodium hydroxide, the paste is diluted with water, and the mass is stirred at 30–40° at pH > 7 until the dye is in solution. The solution is filtered, the dye in the filtrate is precipitated by sodium chloride, separated by filtration, and dried at reduced pressure. The dye gives turquoise blue shades when printed on cotton with good washfastness.

Tartter (234) has improved the fastness to washing and to boiling of water soluble sulfonated phthalocyanines whereby a phthalocyanine containing one or more hydroxyalkylaminomethyl groups is treated at from −10° to +60° with a sulfonating agent.

"The new dyestuffs obtainable by the method according to this invention cannot be defined by way of a structural formula. Nor can they be otherwise defined by their constitution or composition. They can therefore only be described by the manner of their manufacture."

Water soluble phthalocyanines (8) that dye animal, vegetable, and synthetic fibers greenish blue and blue shades are made by substitution of arylmethyl radicals into the phenylene rings of the phthalocyanine molecule. The aryl radicals contain sulfonic acid groups and unsubstituted, alkylated, or acylated hydroxyl or sulfhydryl groups, by reaction of a halomethylphthalocyanine with a hydroxy-, mercapto-, or aminohydroxy-aryl compound.

Water soluble (70) greenish blue to blue phthalocyanines are made by the reaction of phthalocyanines containing aromatic rings fused to the phthalocyanine phenylene rings and which contain at least two tertiary amino groups with ω-halo-N-methyl-imide of a dicarboxylic acid in the presence of an aliphatic carboxylic acid solvent.

"The process according to the present invention is especially suitable for producing dyeings or prints on textiles with water-insoluble tetra-aza-porphins. These dyestuffs are particularly suitable for the dyeing and printing of materials of cellulose or regenerated cellulose. The dye-ings and prints may be effected according to usual methods by leaving the dyeing materials at temperatures in the range of, for example, 20–100°C., for some time in aqueous dye baths containing the water-soluble tetra-aza-porphin dyestuffs. The dyestuffs then draw onto the dyeing ma-terials and are transformed into the water-insoluble tetra-aza-porphine dyestuffs at elevated temperatures. However, the dyeing materials may also be impregnated with the aqueous dyestuff solutions, for example, on the foulard. The insoluble dyestuff formation may then be carried out in the usual manner, for example, by heat treatment such as steaming."

Water soluble blue-green derivatives of phthalocyanines (7) which contain aromatic substituents with sulfonic acid groups and primary amino groups are made by the reaction of a phthalocyanine sulfonic acid chloride with an arylsulfonic acid which contain at least two primary amino groups.

Water soluble greenish blue reactive dyes (136) of the formula

$$-\!\!\!\left[SO_3H\right]_a$$

$$Pc -\!\!\!\left[SO_2L\right]_b$$

$$-\!\!\!\left[SO_2M\right]_c$$

where L = substituted amino group of the formula

$$-NH\left[\underset{\underset{CHCH_2Y}{|}}{\overset{R_3}{|}}\right]_m \underset{\overset{|}{CH}}{\overset{R_4}{|}} - \underset{\overset{|}{CHX}}{\overset{R_5}{|}}$$

M = amino or substituted amino group

R_{3-5} = hydrogen or lower alkyl group

X = halogen atom or a sulfonic group

Y = —NH —, —N alkyl —, —O —, or —S —

m = 0 or 1

a = 0,1, or 2

$b = 1,2,$ or 3
$c = 1,2,$ or 3
$a + b + c \leq 4$

are prepared by treating an aqueous suspension of phthalocyanine sulfonylchloride with a secondary amine and with a compound of the formula L above. These dyes may be applied to cellulosic textiles with an acid fixing agent and to protein-bearing materials such as wool, silk and leather, as well as synthetic polyamides and polyacrylonitriles. The dyed textiles are especially resistant to washing and have good lightfastness.

Tartter (235) prepares water soluble greenish blue to blue dyes for animal, vegetable, and synthetic materials, of the formula

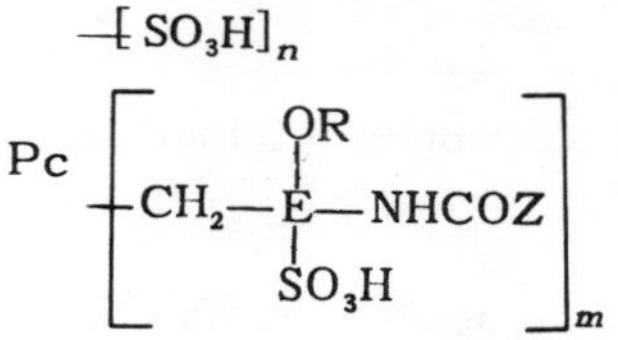

$$Pc \begin{bmatrix} -[SO_3H]_n \\ \begin{bmatrix} & OR \\ -CH_2-E-NHCOZ \\ & SO_3H \end{bmatrix}_m \end{bmatrix}$$

where E = aromatic radical which contains up to two benzene nuclei
R = hydrogen atom, or methyl or ethyl group
Z = vinyl radical
m = integer from 1 to 8
n = integer from 0 to 4

"The new dyestuffs are distinguished by the outstanding fastness to light of the dyeings obtained with them on textiles especially of natural and/or regenerated cellulose."

Fukada (79–83) has prepared a variety of phthalocyanine sulfonic acids and sulfonic acid derivatives, including triammonium monohydrogen copper phthalocyanine tetra-4-sulfonate (79), nickel phthalocyanine tetra-4-sulfonate (79), cobalt phthalocyanine tetra-4-sulfonic acid (80), ferrous and ferric phthalocyanine tetra-4-sulfonates (81), manganese phthalocyanine tetra-4-sulfonic acid (82), and zinc phthalocyanine tetra-4-sulfonic acid (83).

Hashimoto and Isaka (118) have also prepared oil soluble sulfonated copper phthalocyanine dyes.

Spryskov and Kobenin (220) have studied the light absorption and dyeing of cotton fibers of the individual mono-, bi-, or trisulfonic acids of copper phthalocyanine.

Rusznák, Marton, Sello, and Szoke (215) have also considered the dye properties of sulfonated phthalocyanines.

Stefanyak and Borodkin (221) have investigated the dye properties of copper phthalocyanine trisulfonyl chloride and sulfonamides.

SULFONIC ACID CHLORIDES

Although sulfonic acids impart water solubility to phthalocyanine pigments, the phthalocyanine sulfonic acid chlorides are insoluble in water and in organic solvents. However, they are useful adjuncts to dyes because they "... represent valuable starting materials for the preparation of dyestuffs of the phthalocyanine series as the chlorine atoms are capable of being easily exchanged by other groupings, for instance by reaction with alcohols or phenols" (169).

In the Nadler, Hoyer, and Bayer procedure (168,169) phthalocyanine sulfonic acid chlorides are made by reaction of chlorosulfonic acid with phthalocyanines or phthalocyanine sulfonic acids.

For example, a mixture of copper phthalocyanine and chlorosulfonic acid is heated to 145° and is stirred for 1–2 hours at 135–150°. The mixture is cooled and stirred into ice. The bluish green precipitate, probably a copper phthalocyanine tetrasulfonic acid chloride, is filtered off, washed to neutrality, and dried. It is only slightly soluble in most organic solvents.

Phthalocyanine sulfonic acids may also be halogenated at the available carbon sites on the phenylene rings not occupied by the sulfonic acid groups.

"While the higher sulphonated products have no practical significance for the dyeing of textiles according to the usual methods, the disulphonic acids, particularly, possess the quality of dyeing cellulose fibres directly, and their alkali metal salts have sufficient water solubility for dyeing purposes. However, the copper phthalocyanin disulphonic acid for example, in comparison with the generally used direct cellulose dyestuffs shows only a limited affinity, poor take-up and very bad wet fastness properties. When employed according to the usual dyeing procedure for direct dyestuffs, i.e. by dyeing from a dye liquor containing Glauber's salt, up to 50 per cent of dyestuff, according to the desired deepness of shade, is not taken up by the fibres. However, in spite of this, it has attained a great practical significance due to the very pure luminous sky blue nuance which can not be achieved in this purity and fastness to light with any of the known direct cellulose dyestuffs.

"There has been no lack of endeavour to improve the bad take-up of these interesting metal-containing phthalocyanin sulphonic acids. These include, for example, the conversion of the sulphonic acid groups into sulphonic acid amino groups, their complete or partial substitution by carboxyl groups, or the use of diphenyl for building up the phthalocyanin sulphonic acids. However, none of these suggestions has been of practical significance, because either the small degree of improvement did not justify the greater expense or because undesirable changes, particularly an undesired alteration in the shade towards green, becomes apparent.

"In contrast to this, it has now been found that it is possible with technically simple agents to convert the heavy metal, particularly copper and nickel, phthalocyanin disulphonic acid compounds derived from the benzene compounds into products of undoubtedly improved substantivity without an important alteration of the shade. This can be achieved by halogenating them in an alkali chloride or aluminium chloride melt at temperatures from 120–220°C. until at least 2 and at most 7, preferably 4–6 halogen atoms have entered the dyestuff molecule. Preferably temperatures of 140–180°C. are used if the halogenation is effected with compounds giving off halogen. The halogenated copper and nickel-containing phthalocyanin disulphonic acids or their alkali salts so obtained on comparison with the starting material while showing only an unimportant alteration in the shade and maintaining complete brilliance of the shade, are distinguished by an improved affinity to natural cellulose fibres particularly to cotton fibres.

"The structural composition of the new halogenated metal-containing phthalocyanin disulphonic acids cannot be given exactly because even the position of the two sulphonic acid groups in the starting material is not known exactly..." (193).

For example, the sodium salt of copper phthalocyanine disulfonic acid is added to a melt of aluminum chloride to which chlorine is introduced for 6 hours at 170–175°. The reaction mass is poured onto a dilute hydrochloric acid solution. The precipitated dye is filtered off, washed with dilute hydrochloric acid, and dried, yielding copper dichlorophthalocyanine disulfonic acid. "This dyestuff is soluble in alkali and colours cotton in luminous blue shades of improved fastness to water in contrast to the copper phthalocyanin disulphonic acid dyestuffs."

WATER SOLUBLE DYES

Niemann (172) derived a series of water soluble phthalocyanines by the reaction of phthalocyanines with halogen acids such as trichloroacetic acid. "The water-soluble dyestuffs go on to cotton, are stable to acid and have very good fastness to light."

For example, a mixture of copper phthalocyanine and trichloroacetic acid is heated for 6 hours at 170–180°. The reaction mass is discharged into water, filtered, and the residue is boiled with dilute hydrochloric acid, filtered, washed with dilute ammonia solution, heated to 90°, filtered, and precipitated with acid. "It dyes cotton green-blue shades which are fast to acid and very fast to light."

Wyler (254) prepared phthalocyanine polycarboxylic acids, soluble in alkaline media, by heating a mixture of urea and an arylene polycarboxylic acid containing two or more carboxylic acid groups. The phthalocyanine polycarboxylic acids are "... soluble in warm dilute aqueous alkali.... They react further with organic amines to form ammonium salts which are more or less soluble in alcohol, depending on the number of carboxy groups per molecule."

For example, a mixture of hemimellitic acid, urea, boric acid, and anhydrous cupric chloride is heated to 240–300° until the reaction ends, followed by extraction in aqueous, alkaline solution, filtration, drying, dissolution in concentrated sulfuric acid, drowning in water, filtration, water wash, and drying. "The dry product is a bluish-green crystalline powder, which is slightly soluble in weak ammonia."

Hoyer, Schröter, and Rinke (128) prepared direct phthalocyanine dyes soluble in aqueous media, which contain carboxylic acid and phenyl groups in the 4 and 5 positions of the phenylene nuclei. They are capable of directly dyeing cellulosic materials.

For example, 4'-chlorodiphenyl-2,4,5-tricarboxylic acid, urea, and copper chloride yield copper tetrachlorophenylphthalocyanine tetracarboxylic acid, the alkali metal salt of which dyes cotton "... brilliant green shades." 4'-Methoxydiphenyl-2,4,5-tricarboxylic acid, urea, and copper chloride give copper phthalocyanine tetramethoxyphenyl tetracarboxylic acid which dyes cotton in an alkaline solution "... brilliant yellowish-green shades." 2'-Chlorodiphenyl-2,4,5-tricarboxylic acid, urea, and copper chloride make copper tetrachlorophenylphthalocyanine tetracarboxylic acid which dyes cotton in bluish green shades.

Bienert and Thielert (33) prepared phthalocyanines with the "... most greenish shade which has been attained up to the present from among the water soluble phthalocyanine dyes by incorporating a sulfonic acid group and an acylamino group in the 4,5 positions of each of the four phenylene nuclei." They are prepared, for example, from phthalic acids containing a sulfonic acid group in the 4-position and an acylamino group in the 5-position. The new dyes "... exhibit an excellent affinity towards vegetable fibers, such as cotton and viscose or cuprammonium silk and show the most greenish shade which has been obtained to the present within the class of water-soluble dyestuffs."

Mayhew (152) has prepared water soluble phthalocyanines that contain hydroxy groups by attachment to the phthalocyanine phenylene nuclei of from 1 to 4 polyhydroxy sulfonamide groups of the general formula:

$$\begin{array}{c} NHSO_2- \\ | \\ HOCH_2-C-CH_2OH \\ | \\ R \end{array}$$

where $R = CH_3$, C_2H_5, or CH_2OH.

"The new phthalocyanine dyestuffs are characterized by their brilliant blue to greenish-blue shades, their solubility and stability in caustic alkali solution and their relatively good fastness to light. They are capable of dyeing various fibers, such as cotton, wool, and silk, showing particularly good affinity for silk.... Because of their stability in dilute aqueous caustic alkali solution, they are particularly suited as colors in writing inks rendered quick drying by the use of caustic alkali."

Jones (140) synthesized a series of phthalocyanine dyes of the general formula:

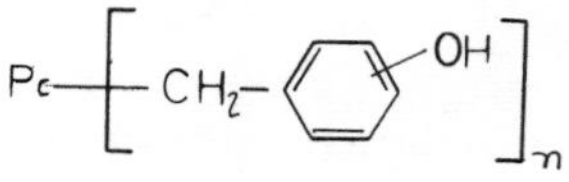

$$\text{Pc} \left[\text{CH}_2 - \underset{}{\bigcirc} - \text{OH} \right]_n$$

where Pc = phthalocyanine radical

  n = integer > 0

The hydroxybenzylphthalocyanines are made from chloromethylphthalocyanines as in the following example: copper trichloromethylphthalocyanine, anhydrous zinc chloride, and phenol are stirred together at 120° for 3 hours. The reaction mixture is steam distilled to remove excess phenol, cooled, filtered off, washed with water, and dried. Copper trihydroxybenzylphthalocyanine is a blue solid, "soluble in dilute aqueous caustic soda solution and Cellosolve, and slightly soluble in ethanol, acetone, and ethyl acetate."

The greenness of shade and solvent solubility increases with increasing number of hydroxybenzyl groups. "The higher members have sufficient solubility in Cellosolve and ethanol to be used as spirit soluble dyestuffs for the colouring of shellac, nitrocellulose or urea formaldehyde resin lacquers."

Martin and Randall (150) have succeeded in preparing a group of phthalocyanine dyes that contain both hydroxy and carboxy groups, with the general formula

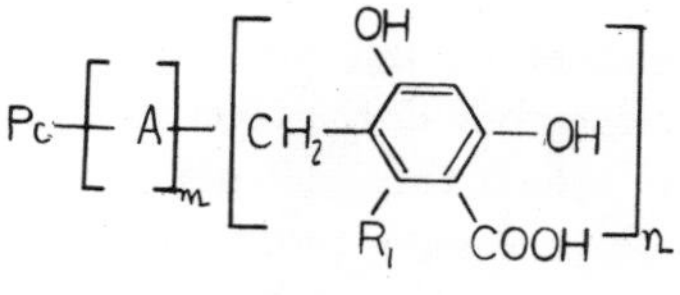

$$\text{Pc} \left[\text{A} \right]_m \left[\text{CH}_2 - \underset{R_1 \quad \text{COOH}}{\overset{\text{OH}}{\bigcirc}} - \text{OH} \right]_n$$

where Pc = phthalocyanine radical

  A = $[-D]_q$Ar— in which D is a bivalent bridging link, q has a value of 0 or 1

  Ar = a pendent aryl nucleus

R_1 = lower alkyl or lower alkoxy

m = from 0 to 8

n = at least 1

The dyes may be made by reacting a phthalocyanine containing one or more chloromethyl groups with a β-resorcylic acid of the formula:

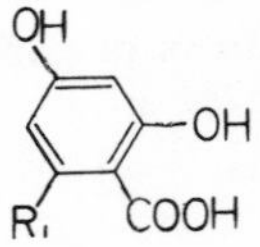

The dyes have excellent lightfastness, are greenish blue to greenish yellow, are soluble in spirit and alkali media, and are insoluble in hydrocarbons.

Buc (46) prepared a series of carboxylic acid derivatives of the phthalocyanines that "... in the form of their alkali metal salts, are completely soluble in water, and are useful in alkaline writing inks, yielding green colorations of exceptional brilliance and fastness to light and other atmospheric influences. They are likewise useful for the coloration of soap, paper, wallpaper, and printing inks."

The carboxylic acid derivatives are prepared from cyano derivatives which in turn are made from the reaction of cuprous cyanide... "with a mixture of a phenyl-cyano-dihalo' derivative, and a cyano-dihalo derivative, of an aromatic hydrocarbon of the benzene or naphthalene series, wherein two of the cyano and halo substituents of each of said reagents are in mutually ortho position and the mol ratio of the aforesaid reagents in said mixture ranges from 1 : 3 to 3 : 1.

"The ensuing reaction results in replacement of the halogen atoms by CN groups, and condensation of the resulting cyano-ortho-dinitriles to form copper phthalocyanines containing four nuclear cyano groups and 1 to 3 phenyl groups as nuclear substituents.... The reaction can be conveniently carried out by merely heating the mixture of dihalocyano compounds with an excess of cuprous cyanide at a temperature of 150 to 400° C.... In order to obtain the corresponding carboxy-substituted phthalocyanines, the tetracyano derivative is hydrolyzed, for example, by boiling with aqueous alkali (e.g. 10 per cent aqueous caustic soda solution) until ammonia is no longer evolved, and a clear solution is obtained. The free tetracarboxy acid can be precipitated from the resulting solution by acidifying with a mineral acid, and recovered by filtration. The tetracarboxylic acids thus obtained are readily and completely soluble in aqueous alkaline solutions, and are characterized by green shades of exceptional fastness to light."

Tartter (224) synthesized water soluble phthalocyanines by reaction of phthalocyanines containing halomethyl groups with tertiary amines which have at least one $-SO_3H$ or $-COOH$ group, dyeing cotton, acetate rayon, and wool in greenish blue to blue shades.

For example, a mixture of copper tetrachloromethylphthalocyanine and pyridine-3-carboxylic acid ethyl ester is heated for 4 hours at 90–95°. After cooling the product is filtered off with acetic acid ethyl ester or acetone. A water soluble dye is obtained and the cotton is dyed in blue shades from a neutral bath. In place of the ethyl ester of the pyridine-3-carboxylic acid, the methyl ester or amide of this acid may be used.

Tartter (225) prepared halomethylphthalocyanines by the reaction of phthalocyanines with halomethylating agents in the presence of sulfuric acid at 40–100°.

For example, paraformaldehyde and chlorosulfonic acid are added to concentrated sulfuric acid. Copper phthalocyanine is added, with heating, to 80°. Sodium chloride is added, followed by additional stirring at 80° for 10 hours, cooling and pouring of the reaction mass into ice water, filtration, washing with alcohol and water, and drying at 50–60°. Copper trichloromethylphthalocyanine containing 14.6 per cent chlorine by weight is obtained as a bright blue powder.

Tartter (227) prepared water soluble phthalocyanine dyes by the reaction of sulfuric acid or sulfonic acid esters with water insoluble phthalocyanines containing one or more carboxy or thiocarboxy groups connected to the phenylene rings of the phthalocyanine molecule by a sulfur bridge. Suitable phthalocyanines are obtained by reaction of diazotized aminophthalocyanines with xanthogenates or isocyanates or when halogen-containing phthalocyanines are reacted with salts of the formula $HS - X$, where X is a carboxy or thiocarboxy group. The reaction takes place upon heating of a phthalocyanine with the sulfuric or sulfonic acid ester, if necessary in the presence of an inert solvent or dilution medium. The new products, green to blue in color, are useful in the dyeing and printing of textiles with good wash- and lightfastness.

For example, a mixture of copper tetrathiocyanatomethylphthalocyanine prepared from copper tetrahalomethylphthalocyanine and potassium thiocyanate and dimethyl sulfate is stirred at 110–120° for 8–9 hours. After cooling, acetone, acetic acid ester, or chloroform is added to the mixture, followed by filtration of the precipitate, and drying. A water soluble dye is obtained which can be used in resist printing on cotton or rayon acetate with greenish blue colors.

Tartter (230) has provided a series of water soluble phthalocyanine dyes "...having a lower or higher content of carboxyl groups, for example of butyric acid radicals in the case of gammabutyrolactone. The new phthalocyanines may be used in part as vat dyestuffs and in part as substantive dyestuffs." The process involves reacting a phthalocyanine with lactones selected from the group consisting of γ-butyrolactone and γ- and δ-valerolactone at 60–180° in the presence of a Friedel-Crafts type of catalyst.

For example, copper phthalocyanine is added to a melt of anhydrous aluminum chloride and sodium chloride. γ-Butyrolactone is then added. The reaction mixture is stirred for 10 hours at 150°, and the dye is precipitated, filtered, washed with water, and dried. "The blue substantive dyestuff thus obtained dyes cotton blue shades."

Brentano (38) has introduced both carboxy and hydroxy groups into the phthalocyanine molecule by making salicylic acid esters of phthalocyanine tetrasulfonic acids, with the general formula:

$$\text{Pc} \begin{bmatrix} [SO_3H]_m \\ \begin{bmatrix} & X & \\ & | & \\ -SO_2OR & - & OH \\ & | & \\ & COOH & \end{bmatrix}_n \end{bmatrix}$$

where Pc = phthalocyanine radical

$-SO_3H$ and $-SO_2OR{<}^{X}_{COOH}OH$ groups are in the 3 or 4 positions

X = hydrogen, halogen, $-OH$, $-CH_3$, or $-SO_3H$

m = number from 0 to 3

n = number from 1 to 4

m + n = 4

R = benzene nucleus in which the hydroxy and carboxy acid groups are in o-position to one another.

The dyes are made by the reaction of sulfonic acid chlorides with dihydroxybenzene carboxylic acids.

"The alkali salts of the (ortho-hydroxycarboxy)-phenyl esters of the phthalocyanine tetrasulphonic acids are easily soluble in water, and are suitable for dyeing or printing vegetable, animal or wholly synthetic fibres, and also for dyeing oxidic protective coatings on aluminium."

Tartter (231) has developed a new group of water soluble phthalocyanine dyes containing carboxylic acids which are "... phthalocyanine or phthalocyanine methylene thiocarboxylic or thiosulfonic acids which, depending on the number of acid groups which have entered into the phthalocyanine molecule, are more or less soluble in water in the form of their alkali, ammonium or amine salts."

For example, a solution of the sodium salts of a mixture of di- and trimercaptomethylphthalocyanine, water, and sodium chloroacetate is heated for 1 to 2 hours at 90° in the absence of oxygen. The reaction mass is acidified with dilute hydrochloric acid, and the resulting precipitate is filtered off and washed with water. "After drying, a blue-green dyestuff is obtained which dyes cotton blue-green shades from alkaline solution or from the vat."

Lacey (144) has prepared water soluble dyes which are sulfonated and unsulfonated carboxyamidomethyl-, imidomethyl-, or aminomethylphthalocyanines.

For example, copper tetra-o-carboxybenzamidomethylphthalocyanine monosulfonic acid:

$$HSO_3-Cu\ Pc\left[-CH_2NH-CO\quad COOH\right]_4$$

is prepared by adding copper phthalocyanine to 10 per cent oleum, stirring, and heating to 80°. Methylolphthalimide is added with heating to 95–100°. The mixture is stirred 4.5 hours at 95–100°, precipitated over ice, filtered, and dried, yielding copper tetra-o-carboxybenzamido-methylphthalocyanine monosulfonic acid.

Copper tetra-o-carboxybenzamidomethylphthalocyanine is dissolved in a dilute aqueous solution of sodium hydroxide. Stearamidopropyl tri-methyl ammonium hydroxide is added. Cotton yarn is added and the mixture is stirred for 20 minutes at 90°. Sodium chloride is added and the stirring is continued for 10 minutes. "The yarn is rinsed and dried. It is dyed a bright green blue."

Schuster, Gehm, Eisele, and Federkiel (218) have improved the fastness properties and especially the moisture fastness of phthalocyanine dyes by treating the dyes with polymers containing basic groups, and their water soluble salts or quaternary ammonium compounds. These polymers include the polymers of N-vinylimidazol and its derivatives, polymers of dimethylaminohydroxyethylvinyl ether, and their copolymers. They may be used in the form of solutions or suspensions.

For example, a staple fiber dyed with copper phthalocyanine disulfonic acid is treated for 30 minutes at 25–30° in an aqueous solution of a copolymer of N-vinylimidazol and a quaternary salt of acrylonitrile and dimethyl sulfate. "After the usual finishing off, a turquoise blue dyeing with very good fastness to moisture and light is obtained."

As another example, a cotton fabric dyed with copper phthalocyanine disulfonic acid is treated for 20 minutes at 25–30° in water containing a copolymer of vinylimidazol and a quaternary salt of vinyl pyrrolidone with dimethyl sulfate. "The turquoise blue dyeings obtained have very good fastness to light and moisture."

Bienert and Baumann (19) have prepared a group of amine bearing phthalocyanines that are soluble in organic solvents and, in the form of their salts, water soluble. The dyes are produced by reacting a phthalocyanine sulfonyl chloride with an aliphatic tertiary amine, yielding

$$Pc \left[SO_2-\underset{\underset{R_1}{|}}{N}-R_2-N \underset{R_4}{\overset{R_3}{<}} \right]_n$$

where Pc = phthalocyanine radical

R_1 = H or lower alkyl radical

R_2 = lower alkylene radical

R_3 and R_4 = monovalent radicals, lower alkyl and hydroxy lower alkyl

n = integer from 1 to 8

"The high affinity of the new basic dyestuffs to fibers derived from various raw materials makes the same, especially in form of their water soluble salts, extremely suitable for the dyeing of cotton, wool, cellulose, regenerated cellulose, fibers of polymides or polyacryl nitrile, paper or paper raw materials as paper pulp etc. The basic dyestuffs go on these materials very easily from a dilute acid solution and the resulting dyeings show an extremely good wet fastness."

Bienert, Breig, and Groll (25) have prepared phthalocyanine sulfonamides of the general formula:

$$Pc \left[R-R_1 \right]_n$$

where Pc = phthalocyanine radical

R = $-SO_2-$ or $-CO-$

R_1 = radical chosen from aminophenyl pyrazolone, aminobenzoyl acetic acid anilide, aceto acetic acid aminophenylamide, 2-hydroxynaphthalene-3-carboxylic acid aminophenylamide, and aminohydroxynaphthalene, with R_1 connected to R with the amino group and containing a coupling position.

n = integer from 1 to 4

"The new phthalocyanine-sulfonamides which are obtainable according to the present invention are themselves suitable for the dyeing of vegetable fibres. They are preferably employed, however, as intermediate products for the preparation of azo dyestuffs."

Bienert and co-workers (27) have also prepared phthalocyanine sulfonamides and carbonamides from phthalocyanine sulfonic acid halides or carboxylic acid halides with esters of coupling hydroxy compounds that contain primary or secondary amino groups.

For example, 1-(3'-nitrophenyl)-3-methyl-pyrazolone-5, sodium hydrox-

additions, such as alkali or alkaline earth halides.

"The dyestuffs obtained are vat dyestuffs, substantive dyestuffs or wool dyestuffs depending on the choice of initial materials, the amount of dicarboxylic acid anhydride and the reaction conditions employed."

Tartter (236) obtains water soluble phthalocyanines by the addition of sulfonating agents to phthalocyanines containing hydroxyalkylaminomethyl groups in inert solvent media, such as chlorinated aromatic hydrocarbons, followed by neutralization. The resulting dyes not only have as good color properties and excellent fastness to light as sulfonic acid derivatives of phthalocyanines but also have good fastness to washing.

"The new dyestuffs obtainable by the method according to my invention cannot be defined by way of a structural formula. Nor can they be otherwise defined by their constitution or composition."

However, in the presence of the dyes, "Structures, such as flocks, threads, woven and knitted fabrics of native or regenerated cellulose, such as cotton, linen, hemp, viscose or staple fiber can be dyed, padded or printed in alkaline medium, for example with the addition of alkaline reagents."

Rösch and Bayer (202) have made water soluble dyes of the formula

$$Pc \text{---} [CH_2NH_2HX]_n$$

where X = halogen

n = from 1 to 8

"The new water-soluble phthalocyanine dyestuffs are blue to green

Harris and Marrable (115) have developed a series of water soluble salts of aminomethylphthalocyanines of the formula:

$$Pc \left[CH_2 - N \begin{array}{c} R_1 \\ R_2 \end{array} \right]_n$$

where Pc = substituted or unsubstituted metal phthalocyanine or naphthalocyanine radical

R_1 = hydrogen atom or aliphatic radical

R_2 = aliphatic radical

for the purpose of coloring paper pulp or finished and dried paper, in greenish blue shades imparting "very high fastness to light, to water and to bleach treatments and of great brilliance of shade."

Tartter, Braun, and Weissauer (237) have prepared water soluble phthalocyanines of the formula:

$$Pc \left[CH_2OR \right]_n$$

where Pc = water soluble phthalocyanine

R = alcohol radical

n = integer from 1 to 8

These greenish blue dyes may color vegetable and animal fibers and synthetic materials with excellent lightfastness and resistance to humidity.

A phthalocyanine of the formula:

$$Cu\ Pc \left[\underset{SO_3H}{\overset{\displaystyle —SO_3H}{\underset{\displaystyle}{}}} \right]$$

is added to an aqueous solution of formaldehyde. Sodium hydroxide solution is added to pH 10.5. The mixture is stirred for 20 hours. The reaction product is precipitated with sodium chloride, filtered, and washed with alcohol. The methylol derivative thus obtained is pasted with concentrated hydrochloric acid and methanol. The mixture is stirred for several hours at room temperature, and is neutralized with an aqueous saturated solution of sodium carbonate, filtered, and dried.

A cotton fabric is immersed in an aqueous solution containing the dye, *N*,*N'*-dimethylol-glyoxal monourein, and zinc chloride, squeezed and dried. A blue turquoise color is obtained of excellent wetfastness.

Tartter, Rohland, Ludsteck, and Schroedel (241) have prepared greenish blue water soluble phthalocyanines of the general formula:

$$\left[HO_3S \right]_n \!\!-\!\! Pc \!\!-\!\! \left[A\text{-}E\text{-}F \right]_m$$

where Pc = radical of phthalocyanine, chlorophthalocyanine, phenylphthalocyanine, phenylmercaptophthalocyanine, or phenylsulfonylphthalocyanine

A = a bridge radical such as —NH—, —CH$_2$—NH—, or

$$E = —CH_2—\overset{\displaystyle R_1}{\underset{\displaystyle}{C}}=\overset{\displaystyle R_2}{\underset{\displaystyle}{C}}—CH_2—,\ or$$

$$—CH_2—C\equiv C—CH_2—$$

and

F = halogen atom or —OSO_3H radical, among others.
m = integer from 1 to 4
n = 0, 1, 2, 3, or 4

For example,

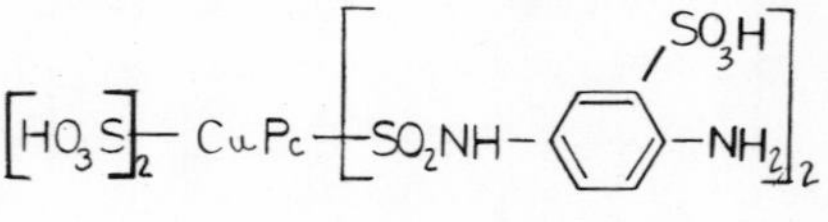

$$\left[HO_3S\right]_2 - CuPc \left[SO_2NH - \langle\rangle\begin{smallmatrix}SO_3H\\-NH_2\end{smallmatrix}\right]_2$$

is pasted in water. The paste is mixed with methanol. Aqueous sodium hydroxide is added to pH 8.5. At 0°, trichloro-1,3,4-butene-2 is added: the mixture is heated to room temperature and the pH is adjusted to 7 by the addition of aqueous sodium carbonate. Alcohol is separated by distillation at reduced pressure. The dye is precipitated with sodium chloride and is filtered off. After drying, a water soluble dye is obtained that dyes cotton of excellent fastness properties in turquoise blue shades.

TERNARY AND QUATERNARY COMPOUNDS

Bradbrook, Coffey, and Haddock (35) have prepared water soluble quaternary ammonium salts of phthalocyanines containing the pyridyl radical:

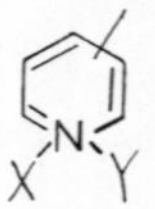

where — means that substitution may be at any carbon atom
X = an alkyl radical
Y = a monovalent acid radical

The quaternary ammonium salts of the pyridylphthalocyanines are made by reacting the pyridylphthalocyanines and the quaternizing agent such as dimethyl sulfate or ethyl chloride.

"The new coloring matters dissolve in water to give intense blue green to green solutions. As dyestuffs they show direct affinity for cotton or viscose artificial silk or film, paper or other cellulosic material and dye these substances in bright blue-green to green shades of excellent fastness properties, particularly as regards washing and light."

The quaternary derivatives of tetrapyridylphthalocyanines prepared from pyridine and tetraazotized tetraaminophthalocyanine are also useful as direct dyes for cotton and other cellulose materials (93).

Linch (148) produces water soluble quaternary ammonium compounds by the condensation of a betainyl chloride with a phthalocyanine compound containing a primary or secondary amino group. Use of the betainyl chlorides such as *N*-chlorobetainyl chloride permits amidation of aminophthalocyanines without the use of excessive amounts of condensing media in the reaction medium such as pyridine and dimethyl aniline. Condensing agents such as thionyl chloride, which produce side reactions with the amine being agitated, are not required.

Haddock and Wood (110) prepared halomethylphthalocyanines that may be reacted with tertiary amines to give quaternary ammonium salts. The halomethylphthalocyanines are prepared by heating an unsubstituted or substituted phthalocyanine with aluminum chloride and sym-dichlorodimethyl ether or sym-dibromodimethyl ether, preferably in the presence of a tertiary amine.

Haddock and Wood (111) prepared a new class of green and blue water soluble phthalocyanines by treating phthalocyanines which contain at least two chloro- or bromomethyl groups with quaternary compounds whereby the chlorine or bromine atoms are replaced by quaternary or ternary salt groups, forming compounds of the formula

$$Pc -[CH_2X]_n$$

where Pc = substituted or unsubstituted phthalocyanine radical
     X = ternary or quaternary salt group
     $n = \geqslant 1$

The chlorine or bromine atoms are replaced by (1) heating the halomethyl derivative with a tertiary amine to convert it to a quaternary ammonium salt, or (2) causing the halomethyl derivative to react with an alkali metal derivative of a mercaptan, or (3) causing the halomethyl derivative to react with a thiourea containing at least one hydrogen atom directly attached to nitrogen to convert it into an isothiouronium salt, or (4) causing the halomethyl derivative to react with tetramethyl thiourea.

"The new phthalocyanine derivatives containing at least two quaternary or ternary salt groups are soluble in water giving bright blue or green solutions from which cotton or other textile material is dyed in bright blue or green shades of very good fastness to washing treatments and to light."

Haddock and Wood (113) have produced water soluble phthalocyanine dyes by reaction of phthalocyanines which carry pendent aryl nuclei, attached to the phenylene nuclei of the phthalocyanine ring, and with —CH$_2$Cl or —CH$_2$Br attached to the aryl nuclei, with the sulfonium, isothiouronium, and quaternary ammonium salts of water soluble acids. In other words, the chlorine or bromine atoms of the chloro- or bromomethyl derivative of phthalocyanine are replaced by quaternary or ternary salt groups by (1) heating the chloro- or bromomethyl derivative with a tertiary amine such as pyridine or triethylamine, to convert it to a quaternary ammonium salt, (2) reacting the chloro- or bromomethyl derivative with an alkali metal derivative of a mercaptan, and treating the sulfide product with suitable esters such as dimethyl sulfate to yield ternary sulfonium salts, and (3) reaction of the chloro- or bromomethyl derivative with a thiourea, such as thiourea or N-methylthiourea, to form an isothiouronium salt.

"The new phthalocyanine derivatives ... are soluble in water giving bright green solutions from which cotton or other textile material is dyed in bright green shades of very good fastness to washing treatments and to light. In some cases, it is advantageous to assist solution in water, for example by the addition of suitable surface tension reducing agents ... condensation products of β-naphthol and ethylene oxide are particularly suitable for this purpose."

As an example of the thiourea route, copper octachloromethyl-tetra-4-phenylphthalocyanine is prepared by adding, at room temperature, copper tetra-4-phenylphthalocyanine to a mixture of anhydrous aluminum chloride and sym-dichlorodimethyl ether. The solution is stirred at 25° for 1 hour, and is poured into hydrochloric acid while maintaining a temperature of 25°. The mixture is filtered; the filter cake is washed with water to neutrality, then with ethanol, followed by drying, yielding bright green copper octachloromethyl-tetra-4-phenylphthalocyanine. A mixture of copper octachloromethyl-tetra-4-phenylphthalocyanine, tetramethylthiourea, and water is heated at 95–100° for 10 minutes, followed by cooling and dilution with acetone. The precipitate is filtered off, washed with acetone, and dried. "It is a green powder, which dissolves in water to give a bright yellowish-green solution. This solution dyes cotton in bright yellowish-green shades."

As an example of the quaternary ammonium salt route, copper tetrachloromethyl-tetra-4-phenylphthalocyanine is boiled in pyridine for 10 minutes. Water is added and the mixture is boiled for an additional 5 minutes. The solution is cooled, and diluted with acetone. The precipitate is filtered off, washed with acetone, and dried. "A bright green powder is obtained which dissolves readily in water to give a bright yellowish-green solution. This solution dyes cotton in bright yellowish-green shades."

As an example of the ternary sulfonium salt route, copper tetramethylmercaptomethyl-tetra-4-phenylphthalocyanine is heated with dimethyl sulfate for 15 minutes at 90°. The mixture is cooled; acetone is added; the suspended solid is filtered off, washed with acetone, and dried. "The bright green powder so obtained is soluble in water and the solution dyes cotton in bright yellowish-green shades."

Haddock and Wood (114) obtain similar dyes starting with phthalocyanine compounds which contain a monatomic bridging link such as $-CO-$, $-S-$, $-O-$, and $-SO_2-$, between the pendent aryl nuclei and the phthalocyanine phenylene nuclei.

For example, tetramethylmercaptomethyl-tetra-4-benzoylphthalocyanine is "...a blue powder which is readily soluble in water giving a bright greenish-blue solution which dyes cotton in bright greenish-blue shades of excellent fastness to washing and to light."

Pedersen (184) finds that metal-free phthalocyanines react with quaternary ammonium hydroxide in a suitable solvent such that the two central hydrogen atoms are replaced by quaternary ammonium cations while the solvent forms an addition compound with the resulting salt. This phthalocyanine system may then be made to dye cellulose fiber "with an agent of the group consisting of water and ionizable metal salts, whereby to convert the dissolved color to a phthalocyanine pigment within the fiber."

Pedersen states the reaction to be:

$$H_2Pc + 2R_4NOH + nS \rightleftharpoons (R_4N)_2Pc \cdot nS + 2H_2O$$

where R = an alkyl radical
> S = solvent molecule from the group pyridine, quinoline, α-picoline, 2,6-lutidine, pyrrole, dimethyl formamide, and tetramethylenesulfone.
> n = unknown integer

The phthalocyanine solution containing $(R_4N)_2Pc \cdot nS$ is then applied to cellulose fiber.

"In the case of textile fiber it is preferable to subject the fiber first to a wetting-out treatment, to open its pores. This may be achieved in any convenient manner, for instance by boiling the fiber successively in water and in a liquid monoalkyl ether of ethylene glycol. Impregnation may be effected in any convenient manner, for instance by immersion or spraying, or by printing the fiber with the color solution.

"The next step is conversion of the solvated color to pigment within the fiber. This may be effected simply by rinsing the treated fabric with water at room temperature or at any other convenient temperature up to the boiling point, or if desired by steaming the impregnated fiber in a customary steam ager. This treatment results in precipitation of the original phthalocyanine within the fiber. The fabric is then soaped to remove any loose pigment, and dried."

Dawson (57) produces dyes for the direct dyeing of cellulosic materials by reacting a polymer of acrylic acid and one or more alkali metal or ammonium salts of a polymer of acrylic acid with the product of the reaction between chloromethyl derivatives of phthalocyanines with tertiary amines or thioureas.

"It has been found that the coloured textile materials obtained by the new process are considerably more resistant to removal of dyestuff by wet or dry abrasive treatments than are coloured textile materials obtained when the pretreatment with polyacrylic acid and polyacrylate is omitted."

Tartter (232) has developed a series of quaternary ammonium compounds based on acylaminomethylenephthalocyanine of the general formula

$$Pc{\left[CH_2-\underset{\underset{R_1}{|}}{N}-\underset{\underset{O}{\parallel}}{C}-\underset{\underset{R_2}{|}}{CH}-Z\right]}_n$$

where Z = hydrogen or halogen atom, alkoxy, dialkylamino, or alkylthio
       group
R_1, R_2 = hydrogen atom or alkyl group
    $n = 2-8$

For example, a mixture of phosphorous pentoxide, copper phthalocyanine, chloroacetamide, and paraformaldehyde is introduced into 100 per cent sulfuric acid. The temperature is maintained at $100°$ for 20 hours. The mixture is then stirred into ice water, forming a precipitate of copper chloroacetylaminomethylphthalocyanines which is washed neutral with water. The dried precipitate, N,N-dimethylcyclohexylamine, and benzyl alcohol are heated together and cooled, followed by precipitation of the quaternary ammonium compound with acetone, and filtration. The compounds "... can be used for printing textiles and give brilliant blue prints of good fastness to light."

SOLVENT SOLUBLE DYES

Several of the green shade phthalocyanines developed by Holzach and Mühlbauer (123) with the general formula $Pc{[O-R]}_n$, where R = alkyl radical, and n is an integer from 1 to 4, are solvent soluble.

For example, a mixture of copper phthalocyanine containing 4–5 atoms of chlorine per molecule, dodecyl alcohol, potassium hydroxide, copper powder, and naphthalene is heated at $350°$ for 8–10 hours. The reaction mass is boiled with alcohol, washed, treated with dilute hydrochloric acid, and washed, yielding a green-blue powder which dissolves readily in benzene, toluene, xylene, nitrobenzene, trichlorobenzene, benzyl alcohol, pyridine, and quinoline "... giving a brilliant green color and is suitable for example for coloring waxes."

Mühlbauer (160) obtained greenish blue to green dyes of the phthalocyanine series by heating a mixture of a phthalocyanine with aromatic halogen compounds such as carbon tetrachloride, tetrachloroethane, dichlorobenzene, and trichlorobenzene.

For example, a mixture of copper phthalocyanine, anhydrous ferric chloride, and trichlorobenzene is heated for 3 hours at 175–180°. Chlorine gas is evolved. After cooling the reaction mass is poured into methanol. The dye precipitates, is filtered off, and is washed with methanol and water. It is boiled with dilute hydrochloric acid and sodium carbonate solution, filtered off, washed, and dried, yielding a yellowish green dye that is soluble in higher boiling organic media such as trichlorobenzene and yields clear yellowish green dyeings that are intense and lightfast.

Substitution of alkyl groups on phthalocyanines may confer solubility in solvents (5). Alkyl groups may be introduced by dissolving a phthalocyanine in an anhydrous aluminum chloride melt with slow addition of alcohol with heating and stirring at 100–150°.

For example, octyl alcohol is poured into a solution of copper phthalocyanine in a melt of anhydrous aluminum chloride and sodium chloride at 130–135° with agitation. "After working up in the usual way, a greenish-blue dyestuff is obtained which is soluble in organic solvents to give a green colouration."

Harrison and Samuels (116) have prepared phthalocyanine dyes soluble in alcohols by reacting sulfonated phthalocyanines with organic quaternary ammonium compounds having an aliphatic radical of from 8 to 20 carbon atoms attached to the nitrogen atom. These alcohol soluble phthalocyanines "...are useful in those arts wherever a spirit soluble or acetone soluble, etc., color is required, for instance in the manufacture of spirit inks, spirit stains, spirit varnishes, etc."

Carleton and Woodward (48) have prepared phthalocyanine dyes soluble in alcohols by reacting.sulfonated or carboxylated phthalocyanines with aryl guanidines. The dyes are useful for coloring paper, wood, leather, and for coloring nitrocellulose lacquers.

Hartmann and Moll (117) prepared phthalocyanine dyes soluble in organic solvents such as alcohol, butanol, ethylene glycol, or cyclohexanone, by the precipitation of sulfonated phthalocyanines with organic bases, producing blue-green shades "...on fibres consisting of or derived from cellulose, such as cotton, viscose artificial silk, paper, cardboard and wood-pulp. The shades of color thus obtained are distinguished by a very good fastness to light."

Holzach and Mühlbauer (125) prepared aminophthalocyanines soluble in solvents by the reaction of amines with phthalocyanines containing halogen groups. The aminophthalocyanines are greenish blue to green in color.

Phthalocyanine derivatives (130) that are soluble with blue to greenish blue colors in "fats or organic solvents such as alcohol, acetone, chloroform, benzene or pyridine and compatible with polystyrene and cellulose triacetate and are suitable for use in varnish lacquers" are prepared by the reaction of aliphatic or hydroaromatic amines with phthalocyanine sulfonyl chlorides.

Nadler, Wegler, and Bayer (170) have prepared phthalocyanines that are solvent soluble but which remain insoluble in water by the addition of sulfonamide groups prepared from sulfonic acid chlorides and amines of the general formula:

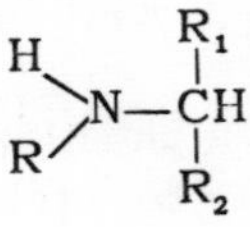

$$\begin{array}{c} H \\ \diagdown \\ R \diagup \end{array} N - \underset{\underset{R_2}{|}}{\overset{\overset{R_1}{|}}{C}} H$$

where R = H or alkyl
R_1 and R_2 = alkyl or cycloalkyl

Fox (76) has prepared phthalocyanine sulfonamidopyridines that are soluble in organic solvents, from piperidine and copper phthalocyanine tetrasulfonyl chloride.

Copper phthalocyanine tetrasulfonyl chloride is stirred into a solution of piperidine and methanol at room temperature for several hours until the reaction is complete. The methanol is removed by heating and the residue is stirred into water. "The resulting water-insoluble precipitate is filtered and dried. A blue powder is obtained which is soluble in acetone, methanol, ethanol and other organic solvents."

Paige (182) obtained phthalocyanine dyes insoluble in water but soluble in alcoholic media and therefore useful in lacquers and spirit varnishes by the reaction of sulfonated copper phthalocyanine with an N-dialkyl ethanolamine of the formula:

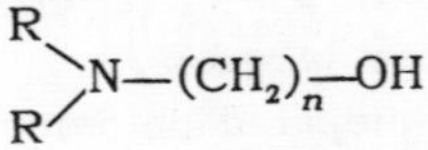

$$\begin{array}{c} R \\ \diagdown \\ R \diagup \end{array} N - (CH_2)_n - OH$$

where R = like or unlike alkyl groups containing 8 carbon atoms
     n = integer > 1

Randall and Martin (196) have prepared phthalocyanine dyes, soluble in hydrocarbon solvents, from chloromethylated metal phthalocyanines and primary or secondary amines. The dyes have the formula:

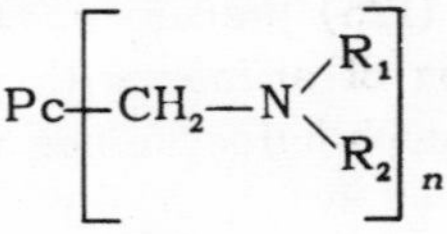

$$Pc \left[CH_2 - N \begin{array}{c} \diagup R_1 \\ \diagdown R_2 \end{array} \right]_n$$

where Pc = a metal phthalocyanine radical
R_1 and R_2 = hydrogen atom and/or alkyl group
        n = integer from 1 to 6

The products are secondary and tertiary aminomethyl-substituted metal phthalocyanines, "...especially copper phthalocyanines, which compounds are blue to green solids, soluble in hydrocarbon solvents possessing excellent light fastness, and suitable for coloration of gasoline, oily printing inks, and hydrophobic resinous polymers, especially of the polyvinyl series, e.g. polystyrene."

Lacey and Waitkins (145) have succeeded to obtain phthalocyanine dyes that are both oil soluble and spirit soluble. The compounds are prepared from o-carboxybenzoamidomethylphthalocyanines which are reacted with a quaternary ammonium compound.

"Attempts have been made in the past to prepare modified phthalocyanines which would have solubility in organic solvents or other media. Among the modifications which have been proposed is the reaction of phthalocyanine sulfonic acid derivatives with secondary amines. While the products of this reaction are somewhat soluble in solvents like alcohol, the products have little or no solubility in hydrocarbon oils or plastics.

"It has also been proposed to produce hydrocarbon-soluble phthalocyanines by the reaction of chloromethyl phthalocyanines with secondary amines. While these products have some oil solubility, they have the disadvantage of requiring the relatively expensive chloromethylation of phthalocyanines....

"It is a surprising feature of the present invention that the novel products of the present invention have such greatly increased solubility in spirits and oils since the substituted ammonium salts of phthalocyanine sulfonic acids have no such solubilities and are limited to alcohol solubility for all practical purposes. This is borne out by the fact that the tetrasulfonic acid of a phthalocyanine when reacted with a long-chain aliphatic quaternary ammonium ion gives a product with only moderate solubility in alcohol and no solubility in hydrocarbons or oils, whereas the tetra-(o-carboxybenzamidomethyl) copper phthalocyanine of the present invention when reacted with the same quaternary ammonium ion produces a product which is highly soluble in both hydrocarbons and alcohol. The reason for the increased solubility of the products of the present invention is not known and, therefore, it is not desired to limit the invention to any particular theory of action...the novel products are blues of a very desirable green shade and the products are much more substantive on cotton and paper than previously available phthalocyanine coloring matters." They have the general formula:

$$\left[\left(Pc - \left\langle \begin{array}{c} \\ \end{array} CH_2NHCO \quad \bigcirc \quad COO \end{array} \right) \right]^{-} Q^+ \right]_n$$

where Pc = phthalocyanine radical
Q^+ = quaternary ammonium ion
n = positive integer less than 9

Martin and Randall (151) have improved the solvent solubility in hydrocarbons of their aminomethylphthalocyanine series of dyes (196) and have extended their range of colors from greenish blue to greenish yellow by the addition from 6 to 16 aminomethyl groups to aryl nuclei which are connected to the phthalocyanine phenylene groups:

$$Pc \left[D_q - Ar \left(CH_2N \begin{array}{c} R_1 \\ R_2 \end{array} \right)_n \right]_p$$

where Pc = phthalocyanine radical
D = monatomic or diatomic bridging link such as —S—, —O—, —CO—, —SO$_2$—, —CH$_2$S—
q = 0 to 1
Ar = aryl nucleus
R_1 = hydrogen, alkyl, aralkyl, aryl, cycloalkyl, or heterocyclic radical group
R_2 = a radical of at least 4 carbon atoms, alkyl, aralkyl, aryl, cycloalkyl, or heterocyclic
n = 1 to 2
p = 1 to 8

These compounds "... have improved solubility in hydrocarbon solvents such as gasoline, petroleum ether, benzene and the like.... They are likewise useful for the coloration of oily printing inks, and hydrophobic vinyl resins such as polystyrene."

Pedersen (183) developed a series of alkali metal salts of phthalocyanine in which the two central hydrogen atoms are replaced by sodium or potassium and a solvent medium forms an addition compound with the resulting salt. Phthalocyanine is treated in an alcoholic solvent such as anhydrous ethanol, isopropanol, n-butanol, sec-butanol, n-amyl alcohol, isoamyl alcohol, sec-isoamyl alcohol, n-octyl alcohol, n-dodecyl alcohol, ethylene glycol monomethyl ether, and cyclohexanol. Alkali metal base such as sodium or potassium hydroxide, alkoxide, or hydride is then added.

The alcoholic solution of color is then applied to cellulose fiber. The solvated color is then decomposed in the fiber by rinsing in water, and precipitating phthalocyanine within the fiber.

Mühlbauer's compounds (167) are soluble in water and in organic solvents. The general formula is given in the section relating to sulfonic acid derivatives.

For example, substituted aluminum phthalocyanine trisulfonamide monosulfonic acid is a "...greenish dark blue powder which dissolves in water or also in lacquer varnish with a deep yellowish-green color."

Randall and Martin (197) state that "...to the present (1956) it has not been found possible to prepare hydrocarbon-soluble phthalocyanine dyes, which are satisfactory as colorants as well as hydrocarbon soluble." The authors find that "...if the chloromethylated copper phthalocyanine dyes or pigments are treated with alkyl aromatic compounds, a reaction occurs by which hydrogen chloride is split out and the alkyl aromatic residue is combined into the phthalocyanine molecule in such a way as to make the material hydrocarbon soluble without injuring or decreasing its tinctorial power, stability or any of the other valuable characteristics of the original phthalocyanine dye or pigment." The general formula of the new dyes is:

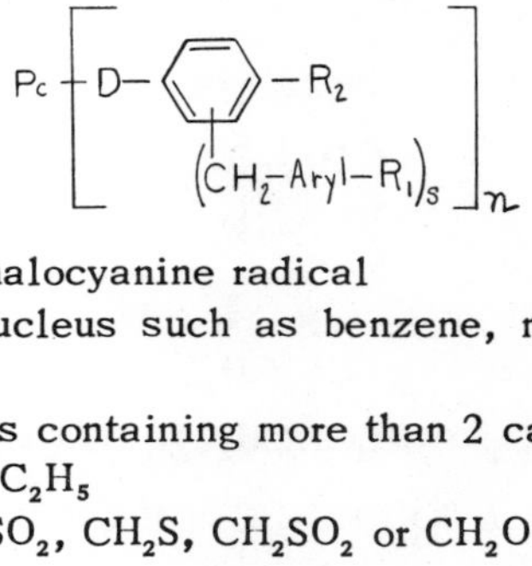

$$Pc \left[D - \langle \rangle - R_2 \atop (CH_2-Aryl-R_1)_s \right]_n$$

where Pc = copper phthalocyanine radical

Aryl = aromatic nucleus such as benzene, naphthalene, thiophene, and furan

R_1 = alkyl groups containing more than 2 carbons

R_2 = H, CH_3, or C_2H_5

D = S, O, CO, SO_2, CH_2S, CH_2SO_2 or CH_2O

s = 1 or 2

n = from 2 to 6

"...these dyestuffs possess good solubility in hydrocarbon solvents and exhibit good lightfastness. Thus these products are suitable for coloring gasoline, for oily printing inks, and the hydrophobic resinous polymers, especially of the polyvinyl series, such as polystyrene."

Bienert and Baumann (20) have produced a series of basic solvent soluble phthalocyanine dyes of the general formula

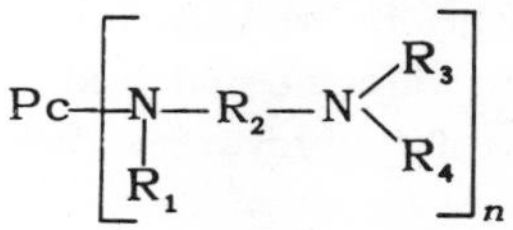

$$Pc \left[N - R_2 - N \genfrac{}{}{0pt}{}{R_3}{R_4} \atop R_1 \right]_n$$

where R_1 = hydrogen atom or alkyl radical

$\quad R_2$ = acyclic bivalent radical

$\quad R_3R_4$ = aliphatic radicals

$\quad\quad n$ = from 1 to 4

The compounds of this series possess solubility in ethyl alcohol, benzyl alcohol, esters, aromatic hydrocarbons, and dimethyl formamide, and may be used for dyeing plastics and varnishes, and in offset printing.

"The high affinity of the new basic phthalocyanine dyestuffs to fibres derived from various raw materials makes these dyestuffs, especially in form of their water-soluble salts, extremely suitable for dyeing cotton, wool, cellulose, regenerated cellulose, fibres of polyamides or poly-acrylonitrile, paper, or paper raw materials such as paper pulp. The basic phthalocyanine dyestuffs take on these materials very easily from a dilute acid solution and the resulting dyeings show extremely good wetfastness.

"It is very surprising that phthalocyanine dyestuffs will become readily soluble in dilute acids such as acetic acid if at least one tertiary amino group is introduced into the molecule."

Tobel (242) has prepared copper phthalocyanine sulfonic acid amides of the formula

$$\begin{array}{c} -R \\ Pc{-}R \\ -R_1 \end{array}$$

where

$$R = SO_2NHCH_2\overset{\displaystyle CH_2CH_3}{\underset{\displaystyle |}{CH}}CH_2CH_2CH_2CH_3$$

$$R_1 = H \text{ or } SO_2NHCH_2\underset{\displaystyle \underset{\displaystyle CH_2CH_3}{|}}{CH}CH_2CH_2CH_2CH_3$$

The amides are soluble in acetone, methylcellosolve, and in lacquers, and are suitable for spin dyeing of synthetic fibers and for coloring polymers.

Zickendraht and Koller (260) have developed a series of phthalocya-nine sulfonic acid amides that are soluble in organic esters, alcohol, and acetone. These spirit soluble dyes, therefore, are useful for coloring resins, waxes, lacquers, and plastics. "...it is possible, for example, to dye cellulose acetate artificial silk by spin-dyeing methods, clear blue tints which are fast to chlorine and flue gases."

Weinmayr (245) produces phthalocyanine dyes containing both at least two fluorosulfonyl groups and one nuclear halogen substituent that are soluble in acetone, alcohol, benzene, and pyridine, of the general formula:

$$Pc \begin{array}{c} [SO_2F]_n \\ -X_y \end{array}$$

where Pc = metal phthalocyanine radical
X = F, Cl, or Br
n = number from 2 to 4
$y \geqslant 1$

Weinmayr sets down useful criteria for the definition of "soluble." A dye is soluble in acetone, for example, if it dissolves therein to the extent of at least 0.1 per cent by weight at 20°. The halogen fluorosulfonylphthalocyanines may be applied from solution to textile fibers to produce blue to green colors "... and usually light-fast dyeings on most of them." Also, they can be used to color inks and lacquers.

The halogen fluorosulfonylphthalocyanines are exceptionally resistant to oxidation—"Thus, whereas copper phthalocyanine and copper phthalocyanine sulfonic acids are readily oxidized by acidic, aqueous, ceric sulfate solutions at room temperature, and whereas even polychlorinated copper phthalocyanine containing as high as 14 Cl-atoms per molecule is quickly oxidized by ceric sulfate solutions upon slight warming, many of the novel compounds of this invention will withstand heating in boiling ceric sulfate solution (110°C.) for several hours without being changed to any perceptible degree." Since the halogen fluorosulfonylphthalocyanines "... are not attacked by peroxides, they may be incorporated as colorants into monomers which are to be polymerized by the aid of dibenzoyl peroxide or similar catalysts into plastics."

Howard and Marrable (126) have prepared phthalocyanines, suitable for coloring cellulose acetate greenish blue shades in acetone, followed by spinning the cellulose acetate into filaments of the formula

$$Pc \left[X-N \begin{array}{c} R_1OCOR_2 \\ R_3 \end{array} \right]_n$$

where Pc = phthalocyanine radical that may carry at most 1 sulfonic acid group
X = $-CH_2-$ or $-SO_2-$
R_1 = alkylene radical
R_2 = alkyl or aryl radical
R_3 = hydrogen or lower alkyl radical or $-R_4OCOR_2$
R_4 = alkylene radical
n = from 2 to 8

These dyes are prepared by heating a hydroxy compound of the formula

$$Pc \left[X-N \left\langle \begin{array}{c} R_1OH \\ R_3 \end{array} \right. \right]$$

with the anhydride or chloride of a carboxylic acid R_2COOH.

Erbe (66) prepares solvent soluble phthalocyanines by reacting phthalo-cyanine-forming compounds in the presence of α, β-dialkylaryl-α, β-di-cyanoethylene. For example, phthalic acid dinitrile and anhydrous ferric chloride are reacted in the presence of di-n-dodecyldicyanostilbene at 270–280°. The product is soluble in benzene with a green color.

SULFUR DYES

In 1942, in U. S. Patent 2,290,906, Coffey, Haddock, and Jackson (55) described a method for the preparation of water soluble sulfur dyes. The dyes were obtained by the reaction of metal tetra-4-alkylthiophthalocya-nine or tetra-3-alkylthiophthalocyanine with alkyl sulfates or sulfites, yielding the corresponding sulfonium derivatives. For example, copper tetra-4-methylthiophthalocyanine and dimethyl sulfate yield copper phthal-ocyanine octamethyltetrasulfoniumtetramethylsulfate. The phthalocyanine sulfonium derivatives may be applied as direct dyes on cotton and other cellulose materials, resulting in dyeings in green shades with good washfastness, or after application to the fabric, they may be oxidized to yield green to blue shades of good light and washfastness. From 1 to 4 sulfonium groups per phthalocyanine molecule may be introduced. How-ever, affinity of phthalocyanine sulfonium compounds for cellulosic fiber decreases with decrease in the number of sulfonium groups.

Haddock (95) has developed a second route for the obtention of phthalo-cyanine sulfur dyes, viz., mercaptophthalocyanines, containing from 1 to 4 mercapto —SH— groups per molecule of phthalocyanine, prepared from the corresponding aminophthalocyanines by their conversion into diazo compounds, xanthate esters, followed by hydrolysis at elevated tempera-ture. The alkali soluble mercaptophthalocyanines are oxidized by air or other agents to form water insoluble disulfides. "These dyes can be re-dissolved in aqueous sodium sulfide solution, forming a vat from which textiles can be dyed much in the same manner as commercial sulfur colors. The final bluish-green or greenish-blue dyeings obtained from these products on cellulosic material show outstanding fastness to wash-ing and light and are in general, equal in fastness properties and clarity of shade to the best known anthraquinone vat dyes."

Haddock and Wood (110) prepared halomethylphthalocyanines that may be reacted with mercaptans to give sulfides, with sulfides to give ternary sulfonium salts, and with thiourea to give isothiouronium salts. The halomethylphthalocyanines are prepared by heating an unsubstituted or substituted phthalocyanine with aluminum chloride and sym-dichlorodimethyl ether or sym-dibromodimethyl ether, preferably in the presence of a tertiary amine.

Haddock (96) has also developed a third route for obtaining phthalocyanine sulfur dyes starting from copper phthalocyanine sulfonyl chloride, such as copper phthalocyanine tetra-4-sulfonyl chloride which is prepared by treating copper phthalocyanine with chlorosulfonic acid at elevated temperature. The phthalocyanine sulfonyl chloride is reduced to the corresponding mercaptophthalocyanine by dilute hydrochloric acid and zinc dust, and in this form has affinity for cellulose fibers. The color is developed and fixed on the fibers by oxidation to a polydisulfide by contact with the atmosphere or in an aqueous suspension containing dissolved oxygen.

Fox (75) has made use of the sulfonyl chloride method to provide another series of phthalocyanine sulfur dyes formed by the condensation of a phthalocyanine sulfonyl chloride with a hydrazine or primary, secondary alkyl, substituted alkyl, alicyclic, aryl, or heterocyclic hydrazine. The products range in color from bluish green to green.

Hinokiyama (121) also prepares phthalocyanine sulfur dyes by reduction of phthalocyanine sulfonyl chloride. A mixture of copper phthalocyanine and chlorosulfonic acid is heated at 130–140° for 3 hours, and is cooled. The product is poured onto ice to precipitate copper phthalocyanine sulfonyl chloride which is then reduced in the presence of ice, concentrated hydrochloric acid and tin powder at 0–10° and heated for 5 hours at 40–60°. The precipitate is filtered and washed with water to give a green sulfur dye.

Gutzwiller (91) developed phthalocyanines, bright green in shade and "possessing an excellent fastness to light" by condensing halogenated phthalocyanines with mercapto compounds of the aromatic series in presence of an alcohol and a catalyst, forming phthalocyanine dyes of the general formula:

$$Pc \begin{bmatrix} X \\ Y \end{bmatrix}_4$$

where X = —S— aryl radical
    Y = hydrogen or —S— aryl radical

These green compounds are insoluble in water and soluble in benzene. Gutzwiller (92) found that the sulfonated products of phthalocyanine arylthioethers are water soluble. The dyes are the condensation products prepared by treating halophthalocyanines with aromatic mercapto compounds forming phthalocyanine thioethers. The shades are brilliant bluish green to yellow-green and are quite fast to light.

For example, symmetrical iron tetra-p-thiocresoxyphthalocyanine is dissolved in 95-100 per cent sulfuric acid and stirred at 70-120°. "The dyestuff isolated in the usual manner dyes paper in grey-greenish shades."

Mayhew (154) states that by replacing zinc in Haddock's process (96) with iron "... and using as little as 2 parts of iron to 1 part of the copper phthalocyanine content of the tetrasulfonylchloride to be reduced, complete reduction of the copper phthalocyanine tetrasulfonyl chloride can be obtained."

Fox (74) has found a fourth route to make phthalocyanine sulfur dyes, viz., by using an addition compound of aluminum chloride and sulfur monochloride, to introduce vattable sulfur atoms into the phthalocyanine molecule, by reacting aluminum chloride with sulfur monochloride at elevated temperature in the absence of a solvent.

Holzach and Mühlbauer (124) prepared sulfur bearing phthalocyanines by heating halophthalocyanines with aliphatic or aromatic mercaptans at 250-350° for about 15 hours that the product contains at least one mercaptan group.

For example, a mixture of xylene, thiophenol, potassium hydroxide, copper powder, and a copper phthalocyanine containing 18 per cent chlorine is heated at 350° for about 15 hours, boiled with methanol, washed in water, and boiled after addition of hydrochloric acid. The dye is filtered off, washed, and dried. "Its shade of colour has been clearly displaced towards green."

Haddock (102) has succeeded to find still another route to the dyeing of textiles with phthalocyanine sulfur dyes by means of phthalocyanine thiocyanates containing from 1 to 4 thiocyanate groups, —SCN, per phthalocyanine molecule. The phthalocyanine thiocyanates are obtained from the corresponding aminophthalocyanines by diazotization followed by conversion of the diazo derivatives into thiocyanates by treatment with an alkali-metal thiocyanate. The phthalocyanine thiocyanates thus obtained "... are suitable directly for dyeing cellulosic fiber by the standard sulfur-dyeing process, that is, by dissolving the compound in an alkaline sodium sulfide vat, impregnating the fiber therewith and then oxidizing the dyeing on the fiber by exposure to air or by treatment with dilute sodium chromate and acid. This effect is again highly surprising, because theory demands that such dyeing must proceed as a result of hydrolysis of the thiocyano compound in the vat to the corresponding mercaptans and oxidation of the latter on the fiber to a disulfide or polydisulfide compound; such easy hydrolysis, however, was not to be anticipated, because in the case of the simpler aryl compounds it has been our experience that their thiocyanates do not hydrolyze readily except under drastic conditions, involving for instance refluxing for six hours with very strong aqueous or alcoholic caustic soda. It is very surprising, therefore, that the relatively cool (82–93°C.) and weakly alkaline (sodium carbonate) aqueous sodium-sulfide vat is capable of hydrolyzing phthalocyanine thiocyanates so readily as to produce a satisfactory dyeing on the fiber."

Haddock (108,109) extends the sulfonyl chloride synthesis of sulfur dyes to include reaction of phthalocyanine sulfonyl chlorides with alkyl or aryl mercaptans (108) or with thioamides (109). Thioamides possess the group

$$\overset{\text{S}}{\underset{\|}{-\text{C}}}-\text{NH}-$$

the tautomeric form of which is

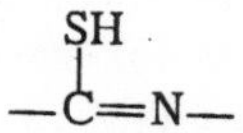

$$\overset{\text{SH}}{\underset{|}{-\text{C}}}=\text{N}-$$

For example, copper phthalocyanine tetra-4-sulfonyl chloride is heated with thiourea for 2 hours at 170–175°. The bright green melt is cooled and extracted with boiling water. The residue is filtered off, washed with water, and dried to a bright green powder which dissolves in hot dilute aqueous sodium sulfide solution yielding a bluish gray vat, which "...dyes cotton in grey to black shades, which on being allowed to oxidise in the air become bright green and are of good fastness properties, particularly in respect of wet treatment."

Wood (250) has further broadened the scope of the possibilities of the phthalocyanine sulfonyl chlorides by reaction with phosphorous sulfide, giving products that are soluble in aqueous sodium sulfide solutions, which if contacted with cotton, produce blue to green colors on the cotton if it is subsequently oxidized. "From this behavior it is assumed that the above reaction effects replacement of the sulfonyl-chloride radicals by mercapto groups."

Haddock, Jones, Page, and Wilkinson (103) prepared water soluble vat phthalocyanines of the formula Pc$-$[CH$_2$$-S-$A], where A = an aryl group, giving bluish green shades on cotton.

For example, the vat dye

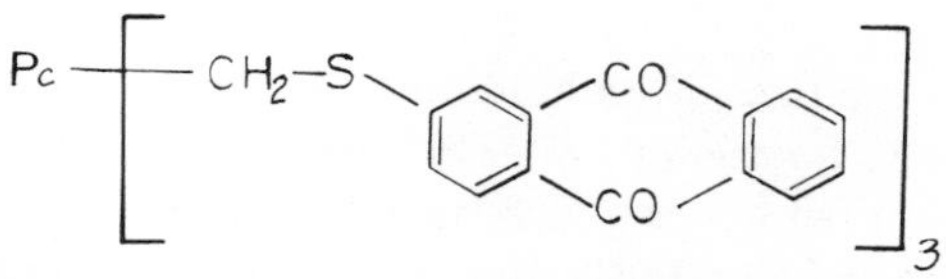

obtained by heating copper trichloromethylphthalocyanine with sodium anthraquinone-2-mercaptide in ethylene glycol monomethyl ether, copper powder, and sodium pyrosulfate are added to dry pyridine. The mixture is stirred for 4 hours at 80°. The product is added to sodium hydroxide solution. Pyridine is removed at 40° at reduced pressure. The residue is diluted with water and filtered. The filtrate is saturated with sodium chloride; the precipitated leuco sulfuric ester is filtered off, mixed with sodium carbonate, and dried at 40°. "When applied to cotton by the usual methods for dyeing and printing and subsequently developed, very bright shades of bluish green are obtained which are fast to light and to washing."

Haddock and Wood (112) prepared a series of phthalocyanine water soluble sulfonium salts of the formula $Pc-[CH_2SR]_n$ where R = alkyl group and n = integer greater than 1. These dyes are made by the reaction of a thiourea and a phthalocyanine containing more than one chloro- or bromomethyl groups, followed by hydrolysis with alkali to replace the salt groups by alkali metal mercaptide groups, alkylating, and reacting the alkyl mercaptomethylphthalocyanine with an ester to make the corresponding sulfonium salt.

This series of phthalocyanine dyes is "... soluble in water giving bright blue or green solutions from which cotton or other textile material is dyed in bright blue or green shades of very good fastness to washing treatments and to light."

Jolles, Wardleworth, and Wood (139) prepared water soluble dyes containing isothiouronium salt groups by heating thiourea with a phthalocyanine containing at least one halomethyl group connected through linking atoms to the phenylene nuclei.

Mühlbauer (165) has found still another route and a new series of phthalocyanine sulfur dyes which contain at least 1 atom of sulfur to each molecule of the phthalocyanine. With increasing amount of sulfur, the tinctorial properties of the dyes improve "... but it is not recommended that more than 24 atoms of sulfur should be used for 4 molecular proportions of phthalocyanine-forming compounds for it has been found that a maximum of only 1 to 2 atoms of sulfur enter into the resulting dyestuff molecule.... Some of the resulting dyestuffs, in particular the sulfur-containing cobalt phthalocyanines, are typical 'sulfur dyestuffs' which yield deep-colored solutions with sodium sulfide alone from which natural or synthetic fibers are dyed greenish blue shades which are fast to light."

For example, a mixture of phthalodinitrile, anhydrous cobalt chloride, and sulfur powder is heated at 180–200° until formation of the crude dye is completed, after which the dye is ground, boiled in dilute sodium hydroxide solution, and boiled again with dilute hydrochloric acid after filtration and washing followed by a water wash and drying. A dark blue dye is obtained that is easily vatted in alkaline sodium hydrosulfite solution at room temperature. "...vat vegetable or synthetic fibres suitable for vat dyeing are dyed powerful greenish-blue shades. The dyestuff can be brought into solution with sodium sulfide, instead of with sodium hyposulphite, and fibres may be dyed with this solution in the same way as with sulfur dyestuffs."

Clarke, Keats, Thornton, and Wood (54) have prepared phthalocyanine isothiouronium salt dyes which contain isothiouronium salt groups attached through methylene links to aromatic nuclei and one or more acidic substances from the class consisting of aliphatic dicarboxylic acids, alkali metal bisulfates, and boron hydroxy acids. The acidic substances prevent the isothiouronium salts from decomposing prior to their use as dyes, by enhancing the stability of the dry dyes during storage.

Zerweck, Ritter, and Stier (258) have synthesized yet another group of phthalocyanine sulfur dyes that are mixtures of metal phthalocyanines containing amino and mercapto groups represented by:

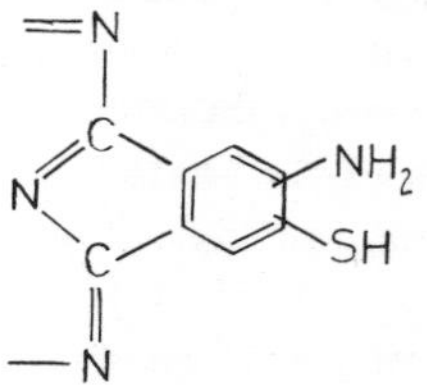

"These sulfur dyestuffs are of a greenish-grey to bluish-grey shade, shades unknown in the phthalocyanine series prior to this invention. As in the case of other sulfur dyestuffs, the dyestuffs of the present invention are oxidized during dyeing to contain disulfide groups instead of the SH groups of the above formula."

The dyes are prepared by reacting a copper, nickel, or cobalt tetra-aminophthalocyanine with chlorosulfonic acid between 70° and 150°, and reducing the product with iron and zinc in a mineral acid.

Zerweck, Ritter, and Stier (259) obtained dyes of improved properties by adding sulfur monochloride with hydroxylamine, before treatment with reducing agents, as described in German Patent 947,409 (258).

Zerweck, Ritter and Stier (257) also prepared phthalocyanine sulfur dyes by the reaction of polyaminophthalocyanines and chlorosulfonic acid at 100–150°.

Tartter (226) obtained phthalocyanine dyes more or less soluble in organic media by reaction of phthalocyanine containing halogen, or halomethyl groups, with salts of a compound containing a mercapto group.

For example, carbon disulfide is added to a solution of sodium butyrate in butanol at room temperature, to which cobalt tetrachloromethylphthalocyanine is added. The reaction mass is stirred for 10 hours on the boiling waterbath, filtered off, washed with alcohol and water, and dried. Cobalt tetrabutylxanthogenomethylphthalocyanine is obtained. It is insoluble in water but dissolves with a blue color in organic media such as benzene, toluene, benzyl alcohol, chloroform, tetrahydrofuran, or pyridine.

Tartter (228) obtains phthalocyanine dyes from water insoluble phthalocyanines which contain at least two $-CH_2-S-X$ groups, where X is an acyl, thioacyl, carboxy, or thiocarboxy group, with alkaline media, the mercaptans being converted to thioethers and to ternary sulfur compounds. Suitable phthalocyanines are obtained from the reaction of halomethylcyanines with salts of thio or dithiocarboxy acids or with compounds of the formula $HS-X$, where X is a carboxy or thiocarboxy group. Treatment with alkaline media such as solutions of alkali metal hydroxides, ammonia, amines, or hydrazine with heating yields the corresponding mercaptans. The products are soluble in water or in dilute formic acid and light- and washfast colors are obtained on textiles.

For example, copper tetraacetylthiomethylphthalocyanine, prepared by heating copper tetrachloromethylphthalocyanine in glycol with the potassium salt of thioacetic acid, is heated at 95–100° in water containing sodium hydroxide and sodium sulfide. The mixture is cooled, and ethyl alcohol and methyl iodide are added at 40° until the end of the reaction. The precipitate is filtered off, washed with water, and dried. The thioether is heated with dimethyl sulfate at 100–105° until water soluble, and cooled with precipitation of the reaction product with acetone. The product dyes cotton blue from aqueous solution.

Tartter (229) has extended the range of sulfur bearing phthalocyanines to include carboxylic and sulfonic acid groups, forming phthalocyanine or phthalocyanine methylene thiocarboxylic or thiosulfonic acids the alkali, ammonium, or amine salts of which possess water solubility. The general formula is

$$Pc \hspace{-2pt}-\hspace{-4pt}\left[CH_2-S-R-X \right]_n$$

where R = alkylene, phenylene, or naphthylene radical

X = carboxylic acid or ester or amide, cyano, sulfonic acid, or sulfonic acid amide.

n = from 4 to 8

wherein each phthalocyanine phenylene nucleus may carry one or two of the $-CH_2-S-R-X$ groups.

They are prepared by reacting the salts of phthalocyanines containing mercapto groups with salts of halogen carboxylic or halogen sulfonic acids or their functional derivatives or by reacting halophthalocyanines, such as halomethylphthalocyanines, with salts of carboxylic or sulfonic acids containing mercapto groups.

Tartter (6) has also prepared sulfur containing dyes of the formula:

$$Pc\text{---}[CH_2\text{---}X\text{---}S\text{---}R]_n$$

where X = bivalent aromatic radical
R = alkyl group
n = integer from 1 to 8

by reacting alkyl aryl sulfides with chloromethylphthalocyanines, in the presence of a Friedel-Crafts catalyst, such as zinc chloride, ferric chloride, aluminum chloride, or boron fluoride.

For example, a mixture of copper tetrachloromethylphthalocyanine, sodium chloride, zinc chloride, and methylphenylthioether is heated to 100–110° for several hours until the evolution of hydrogen chloride ceases. The reaction product is washed with methanol and water, and is dried. The product is soluble in higher aromatic hydrocarbons, benzyl alcohol, and dimethyl formamide. The dye is suspended in dichlorobenzene, heated with dimethyl sulfate on a steam bath, precipitated with acetone, decanted, treated with acetone, and filtered.

"If the tertiary sulphur compounds are worked up to printing pastes and cotton cambric, linen or natural silk, for example, printed therewith in the usual way, blue prints of good fastness to light are obtained after drying and steaming."

Haddock, Slinger, and Wood (107) synthesized a new group of water soluble isothiouronium dyes of the formula

$$[CH_2X\text{---}]_n Pc\text{---}[Y\text{---}R]_m$$

where Y = —O— or —S—
R = aryl radical
X = isothiouronium salt group
m = 3, 4, or 5
n = >1

These compounds are prepared by heating with thiourea or with a mono-, di-, tri- or tetraalkylthiourea, a phthalocyanine which contains 3, 4, or 5 pendent aryloxy or arylmercapto radicals and at least 2 chloro- or bromomethyl groups.

These compounds are superior in lightfastness and tinctorial strength to the comparable dyes made by reacting a chloromethylphthalocyanine containing at least 2 chloromethyl groups with compounds that replace the chloromethyl groups with isothiouronium groups.

The new dyes "...are especially valuable for use in printing textile materials, for example cotton, wool, silk, regenerated cellulose, cellulose acetate and rayon or mixtures of these. They are conveniently applied to cotton in faintly acid medium and subsequently fixed in alkaline medium, for example they may be applied in the presence of a mixture of weakly acidic substance and an alkaline salt of a weak acid which on steaming or heating changes from a weakly acid to a weakly alkaline state."

Tartter (232) has prepared isothiouronium compounds such as

$$Pc\left[CH_2-NH-\overset{\overset{O}{\|}}{C}-CH_2-S^+=C\overset{N(CH_3)_2}{\underset{N(CH_3)_2}{<}}\right]_n Cl^-$$

where n = from 2 to 8

This compound "produces on cotton brilliant blue dyeings of very good fastness properties." It is prepared from a mixture of copper phthalocyanine, phosphorous pentoxide, N-hydroxymethylchloroacetamide, and 100 per cent sulfuric acid heated for 12 hours at 95°. The reaction product is then heated with tetramethylthiourea yielding the above isothiouroniumphthalocyanine.

Wood (251) prepared water soluble copper isothiouroniumphthalocyanines from thiourea and chloromethylphthalocyanines, the stability of which in alkaline media is improved by the addition of dimethyl sulfate.

For example, the isothiouronium salt of copper trichloromethylphthalocyanine and tetramethyl thiourea, and dimethyl sulfate are heated for 10 minutes at 100–110°. The solution is diluted with acetone and the precipitate is filtered off, washed with acetone, and dried, giving a blue powder that dissolves in water to give a bright blue solution.

Wood (252,253) prepared cobalt phthalocyanines containing at least one chloromethyl or bromomethyl radical of value as intermediates in the preparation of water soluble dyes such as isothiouronium salts by reaction with thiourea. For example, pyridine is added to aluminum chloride, with the temperature rising to 150°. The mixture is heated at 120–150° until dissolution of the aluminum chloride is complete. The solution is cooled to 60° and sym-dichlorodimethyl ether is added at 70°. The mixture is cooled to 45° and cobalt phthalocyanine is added at 50° or below, heated at 50° for 30 minutes, poured into cold water, filtered, washed free from acid with water, and dried to give a mixture of cobalt mono- and dichloromethylphthalocyanine. This mixture is reacted with thiourea and water at 90–100° for 30 minutes. Acetone is added; the suspension is filtered, washed with acetone, and dried, yielding a blue powder that dissolves in water to give a reddish blue solution that dyes cotton in reddish blue shades of good fastness to washing and to light.

Tartter (233) has synthesized a series of basic phthalocyanine dyes by the reaction of phthalocyanine sulfonyl chlorides with compounds of the formula $NH_2-R-NH-R'$, where R is an alkylene or cycloalkylene group, and R' is a branched aliphatic or cycloaliphatic radical. The products are insoluble in most organic solvents but are soluble in benzyl alcohol.

For example, copper phthalocyanine is heated in chlorosulfonic acid for 2.5 hours at 120°. The cooled solution is precipitated on ice, filtered, and washed to neutrality with ice water. The precipitate is pasted with ice water and is stirred with water, ice, and N-cyclohexylpropylene-diamine-1,3. After 15 hours agitation the mixture is diluted with water, heated to 60°, filtered off, and dried, yielding a dye that is almost insoluble in acetone and in alcohol but that is easily soluble in benzyl alcohol with a blue color.

Ono and Tsutsumi (173–178) have concerned themselves with phthalocyanine isothiocarbamides. They prepare (173) copper phthalocyanine tetra-4-S-isothiocarbamide hydrochloride by suspension of copper tetra-4-aminophthalocyanine in 20 per cent hydrochloric acid, diazotization with sodium nitrite, thiourea, and ice water, followed by washing with 10 per cent hydrochloric acid, and drying. They prepare (174) copper phthalocyanine tris-4-S-isothiocarbamide hydrochloride as follows. A mixture of 4-nitrophthalimide, phthalic anhydride, urea, ammonium molybdate, cuprous chloride, and o-dichlorobenzene is heated at 170° for 15 hours. The solvent is evaporated and the residue is heated with 35 per cent hydrochloric acid and water at 90° for 2 hours to give copper tri-4-nitrophthalocyanine which is reduced with sodium sulfide, diazotized with hydrochloric acid, sodium nitrite, and water, followed by treatment with thiourea, water, and ice to give copper phthalocyanine tris-4-S-isothiocarbamide hydrochloride. Phthalocyanine disulfide (175) is prepared from copper phthalocyanine tetra-4-S-isothiocarbamide hydrochloride in water, treated with dilute sodium hydroxide solution at 40–50°, followed by addition of dilute hydrochloric acid, the mixture filtered and washed with water to give a paste that contains copper tetramercaptophthalocyanine, oxidation of which gives phthalocyanine disulfide. Copper phthalocyanine tetra-4-S-isothiocarbamide hydrochloride (176) also gives copper phthalocyanine disulfide by boiling in water for several hours with continuous addition of air, followed by filtration, and water wash.

The phthalocyanine isothiocarbamides dye vegetable fibers in blue green shades (177,178). Copper phthalocyanine tetra-4-isothiocarbamide hydrochloride in water is treated with sodium sulfide. Cotton fiber is immersed in this solution and is heated at 90° for 30 minutes. The dyed fiber is washed with water, immersed in a solution of hydrochloric acid for several minutes, washed with water, and dried to give a bluish green fiber (177). Also, vegetable fiber is dyed with an aqueous solution of an acid salt of phthalocyanine-S-isothiocarbamides (178) followed by alkaline and acid treatment or by treatment with a mild oxidizing agent in a neutral or alkaline solution at a higher temperature. Yagi and Hori (255) reduce phthalocyanines containing 3 or 4 sulfonyl chloride groups per molecule of phthalocyanine with hydrogen iodide to give phthalocyanines containing sulfur.

Iino (132,133) makes phthalocyanine sulfur dyes that color cotton and wool green.

For example (132), a mixture of 4-nitrophthalimide, cupric chloride, urea, and boric acid is heated for 3 hours at 220°. The reaction product is treated with boiling sodium hydroxide and hydrochloric acid solutions to give copper tetranitrophthalocyanine. A mixture of copper tetranitrophthalocyanine sodium hydrosulfite, water, and polyoxyethylene alkyl ether is refluxed for 2 hours, then for 3 hours with sodium hydrosulfite. Hydrochloric acid is added and the product is filtered to give copper tetraaminophthalocyanine which is poured into ice water. Hydrochloric acid, sodium nitrite, and potassium thiocyanate are added. The mixture is heated for 30 minutes at 80–90° and filtered, to yield a sulfur dye that dyes cotton green. Also, a mixture of methyl sulfide, water, acetone, and copper phthalocyanine containing at least 3 chloromethyl groups (133) is refluxed for 13 hours, cooled, filtered, and washed with acetone to yield a water soluble dye that colors cotton and wool green.

Hiyama and Manabe (122) suspend copper phthalocyanine disulfonyl chloride in cold water to which a solution of p-phenylene-diamine in water is added at 0–5° and stirred for 6 hours. The solution is acidified, and filtered, and the precipitate is suspended in water, diazotized, and treated with sodium thiocyanate at 5–10° for 4 hours to give a product that dyes cotton and nylon in a clear bluish green color.

AZO DYES

In his search for green shade phthalocyanines, Bienert (18) prepared acylaminophthalocyanines which can be modified to create azo phthalocyanines by splitting off the acyl groups in 95 per cent sulfuric acid. The aminophthalocyanines can be diazotized by suspension in an acid medium and addition of sodium nitrite. The resulting diazo compounds are in general greener compounds.

Haddock synthesized tetradiazonium derivatives of metal-free and metal phthalocyanines from tetraaminophthalocyanines which, in turn, were formed from tetranitrophthalocyanines (94,97–99). The tetranitrophthalocyanines themselves are made from mixtures of urea and nitrophthalodinitrile or nitrophthalic anhydride (94). The tetranitrophthalocyanines are reduced to the corresponding tetraaminophthalocyanines with stannous chloride, sodium hydrosulfite, or alkali sulfide reducing agents (94). For example, copper tetra-4-nitrophthalocyanine, slurried in water, to which is added 33 per cent aqueous sodium hydroxide, and sodium hydrosulfite, the mixture stirred at 50–55° for 1 hour, filtered, and the filter cake stirred with boiling 20 per cent sodium chloride solution, filtered, washed with 10 per cent sodium chloride solution, and dried yields a dark green copper tetra-4-aminophthalocyanine. Copper tetra-3-aminophthalocyanine may also be prepared from the corresponding nitro precursor. The tetraamines are insoluble in water. However, they are readily diazotized and may be stored as dry phthalocyanine diazonium compounds available for use to make coloring matters. The dry phthalocyanine diazonium compounds are green in color. They are applied to textiles from cuprous solutions by the action of suitable reagents for the decomposition of the diazonium groups, liberating nitrogen, and producing insoluble phthalocyanine derivatives on the textile. For example, an aqueous slurry of copper tetra-4-aminophthalocyanine is mixed with concentrated hydrochloric acid. The mixture is cooled to 5° or below and an aqueous solution of sodium nitrite is then added. The dark green diazo solution is added with agitation to an aqueous mixture of potassium hydroxide at −10°, yielding a green solution, after which another mixture of potassium hydroxide in water is added at 120°. The mixture is cooled to 100°, filtered, and dried. The dry copper tetra-4-potassium diazotate is a dark green powder that is soluble in cold water (97). Haddock further developed stable modifications of the tetra-4-isodiazotate, viz., preparation of double salts, stabilization with naphthalene-1,5-disulfonic acid, and preparation of the corresponding diazoimino and diazosulfonate compounds (98). These compounds may be used to dye cotton cloth. For example, dyeing with the copper tetra-4-potassium diazotate can be accomplished by treating the diazotate in the cold with concentrated hydrochloric acid, which decomposes the isodiazotate, yielding an aqueous solution of the normal diazonium compound (98,99). Printing on cotton cloth may be accomplished using printing pastes containing alkali, the isodiazotate, a coupling component such as β-naphthol, and a thickener. "Such pastes, when printed on cloth and steamed under acid conditions, or when passed into an aqueous bath containing weak acids (e.g. acetic acid) or acid salts (e.g. sodium bichromate), form the dye on the fiber and yield green to brown prints" (99).

Libby and co-workers (146,147,211) have developed methods for the application of azo phthalocyanine dyes directly on a variety of textile materials including cellulose, cellulose esters, nylon, silk, and wool, by the use of water soluble coupling components. Color is developed on the fiber by impregnating the fiber with an aqueous solution of the phthalocyanine diazotate between 0° and 30° and then generating the color on the fiber with a coupling component by "rinsing the impregnated fiber in cold water and then treating it with an aqueous solution of a coupling component containing water solubilizing groups, such as carboxylic acid, sulfonic acid, or their alkali-metal salts. An alternative procedure is to impregnate the fiber first with the coupling component, and then treat the fiber with a neutral aqueous solution of the azotized polyamino-phthalocyanine. This procedure is to be preferred in the case of animal fibers such as wool or silk. In either of the above cases, the color may be developed in local designs, if desired, by printing from an engraved roll. For instance, a thickened paste containing an azotized aminophthalocyanine may be printed on cotton cloth impregnated with the coupling component" (146). As an example of a dyeing of a fiber in its entirety, a slurry of copper tetra-4-aminophthalocyanine is mixed with concentrated hydrochloric acid and an aqueous solution of sodium nitrite at 5–10°. The resulting solution is cooled to 0° by the addition of ice. Cotton piece goods are stirred in this solution for 1 hour. The piece is removed, rinsed in cold water, and treated at 5–10° for 15 minutes in an aqueous solution of sodium carbonate and 1-(4'sulfo-phenyl)-3-methyl-5-pyrazolone. Other effective coupling components with water solubilizing groups include 2-naphthol-6-sulfonic acid, 8-hydroxyquinoline-5-sulfonic acid, and 2-amino-5-naphthol-7-sulfonic acid. The different coupling components give a variety of shades including green, gray, and brown. The dyeing is removed, rinsed, and ironed dry. The dyeing is bright green in color with good washing, crocking, and lightfastness (146).

Libby and his associates (147,211) also found that if azo phthalocyanines formed in substance or on the fiber are then treated "... with aqueous solutions of compounds of metals capable of forming metallic complexes with ortho-hydroxy-azo dyes, new metal complex azo pigments of the phthalocyanine series are formed, which are in general faster to light than the unmetallized pigments" (147). Copper acetate, copper sulfate, cuprammonium sulfate, copper chloride, nickel acetate, cobalt acetate, cobalt chloride, chromium acetate, and chromium fluoride are among the effective metal compounds. If, for example, in the dyeing of the cotton piece good described above, an aftertreatment of alkaline copper acetate solution is made for 15 minutes at 5–10°, a dull green dyeing with excellent wash- and lightfastness is obtained.

The variety of azo phthalocyanines may be increased by using less than 4 moles of nitrous acid per mole of tetraaminophthalocyanine. Satisfactory dyeings by diazotization of only three of the amino groups in tetraaminophthalocyanine have been obtained (147).

Haddock (100) also offered the method of converting the polydiazophthalocyanines into dyes by coupling them to components containing water solubilizing groups such as sulfo or carboxy. The same components without water solubilizing groups yield azo phthalocyanine pigments (101). The water solubilized form may also be converted into lakes by reaction with, for example, barium chloride, or other compounds used for the obtention of lakes (100). For example, to the mixture of an aqueous paste of copper tetra-4-aminophthalocyanine, and concentrated hydrochloric acid, is added an aqueous solution of sodium nitrite at 10–12°. After 1–2 minutes the green diazo solution is quickly added with agitation to an aqueous solution of 1-*m*-sulfophenyl-3-methyl-5-pyrazolone. "During the addition the mixture is kept alkaline by addition of sodium carbonate as needed and the temperature is kept below 5°C. When coupling is complete, the solution is heated and sufficient common salt added to precipitate the dyestuff. It is filtered off, washed with 20 per cent aqueous solution of common salt, dried, and pulverised" (100).

The product, soluble in water, dyes cotton at the boil in yellow-green shade. Other coupling components dye cotton in red-violet, blue-gray, and violet shades.

Douglas, Parkinson, and Wakefield (60) prepared water insoluble green azo dyes "having a high tinctorial value and good wet fastness" from aminophthalocyanines carrying the amino groups in pendent aryl nuclei. The aryl nuclei each carry at least 2 amino groups and are attached directly or through linking atoms to the phthalocyanine nucleus.

Acetoacetylamino derivatives of phthalocyanines (134) that are useful dye intermediates for coupling with diazotized amines give azoic compounds of yellowish green to green shades. The acetoacetylaminophthalocyanines are prepared by reaction of diketene with phthalocyanine compounds containing one or more amino groups attached to the phthalocyanine molecule or to aryl nuclei that are connected to the phthalocyanine molecule.

Haddock, Parkinson, and Rowe (106) addressed themselves to the problem of stabilizing diazo phthalocyanines. "...it may be said that diazonium salts in general are rather unstable. Nor do diazonium salts derived from aminophthalocyanines form any exception to this rule. Consequently in coupling them, decomposition tends to occur as it does in azo couplings in general, the degree of decomposition depending especially on the temperature. Further the decomposition products thus arising are apt to vitiate the resulting azo colouring matter and so may impair its technically useful properties. Accordingly the less the decomposition of the diazonium salt the better. We have now found that if the amino groups instead of being directly attached to the phthalocyanine molecule are carried on pendant phenyl groups, themselves connected to the phthalocyanine molecule by various linking atoms or groups of atoms, then the stability of the corresponding diazonium salts is notably greater."

In Haddock's, Parkinson's, and Rowe's work, the phthalocyanine phenylene group contains an aminophenyl radical attached by one of the linking atom and groups of atoms: —CO—, —SO$_2$—, and —O—, by "...heating a phthalic acid derivative which is phthalic acid carrying a nitrophenyl group attached by one of the aforesaid linking atom and groups of atoms, or the corresponding derivative of phthalic anhydride, phthalimide or phthalamide, together with urea and a substance containing a metal, and reducing the resulting phthalocyanine having four nitrophenyl groups linked to it."

Fox (76) has prepared a type of phthalocyanine azo dye from diazonium salts and sulfonamide derivatives of the phthalocyanines. This type of diazo dye possesses "valuable dyeing properties towards certain fibers. Of this particular type may be mentioned those prepared from 1-(3′-aminophenyl)-3-methyl-5-pyrazolone."

Haddock and co-workers (105) claim that "...if the amino groups, instead of being attached directly to the phthalocyanine molecule, are attached to pendent aryl nuclei which are connected to the phthalocyanine nuclei either directly or through linking atoms or groups of atoms, then the stability of the corresponding diazonium salts is increased."

Brentano, Grossmann, and Müller (39) have prepared water soluble, mordant azo phthalocyanine dyes, in conformity with the definition of mordant dyes, viz., dyes that combine with both a mordanting substance, such as hydrous chromic oxide, and with the fiber to be colored, and in which the mordant provides attachment to the fiber and forms a lake with the dye. The mordant azo phthalocyanines prepared by Brentano, Grossman, and Müller are derived from a phthalocyanine tetrasulfonic acid, contain at least one —SO$_2$NH— group, at least one azo linkage, and at least one salicylic acid group. These mordant azo phthalocyanines print or dye textiles in green to olive shades. The mordant azo phthalocyanines are represented by

where Pc = a metal phthalocyanine molecule

  —SO$_2$NH— group is present in 3 or 4 position

  —SO$_3$H— group is present in 4 or 3 position

      X = a hydrogen atom, a halogen atom or methyl, hydroxy, nitro, or sulfonic acid group

Y = a hydrogen atom, a halogen atom, or an alkyl, alkoxy, nitro, sulfonic acid or carboxylic acid group

Z = hydrogen or halogen atom, or alkyl or alkoxy group

n = integer from 1 to 4

m = integer from 0 to 3

$m + n = 4$

and where the —SO_2NH— group occupies a m- or p-position relative to the azo group.

Brentano (40) has also prepared water soluble mordant azo phthalocyanine dyes which yield green to olive tints, especially in chrome printing, with the formula

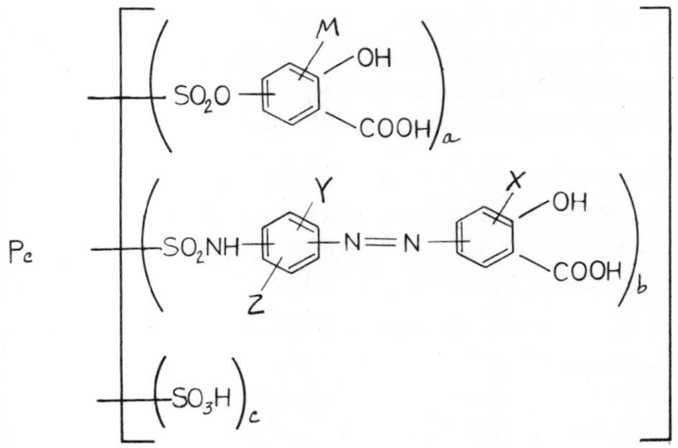

and the alkali salts thereof, where

Pc = metal phthalocyanine

—SO_2O—, —SO_2NH—, and —SO_3H groups are severally present in one of the 3- and 4- positions

M = a hydrogen atom, halogen atom, and methyl group ortho to the —SO_2O— linkage

X = a member from the group of H, CH_3, OH, NO_2, and SO_3H

Y = a member from the group of H, CH_3, OCH_3, SO_3H, and COOH ortho to the azo group

Z = a member from the group of H and OCH_3 ortho to the —SO_2NH— linkage

a = integer from 1 to 3

b = integer from 1 to 3

c = integer from 0 to 2

$a + b + c = 4$

and where the —SO_2NH— group occupies one of the positions m- and p-to the azo linkage.

Gottlieb (89) also has prepared water soluble chromable azo phthalocyanine dyes for cellulose and wool fibers of good fastness to washing and to light. The dyes correspond to the formula

$$Pc \left[\left(SO_2O - \bigcirc - \bigcirc - N{=}N - \bigcirc \begin{smallmatrix} -OH \\ COOM \end{smallmatrix} \right)_n \left(SO_3M \right)_{4-n} \right]$$

where Pc is a copper phthalocyanine molecule
M and M' are cationic atoms or groups
    n = number from 1 to 3

These dyes are chromable and may be converted into washfast and lightfast dyes on the fiber. Their shade range is bluish to yellowish green.

Rösch and Gehringer (205) have produced azo phthalocyanine dyes in which the azo group is removed from the phenylene rings of the phthalocyanine molecule by the linkage $-CH_2-NH-CO-\overset{\|}{C}-$ as given by the general formula

$$Pc \left[CH_2NHCO-\underset{N=N-R}{\overset{OH}{\underset{|}{C}}}{=}\underset{}{\overset{|}{C}}-CH_3 \right]_n$$

where Pc = metal phthalocyanine
    R = radical of a diazo compound chosen from the group consisting of benzene, azo benzene, diphenylether, and diphenyl sulfone.
    n = integer from 1 to 8

The dyes with n = 4 to 8 are soluble in aqueous alkalies. The diazo components may or may not contain water solubilizing groups. The coupling of the diazonium compounds with the phthalocyanine acetoacetic acid amides is carried out in aqueous solution or suspension in substance or on the fiber. Bluish green to yellowish green dyes are obtained.

Haddock and colleagues (104) have broadened the possibilities of the azo phthalocyanines by developing the synthesis of phthalocyanines of the formula

$$Pc[S-Ar-NH_2]_n$$

where Pc = the phthalocyanine nucleus,
    Ar = substituted or unsubstituted arylene nucleus
    n = integer not greater than 4

"The new phthalocyanine derivatives consist of blue or green powders which may be diazotised and the so-obtained diazonium salts used as diazo components for the manufacture of new dyestuffs, by coupling them with the conventional coupling components. For this purpose it is convenient to use the new phthalocyanine derivatives in the form of aqueous pastes."

Bienert and colleagues (26) have extended the azo phthalocyanine group of dyes to include compounds of the formula

$$Pc+[R-R_1-N\!=\!N-R_2]_n$$

where Pc = phthalocyanine nucleus
    R = $-SO_2-$ or $-CO-$ group
    R_1 = an amino-group-containing organic radical
    R_2 = radical of a diazo compound
    n = number from 1 to 4

"The new dyes usually impart green shades to vegetable fibres, which distinguish themselves by excellent fastness properties. The dyes which are prepared in substance are valuable pigment dyes which can be applied for the coloration of lacquers, resins, plastic masses, and others."

Fleischhauer (73) has prepared a new series of azo phthalocyanines of the formula

$$mZ-Pc+\left[SO_2-\overset{\overset{X}{|}}{N}-R_1-N\!=\!N-R_2-\overset{\overset{X}{|}}{N}-Y\right]_n$$

where X = hydrogen or alkyl, aralkyl, cycloalkyl, or aryl radical
    R_1 = residue of a keto, hydroxy, or amino compound
    R_2 = arylene radical
    Y = residue of a saturated or unsaturated halofatty acid or of a mono- or dihalo-triazine compound
    Z = $-COOH$ and/or $-SO_3H$
    m = integer $\geqslant 2$
    n = integer from 1 to 4

"The new dyestuffs can be used for the dyeing of animal fibres and synthetic polyamide fibres. In particular, in the case of dyeing or printing of cotton or artificial silk made from regenerated cellulose in the presence of acid-binding or alkaline-acting agents at elevated temperatures, for example, by steaming, they usually give light stable and clear green, dark green, olive green, brown, blue, marine blue or grey to black shades. The dyeings are characterised by a good water-stability since the dyestuffs combine chemically with the fibres."

Sander (216) prepared aminophthalocyanines by reduction of nitrophthalocyanine in a mixture of sulfur and sulfuric acid at 40–60°.

Dortmann and Schmitz (59) have prepared azo phthalocyanines of the formula

$$Pc \underset{}{\vdash} R_6 - R_7 - N = N - R_8 - (R_6' - R)_m]_n$$

where   R = groups including $-CH_2CH_2-OSO_3X$, $-NH-R_1-OSO_3X$,
$-NH-R_2-Cl$

R_1 and R_2 = bridge elements with 2 or 3 carbon atoms between N and O or halogen atom

$R_6 = -SO_2-$ or $-CO-$

R_7 = radical bearing amino groups of the benzene, naphthalene, pyrazolone or acylacetamide series.

$R_6' = -SO_2-$ or $-CO-$

R_8 = diazo radical

X = hydrogen or alkali metal atom

n = from 1 to 8

m = integer

yielding yellow-green to blue-green dyes. They are suited for the dyeing or printing of materials that contain hydroxy or amide groups, in particular cellulose or regenerated cellulose, wool, silk, and synthetic polyamides. Dyes that are wash- and boilfast are obtained.

Water soluble azo phthalocyanine dyes (69), that yield yellowish green to bluish green as well as reddish blue shades on cotton, of the formula

$$Pc \underset{}{\vdash} R - R_1 - N = N - R_2]_n$$

where R = $-SO_2-$ or $-CO-$

R_1 = amino containing radical of naphthalene, pyrazolone, or acylacetic acid arylamide series linked by the amino group to the radical R

R_2 = radical of a diazo component containing at least one water solubilizing group

n = integer from 1 to 4

are prepared by the coupling of a diazo compound, containing at least one water solubilizing group with a phthalocyanine sulfonamide or carbonamide of the formula

$$Pc \underset{}{\vdash} R - R_1]_n$$

VAT DYES

Only ten years ago, on October 7, 1952, the patent literature of cobalt phthalocyanine vat dyes was born, with the issuance of U. S. Patent 2,613,128 to Baumann and Bienert (11) and of U. S. Patent 2,613,129 to McCormack and Stilmar (157). "We have now found that cobalt phthalocyanines are far superior to all other phthalocyanines as far as vatting properties are concerned. Contrary to the unsubstituted copper and nickel complex the unsubstituted cobalt phthalocyanine is capable of use as a vat dye...." (11). "That certain of the phthalocyanine compounds have the property of being vatted has been known since their earliest appearance in the literature (British Patent 322,169 which was issued in 1929). Nevertheless, they have not found much use as vat dyes up to now, principally because of the dull shades produced and lack of lightfastness. In recent years it has become known through the work of Bienert (P.B. 70339, frame 11206, 1948) that cobalt phthalocyanine, when vatted with sodium hydroxide and sodium hydrosulfite, will dye cotton (upon subsequent oxidation) to a clear, greenish blue shade. This suggestion nevertheless was still insufficient to produce a practical phthalocyanine vat dye, in view of the very poor solubility of cobalt phthalocyanine in the vat, producing as a result very weak dyeings" (157).

The action of alkaline reducing agents, such as the sodium hydroxide-hydrosulfite vat, may yield a sort of leuco compound (90):

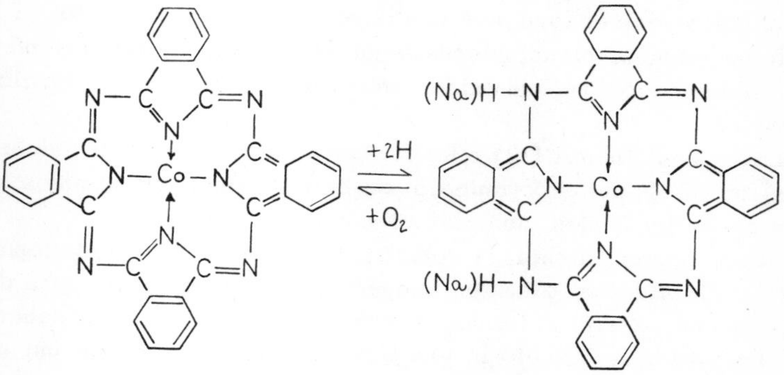

"Although the reducible quinone groups typical of vat dyes are not present in the molecule, displacements presumably occur in the quinonoid bonds of the phthalocyanine ring system under the influence of the reducing agent, so that the molecule is able to take up hydrogen atoms which can be replaced by alkali, i.e. this hydro compound can be ionized" (90).

McCormack and Stilmar found that the solubility of cobalt phthalocyanine in the vat and the strength of dyeing can be improved upon the addition of the phosphonous acid group, $—P(OH)_2$, into the phthalocyanine molecule, to the extent of 0.2 to 0.4 moles $P(OH)_2$ per mole of cobalt phthalocyanine. "The theory is not well understood, but it is obvious that the cobalt phthalocyanine phosphonous acid helps the unreacted cobalt phthalocyanine to dye."

Baumann and Bienert (11) on the other hand, increase the solubility of the cobalt phthalocyanine for vatting, by the addition of other water solubilizing groups, such as sulfonic acid, sulfonamide, sulfinic acid, carboxylic acid, carboxylic amide, cyano, hydroxy, alkoxy, mercapto, sulfur alkyl, nitro, amino, and acylamino groups. "Cobalt phthalocyanine and the various hydrophilic substitution products...will dye cellulose fibers according to the methods usually applied to vat dyestuffs. In general, the best affinity is reached when dyeing from the hot vat. Many cobalt phthalocyanines are capable of being vatted even in a weakly alkaline medium, for instance, in the presence of ammonia and, therefore, may also be used for dyeing animal fibers from the vat."

Motokawa, Tsutsumi, and Nomoto (159) prepare a cobalt phthalocyanine vat dye by addition of cobalt phthalocyanine to 96 per cent sulfuric acid, stirring at 130° for 3 hours, cooling, precipitating in ice water, filtration, washing with water, and drying to give a vat dye that is insoluble in water, almost insoluble in alkali, but soluble in alkaline hydrosulfite solution to dye vegetable fibers blue.

Mühlbauer (164) prepared cobalt vat dyes for dyeing vegetable fibers from phthalocyanines and non-oxidizing, water soluble salts of acids containing oxygen, or soluble salts of metals the hydroxides of which are soluble in sodium hydroxide, or complex compounds with alcohols and amines.

Baumann and Bienert (12) offer further examples of water solubilizing groups for cobalt phthalocyanine in the form of monosulfonamides, monoalkyl monosulfonamides, and dialkyl monosulfonamides.

Vat dyes of iron, nickel, or cobalt phthalocyanines (3) are prepared in inorganic chlorides at elevated temperature in the presence of a diluent and phosgene, oxalyl chloride, or sulfonyl chloride. After saponification, the dyes are vattable in alkaline hydrosulfite solution but are insoluble in alkali metal hydroxide solutions. "The products thus obtained contain probably acid chloride groups. Since the said acid chloride groups are saponified by treating the products with an alkaline sodium sulfite solution to give free acid groups and their corresponding salts, the first products may be used as vat dyestuffs for dyeing cotton and other cellulose fibres from the vat in clear, fast shades."

For example, cobalt phthalocyanine is stirred in a melt of anhydrous aluminum chloride and sodium chloride at 100°, phosgene is added, the melt is stirred into water, concentrated hydrochloric acid is added, followed by boiling and filtration, hot water wash, and drying. The product "...dyes vegetable fibres from a yellow-brown vat powerful blue shades."

Ono, Tsutsumi, and Chiba (179) melt a mixture of aluminum chloride and sodium chloride at 120°. Cobalt phthalocyanine and sulfur are added. The system is heated for 2 hours with stirring, precipitated in hydrochloric acid at 70–80°, filtered, and washed with water to yield a blue vat dye for cotton.

Cobalt vat dyes (4) may be prepared by heating phthalic anhydride or phthalimide, sulfophthalic anhydride, cobalt chloride, urea, ammonium molybdate, and trichlorobenzene, filtering, and boiling with dilute hydrochloric acid, to give a blue powder, dyeing cotton and viscose in bright blue shades from a yellow-brown vat. Monochlorophthalic anhydride and ammonium sulfophthalate give a blue dye that forms green-blue shades from a yellow-brown vat. Phthalodinitrile, sulfophthalic anhydride, and cobalt chloride give a dye that forms clear blue shades from a yellow-brown vat.

Mühlbauer (162) forms cobalt phthalocyanine vat dyes containing from 1 to 4 moles of the water solubilizing group —RCOOH per mole of cobalt phthalocyanine, where R is an aliphatic radical, specifically —CH$_2$—, —CHCl—, or —CCl$_2$—. These dyes are soluble in alkaline hydrosulfite solution and color cotton cellulose or viscose artificial silk in clear blue to greenish blue shades.

For example, a mixture of cobalt phthalocyanine, trichloroacetic acid, trichlorobenzene, and ferric chloride is heated at 180–190° with agitation from 4 to 5 hours. After cooling the trichlorobenzene is removed by blowing in steam; the dye material is boiled with dilute hydrochloric acid, filtered by suction, washed with water, and dried. A dark blue dye is obtained that dyes cotton in clear blue shades, with good lightfastness, from a yellow-brown vat.

Ruppel (214) has prepared cobalt phthalocyanine vat dyes in which the cobalt phthalocyanine itself does not contain water solubilizing groups but is treated with dispersing agents. Suitable dispersing agents include gum arabic, dextrin, tannin, saponin, sulfonated fatty acids, and condensation products from naphthalene sulfonic acids with formaldehyde.

For example, a mixture of cobalt phthalocyanine and a condensation product from β-naphthalene sulfonic acid and formaldehyde is dissolved at room temperature in concentrated sulfuric acid. The solution is poured onto ice and the dye material is applied to textiles in the usual manner, to vegetable fibers in alkaline hydrosulfite solution. An olive green vat dyes cotton in strong, clear blue shades of good light- and washfastness.

Ruppel (213) has also succeeded to make a vattable cobalt phthalocyanine which does not contain water solubilizing groups by mixing the cobalt phthalocyanine with vattable compounds in fine dispersions with the aid of dispersing agents. Suitable vattable compounds are the anthraquinone vat dyes. Vatting of vegetable fibers takes place in alkaline hydrosulfite solution.

For example, a mixture of cobalt phthalocyanine and anthraquinone is dissolved in concentrated sulfuric acid. The solution is poured over ice and the precipitate is worked up into a paste which yields strong, clear blue colors of high light- and washfastness from olive-green vats.

Baumann, Bienert, and Vollmann (16) prepare cobalt phthalocyanine dyes by reaction of the cobalt phthalocyanine intermediate of German Patent 839,939 with a solvent such as dimethyl formamide, glycerin, and thiodiglycol, followed by the addition of sodium hydroxide solution until the cobalt phthalocyanine intermediate is in solution. O- or p-toluenesulfonamide and a mixture of solvent such as formamide, triethanolamine, and acetone is added with tragacanth thickener, benzaldehydebisulfite, and water, yielding a printing paste that prints cellulosic fabrics, followed by formic acid aftertreatment, washing, and soaping, in powerful clean blue shades with excellent light- and washfastness.

A cobalt phthalocyanine vat dye has been marketed under the trade name Indanthren Brilliant Blue 4G (90) prepared by the methods of reference 11. Gund (90) states: "Amongst the fastest-to-light blue vat dyes Indanthren Brilliant Blue 4G is outstanding for its remarkably pure greenish shade. Owing to its poor fastness to chlorine, however, the field of application of this dye is limited. . . . This product should be of interest, for example, for articles made from filament or staple viscose rayon, for which fastness to chlorine is not required. The dye shows normal stability as a printing paste, but it is advisable to steam the goods soon after printing. Their tinctorial strength deteriorates appreciably if the prints are left under unfavorable conditions for some little time prior to steaming. Although this dye can also be combined with other vat dyes, the bright self-shade should be of the greatest interest."

Cobalt phthalocyanines may be converted into dyes for textile fibers (88) by reaction with a 1,2-dicarboxylic acid N-methylolimide.

The resulting cobalt phthalocyanine dyes ". . . may be vatted in known manner with caustic and hydrosulfite, and the vats employed for dyeing textile fibers in strong bright blue shades of excellent light fastness. Subsequent oxidation may be achieved in known manner by exposing the dyed fiber to the air or by dipping it in an oxidizing bath, for instance a solution of sodium perborate or aqueous acetic acid solutions of sodium dichromate. The dyestuff mixtures of this invention are capable of being vatted even in a weakly alkaline medium, for instance in the presence of ammonia, and therefore may also be employed for dyeing animal fibers from the vat in addition to fibers having a basis of synthetic polymeric materials."

Randall and Taras (198) have found that the solubility of a cobalt phthalocyanine in the vat and therefore the strength of dyeing is improved by reacting at least part of the color with formaldehyde, paraformaldehyde or trioxane, in the presence of a strong mineral acid having a concentration of at least 90 per cent by weight. The reaction may be carried out in the presence of an amide "... it having been found that the use of the amide yields products dyeing a strong bright blue shade in comparison with products obtained in the absence of the amide which are generally greener. As amides which may be employed in the process of this invention, there may be mentioned simple aliphatic and aromatic amides such as propionamide, butyramide, benzamide, urea, biuret, and the like, and especially formamide and acetamide."

Ono, Tsutsumi, Chiba, and Nomoto (181) dye cotton green by treating a mixture of 96 per cent sulfuric acid and cobalt phthalocyanine at 125° with formaldehyde and sodium chloride, precipitating the reaction product in ice water, filtering, and washing with water to give a green powder, reducible to clear yellow-brown by sodium hydrosulfite.

Wilkinson (248) uses a mixture of cobalt phthalocyanine and cobalt phthalocyanine carrying one or more isothiouronium salt groups attached by a methylene linkage to an aromatic nucleus of the phthalocyanine molecule, which "dye cellulosic textile materials in clear blue shades of good fastness to light and washing. They are superior to previously known compositions comprising cobalt phthalocyanine in that when the dyeings from these compositions are subjected to severe washing in contact with adjacent white materials, for example in textile material woven from blue and white threads, they show less staining of the adjacent white materials than the dyeings from previously known compositions."

The chloromethyl derivative of cobalt phthalocyanine is made by addition of sym-dichlorodimethyl ether for 15 minutes to a mixture of aluminum chloride and pyridine at 60°. The mixture is cooled to 45°. Powdered cobalt phthalocyanine is added during 0.5 hour at 50°. The mixture is stirred at 50° for 1 hour and the chloromethyl derivative is precipitated on ice, filtered off, and washed free from aluminum chloride, and dried. The product contains 1.5 —CH_2Cl groups per molecule.

Ono, Tsutsumi, and Chiba (180,243) have also used cobalt chloromethylphthalocyanines. A mixture of an equal number of molecules of cobalt phthalocyanine and cobalt monochloromethylphthalocyanine (180) is boiled with a 5 per cent sodium hydroxide solution for 10 hours, cooled, filtered, and washed with water to give cobalt hydroxymethylphthalocyanine, which dissolves in alkaline hydrosulfite solution to give a clear yellow-brown solution that dyes cotton a clean blue color. The

chloromethylphthalocyanine is prepared as follows (243). Paraformaldehyde and cobalt phthalocyanine are dissolved in 96 per cent sulfuric
acid. Sodium chloride is added and the mixture is heated at 100° for 4
hours, cooled, poured into ice water, filtered, washed with water, and
dried at 60° to give cobalt chloromethylphthalocyanine containing 0.2–
1.2 chloromethyl radicals per molecule of phthalocyanine.

Phthalocyanine vat dyes (2) may be obtained by introducing sulfonic
acid and sulfonic acid chloride groups to such an extent that they become vattable but remain from difficultly soluble to soluble in aqueous
solutions of alkali metal hydroxides. The process involves treatment of
the initial compounds with the sulfonating agents such as fuming sulfuric
acid or sulfur trioxide containing pyridine or dioxane or chlorosulfonic
acid under mild conditions, imparting one sulfonic acid group or one
sulfonic acid chloride group to from 2 to 120 molecules of phthalocyanines.

"The new vat dyestuffs may be used for dyeing in the manner known
for vat dyestuffs. They go well on to vegetable fibres and also fibres of
regenerated cellulose, and the resulting dyeings are distinguished by
excellent fastness properties."

Martin (149) has developed a new type of cobalt phthalocyanine vat
dye based on the addition of phenylsulfonyl groups to the phthalocyanine
phenylene nuclei which have improved fastness to chlorine and which
"...upon vatting dye cotton fabrics yield bright blue to greenish blue
shades and show excellent fastness to light, washing and improved fastness to chlorine." Previous cobalt phthalocyanine vats did not exhibit
as good fastness to chlorine. The general formula of the new cobalt
phthalocyanine dyes is

$$P_C \left[SO_2 - \underset{}{\bigcirc}^R \right]_n$$

where P_C = cobalt phthalocyanine radical
        R = halogen such as chlorine or bromine, hydrogen, lower alkyl,
           or nitro group
        n = 1 to 4

These dyes are prepared by the reaction of a benzene sulfonyl chloride
on cobalt phthalocyanine or by the reaction of cobalt phthalocyanine
sulfonyl chloride and either benzene, halogenated benzene, or alkylated
benzene. Benzene sulfonyl chloride is prepared by the reaction of
chlorosulfonic acid and benzene or phosphorous pentachloride on alkali
salts of benzene sulfonic acids. Cobalt phthalocyanine sulfonyl chlorides are prepared by heating cobalt phthalocyanine with chlorosulfonic

acid or by the action of phosphorous pentachloride on the alkali salts of cobalt phthalocyanine sulfonic acids.

Taras and Randall (223) also have improved cobalt phthalocyanine vat dyes the solubility of which in the vat is greater than that of cobalt phthalocyanine, in order to improve the strength of the dyeings. The improved cobalt phthalocyanine vat dyes are made by the reaction of cobalt phthalocyanine with sulfur dioxide in aluminum chloride, with or without the presence of sulfuryl chloride or chlorine, or paraformaldehyde. The vat dyes produced are greener with increasing reaction temperature or with longer reaction time. Addition of chlorine or sulfuryl chloride increases the chlorine fastness of the cobalt phthalocyanine vat dyes.

"The cobalt phthalocyanine derivatives of this invention may be vatted in known manner with caustic and hydrosulfite, and the vats employed for dyeing textile fibers in strong, bright blue shades of excellent light fastness. Subsequent oxidation may be achieved in known manner by exposing the dyed fiber to the air or by dipping it in an oxidizing bath, for instance a solution of sodium perborate or aqueous acetic acid solutions of sodium dichromate. The dyestuff mixtures of this invention are capable of being vatted even in a weakly alkaline medium for instance in the presence of ammonia, and therefore, may also be employed for dyeing animal fibers from the vat in addition to fibers having a basis of synthetic polymeric materials."

Cobalt phthalocyanine (67) may be formed in the fiber by preparation of complex cobalt compounds of phthalonitrile that are soluble in sodium hydroxide. For example, a mixture of phthalic anhydride, urea, anhydrous cobalt chloride, ammonium molybdate and nitrobenzene is heated at 170° for 10 hours. The reaction mass is cooled, diluted with methyl alcohol, and the complex cobalt phthalonitrile paste is filtered off, and is purified by dissolving in aqueous sodium hydroxide-methanol solution, followed by filtration and precipitation with acetic acid. The conversion to cobalt phthalocyanine takes place such as by heating with hydrazine sulfate in glacial acetic acid for 0.5 hour; by heating alone at 300–320° or by refluxing in quinoline. The complex may be used in printing pastes with hydrazine sulfate and other addition agents. Steaming yields a clear blue color with good fastness to light, rubbing, washing, and boiling alkaline solutions. Improved yields of the complex cobalt compounds (68) are obtained by the reaction in the presence of ammonium nitrate. "It may be presumed that the ammonium nitrate has an oxidizing action on the cobalt phthalocyanine which is intermediately formed, although it is probable that the nitrate radical enters also into the new complex cobalt compounds and thus renders them more stable."

Mühlbauer (163) prepares cobalt vat dyes by heating aromatic or heterocyclic *o*-dinitriles or *o*-cyanocarboxylic acid amides or *o*-dicarboxylic acid diamides with cobalt compounds in the presence of acids or salts. The product dyes in pastes "...may be very readily vatted in caustic soda alkaline hyposulphite solution and yield powerful blue dyeings of very good fastness properties on vegetable fibres."

Bruck (45) made vat dyes by heating a phthalocyanine with carboxylic acid halides containing radicals capable of vat dyeing in the presence of iron or of iron compounds and inert solvents such as polyhalohydrocarbons, dyeing cotton blue to green.

For example, a mixture of copper phthalocyanine, trichlorobenzene, anthraquinone-1-carboxylic acid halide, and iron chloride is heated at the boil for 5 hours. The reaction mass is filtered at 50° and boiled with hydrochloric acid and a solution of sodium carbonate to remove iron salts and excess anthraquinone carboxylic acid. The product yields a blue shade on cotton.

Braun (37) prepares dyes by reaction of a phthalocyanine with hydroxylamine in an aluminum chloride melt at about 100°.

For example, cobalt phthalocyanine and hydroxylamine hydrochloride are introduced into a melt of anhydrous aluminum chloride and sodium sulfite at 100–105°. The dye is precipitated over ice, filtered off, washed with water, and dried. The dye colors "...cotton from an olive-green vat blue-green shades of excellent fastness to light and weather."

Woerth and Chabrier (249) have made vat dyes by the reaction of cobalt phthalocyanine in a sulfuric acid medium with a condensation product of an aliphatic amino acid with formaldehyde.

Mühlbauer and Pfitzner (166) find that cobalt and iron phthalocyanines may be used as vat dyes in the presence of small amounts of water soluble accelerators such as monoethanolamine, methyl taurine, cane sugar, and the sodium salt of copper phthalocyanine trisulfonic acid.

For example, cobalt phthalocyanine is mixed at 60 to 80° with sodium hydroxide solution, sodium hydrosulfite, and water. Under these conditions the dye is not vattable. With the addition of monoethanolamine, in a short time an intense yellow-brown vat is obtained that dyes cotton or viscose silk in powerful clear blue shades of good lightfastness.

Bienert, Baumann, and Vollmann (23) prepare cobalt phthalocyanine vat dyes containing alkyl thio groups by the reaction of urea and o-dicarboxylic acids or their imides in the presence of toluene sulfonamide or nitrobenzene. The vat dyes produced are easily reduced to the vat form by sodium hydrosulfite and sodium hydroxide or ammonia, dyeing cotton with intense green shades.

Koberle, Bienert, and Braun (141) prepared phthalocyanine vat dyes based on attachment of anthraquinone to the phenylene rings directly or by a —NH—, —CO—, —NH—CO—, or —CO—NH— bridge.

LEUCO DYES

Brooks (41) has prepared a dye capable of generating phthalocyanine on the fiber by reduction of a solvent soluble form of calcium phthalocyanine. The solvent soluble phthalocyanine is prepared by reacting phthalonitrile with ammonia and calcium oxide or hydroxide. The product "... seems to be made up of 6 phthalonitrile units, an atom of calcium and an NH_3 group. It also seems to contain 3 molecules of water of crystallization or hydration. Without limiting this invention thereby, it is my belief that my novel compound possesses a structure which may be expressed by the empirical formula $-Ca(C_8H_4N_2)_6 NH_3 \cdot 3H_2O$."

This leuco compound is soluble in alcohol, benzene, and chloroform; it is barely colored and has no tinctorial properties.

Upon reduction, the leuco calcium phthalocyanine decomposes into phthalocyanine, ammonia, and a calcium salt of the reducing agent. Effective reducing agents are ascorbic acid, sodium sulfide, and sodium hydrosulfite.

For example, calcium oxide and phthalonitrile are heated together in ethylene glycol monoethyl ether at 90° for 20 hours. The reaction mixture is filtered and the filter cake is extracted with dimethyl formamide at 60°. The extracts are added to the original filtrate and the dissolved leuco calcium phthalocyanine is precipitated by drowning the mixture in water. After separation by filtration the leuco dye is washed with water, and dried. Reduction of the leuco dye with ascorbic acid in boiling diethylene glycol monobutyl ether yields phthalocyanine. In this example, the necessary ammonia may come from alcoholysis of a portion of the phthalonitrile.

In general, the leuco calcium phthalocyanine "... may be used for dyeing or printing textile fibers, particularly cotton and rayon, by conventional padding or printing processes, followed by reduction of the color on the fiber by the aid of aqueous or aqueous-alcoholic solutions of reducing agents commonly employed in textile treatments, for instance sodium sulfide or sodium hydrosulfite, whereby to develop the fast, greenish-blue color of metal-free phthalocyanine upon the fiber."

Randall and Wowk (199) and Randall, Wowk, and Taras (200) have prepared solvent soluble phthalocyanine dyes by reacting metal phthalocyanines, such as copper, cobalt, chromium, nickel, and iron phthalocyanines, with an aryl sulfondihaloamide oxidizing agent (199) such as Dichloramine *T*, *p*-toluenesulfondichloroamide or with an *N*-haloimide such as *N*-bromosuccinimide (200). The resulting leuco phthalocyanines are then converted to dyes by use of heat or by means of reducing agents.

For example, copper phthalocyanine is slurried in methyl Cellosolve, followed by addition of *N*-bromosuccinimide. The mixture is stirred at room temperature for 24 hours. Unreacted pigment is filtered off, the filtrate is added to water salted out with sodium chloride, stirred for 30 minutes, and filtered. The filter cake is washed with water and is dried at room temperature. "This brown material when padded on cotton cloth from a solution in Carbitol and developed with hydrosulfite yielded blue dyeings" (200).

Baumann, Bienert, Vollmann, and Rösch (17) prepared leuco cobalt phthalocyanines by heating at 150–230° a cobalt salt with phthalic anhydride, phthalic acid, phthalimide, or phthalonitrile, urea or biuret, and molybdenum or titanium tetrachloride catalyst, in the presence of ammonium nitrate; stopping the heating when the reaction product becomes light to dark red, and reacting it with a lower alkyl polyamine at room temperature.

For example, a phthalocyanine cobalt complex, soluble in acetic acid, is prepared from a mixture of phthalic anhydride, urea, cobalt chloride, ammonium nitrate, and ammonium molybdate, heated to 178–182° in nitrobenzene with introduction of a stream of air or nitrogen, stirring, and refluxing, for 12–16 hours, cooling to 70°, diluting with methanol, cooling to 28°, adding sodium hydroxide solution and ethylene diamine, and stirring. The ethylene diamine complex precipitates at 55–60°. The mixture is filtered; the filtrate is washed with methanol to remove nitrobenzene and water, and is dried at 70–80°. The product dissolves in acetic acid and has affinity for vegetable, animal, and synthetic fibers and yields cobalt phthalocyanine upon addition of reducing agents such as sodium hydrosulfite.

Baumann and Bienert (13) prepared phthalocyanine containing 6 molecules of phthalonitrile per atom of cobalt when cobalt salts were heated with phthalonitrile, phthalic acid, or phthalic anhydride, and urea at 160–170°.

Leuco copper and leuco nickel phthalocyanine dyes have been prepared also, by Barnhart and Skiles (10), who propose the structure on page 266 for the leuco phthalocyanines.

"...whereas copper phthalocyanine has been proven by X-ray diffraction patterns and similar investigations to be essentially flat, it is believed that the novel complex molecule of the above type lies in 3 planes joined together at a common axis running through the middle vertical sequence of C —N, N —C atoms in the above formula. When a reducing agent is applied, the "wing" shown on the extreme left breaks off, liberating two phthalonitrile molecules and one molecule of NH_3, and the remaining 2 'wings' spring into a single plane forming the molecule of the corresponding metal phthalocyanine ... Apparently, the planar structure of the metal phthalocyanines is essential to the intramolecular valence-bond resonance which is generally considered responsible for producing color, and this planar structure is absent in our novel compounds."

Leuco copper and leuco nickel phthalocyanines are barely colored and possess no tinctorial properties. They are soluble in alcohol, benzene, and chloroform.

The new dyes are supposed to overcome the deficiencies of the other phthalocyanine dyes with respect to "...lack of fastness to bleach, to washing or to crocking."

The new dyes are called leuco phthalocyanines "...by analogy to the term employed in the vat dye field, it being remembered, however, that whereas a leuco vat compound is a reduction product of the dye, the leuco-phthalocyanines are in a sense a higher oxidation stage than the corresponding phthalocyanines, inasmuch as they yield the latter upon treatment with reducing agents."

Leuco copper and nickel phthalocyanines may be made by the reaction of phthalonitrile with anhydrous ammonia and an anhydrous salt of the desired metal, at 60–90°, for from 10 to 40 hours in solvents such as methanol, ethanol, or Cellosolve, in the presence of methyl glucamine or urea.

For example, ammonia gas is passed into a mixture of nickel chloride and glycol monoethyl ether for two hours. Phthalonitrile and methyl glucamine are added and the reaction mass is heated to 60° with introduction of ammonia gas with stirring for 16 hours. The reaction mass is filtered hot and the filtrate is drowned in water. The leuco nickel phthalocyanine precipitate is filtered, washed with water, and air dried. It is dissolved in Cellosolve monoethyl ether of ethylene glycol. Cotton piece goods that have been swollen by boiling in water and in Cellosolve are padded with the leuco nickel phthalocyanine solution. The fabric is dried and boiled for 20 minutes in an aqueous solution of potassium ferrocyanide, followed by boiling in lactic acid solution and soaping for 20 minutes.   "Deep green-blue shades of good brightness are obtained. They are very fast to light and to crocking, and they exhibit good fastness to washing, including the application of bleaching agents such as sodium hypochlorite."

Brooks (42) offers another method to produce leuco copper phthalocyanine, starting from 1,3-diimino-isoindoline instead of from phthalonitrile.   For example, 1,3-diimino-isoindoline and cupric chloride are added to ethylene glycol monoethyl ether. The mixture is heated to and kept at 80° for 90 minutes. Ammonia is liberated during the first 60 minutes.   The reaction mass is filtered and the filtrate is drowned in cold water. The precipitate of leuco copper phthalocyanine is filtered, washed with water, and dried at room temperature. Reduction with ascorbic acid in boiling ethylene glycol monoethyl ether yields copper phthalocyanine.

Stevenson (222) increases the reaction rate of the process of Barnhart and Skiles by reduction in reaction time from 16 or more to 4 or less hours by contacting the reaction mass with oxygen gas in the form of air throughout the reaction period. "The explanation for the observed effect of oxygen is not clear to me." Stevenson also finds that the reaction system tolerates a limited amount of water, up to 8 per cent of the organic liquid used as solvent, such that hydrated as well as anhydrous copper salts may be used.

As an example of the Stevenson process improvement, cupric chloride is mixed with ethylene glycol monoethyl ether. Ammonia is passed into the mixture until it is saturated. Phthalonitrile and methyl glucamine are added and the reaction mass is stirred at 70–78° for one hour, during which time a stream of air is passed into the mixture. The insoluble residue that is produced is filtered off and washed with ethylene glycol monoethyl ether.   The combined filtrate and washings are drowned in water; the precipitated yellow-brown leuco copper phthalocyanine is filtered off, washed with water, and dried. The yield is twice as great as by the process not utilizing the air technique.

Perkins and Whelen (189) have broadened Stevenson's oxygen process improvement to liquid and solid oxidants such as hydrogen peroxide, mercuric oxide, aromatic nitrohydrocarbons, calcium hypochlorite, alkali metal nitrites, nitrates, ferricyanides, nitrobenzene sulfonates, and 2-anthraquinone sulfonates. "The advantages of our invention are that the quantity of oxidizing agent is easier to control than in the case of air, with the results that purer precursor products are obtained. The rate of reaction is more readily controllable, it being noted here that the synthesis of copper phthalocyanine precursor according to the general method of Barnhart and Skiles is an exothermic reaction. Where air and ammonia mixtures are employed or where such mixtures are formed in the reaction, danger exists that the effluent gasses will contribute an explosive mixture. This hazard is eliminated by our invention.''

For example, ammonia gas is passed into a mixture of dimethyl formamide and cupric chloride to saturation. Phthalonitrile and methyl glucamine are added; the reaction mass is heated to 81°. Aqueous hydrogen peroxide, dissolved in dimethyl formamide, is then added at 81–84° for 2 hours. The reaction mass is filtered and the filtrate is poured into water. The precipitated leuco copper phthalocyanine is filtered off, washed with water until free of dimethyl formamide, and dried.

Perkins (186) has further improved the process for the synthesis of leuco copper phthalocyanine by using an organic sulfoxide compound as solvent, such as dimethyl sulfoxide, diethyl sulfoxide, methylethyl sulfoxide, and tetramethylene sulfoxide.

For example, ammonia is passed into a mixture of dimethyl sulfoxide and copper sulfate for 2 hours at 25–40°. Phthalonitrile and methyl glucamine are added to the mixture; the reaction mass is agitated at 85–89° for 1.5–2 hours while air is bubbled through. The mixture is filtered hot to remove copper phthalocyanine; the filter cake is washed with dimethyl sulfoxide; the filtrate is drowned in water and the precipitate is recovered by filtration. The solid is washed with water and dried to give leuco copper phthalocyanine in excellent yields.

Perkins (187) has extended the sulfoxide solvent process improvement to include the preparation of leuco copper phthalocyanine from 1,3-diimino-isoindoline.

For example, a mixture of 1,3-diimino-isoindoline, cupric chloride, and dimethyl sulfoxide are heated, with agitation, at 75° for 2 hours. The temperature is increased to 91° over 1.5 hours and the reaction mass is filtered. Residual copper phthalocyanine on the filter is washed with dimethyl sulfoxide. The filtrate is drowned in water; the light tan precipitate is recovered by filtration. The solid is washed with water and dried to give an excellent yield of leuco copper phthalocyanine.

Whelen (246) has improved the properties of leuco copper phthalocyanine by making it stable toward atmospheric moisture. The unimproved product hydrolizes readily when in contact with moisture; it is amorphous and has a high surface area. Whelen obtains a crystalline product by drying the reaction product from a nonaqueous medium. ''To achieve this, the water-wet filter cake is slurried in a low boiling water-miscible alcohol such as methyl, ethyl or isopropyl, and is then dried at a temperature not exceeding 60°. In this process the reaction product is transformed into a crystalline form which can be readily distinguished from the aforementioned amorphous form both by its X-ray diffraction pattern and by its appearance under the microscope (both optical and electron).''

For example, a mixture of copper sulfate and dimethyl formamide is saturated with ammonia at below 40°. Phthalonitrile and methyl glucamine are added and the mixture is heated to 70°. Air is bubbled through while heating to 88° over 15 minutes and the bubbling is continued for 2 hours at 88–90°. The reaction mass is filtered and the filtrate is poured into cold water. The leuco copper phthalocyanine is precipitated and is filtered off. Residual soluble matter is removed by a water wash. The product appears to be amorphous when observed under an optical microscope. The filter cake is then slurried with methyl alcohol for 2 hours. The leuco copper phthalocyanine is filtered off, washed with methanol, and dried at 50° in vacuum. The product is tan colored crystalline leuco copper phthalocyanine.

Pedersen (185) and Zemp (256) have made use of the chemical properties of the leuco phthalocyanines in photography, in conjunction with reducing agents that can be activated by light. In Pedersen's work, "It has been found that photosensitive elements can be prepared by applying on the surface of a suitable support... an organic solvent solution of a solvent-soluble phthalocyanine intermediate complex (hereinafter sometimes referred to as a leuco-phthalocyanine) and a light-activatable reducing carboxylic acid or salt taken from the group consisting of oxalic acid and α-hydroxy-carboxylic acids and their alkali metal salts, e.g., sodium and potassium and their ammonium salts ... While the exact nature of the colorant-producing reaction is not known, it is believed that the weak reducing action of the reducing acid or salt is augmented by the ultraviolet light [portion of the incident light] to permit reduction of the leuco phthalocyanine ... The period of exposure will, of course, depend upon the intensity of the light source, the particular leuco-phthalocyanine and the particular reducing agent ... In general, a period of 0.1 to 10 minutes is required to give an image of satisfactory intensity" (185).

In Zemp's work the reducing agent is a light sensitive diazonium compound "which upon exposure to light yields a reducing agent taken from the group consisting of 1,2- and 1,4-aminohydroxybenzene and -dihydroxybenzene" (256).

Brooks (43) has extended the color range of the leuco phthalocyanine dyes by substitution of the phenylene hydrogen atoms with chlorine atoms, in the number of 10 to 20 per leuco phthalocyanine molecule. For instance, the cobalt leuco product obtained from tetrachlorophthalic anhydride yields cobalt hexadecachlorophthalocyanine which is noted for its strongly green shade.

Brooks (44) has also synthesized useful halogenated copper or nickel leuco phthalocyanines where the halogen atoms are chlorine or bromine, and where the leuco phthalocyanine contains 6 phthalonitrile units and from 6 to 12 halogen atoms per molecule.

Perkins, Oken, and Whelen (188) have extended the shade range of leuco phthalocyanine dyes by making "...novel precursor compounds of the copper and nickel phthalocyanine series...which distinguish from the copper and nickel precursors of Barnhart and Skiles by having phenyl as a substituent in at least one of the Bz [phenylene] rings, and by producing on the fiber dyes of shades varying from turquoise blue to green. The novel precursors are also distinguished by having only 5 phthalonitrile units in their complex formula as compared to the 6 units which characterize copper phthalocyanine precursor." The structural formula as written is (188):

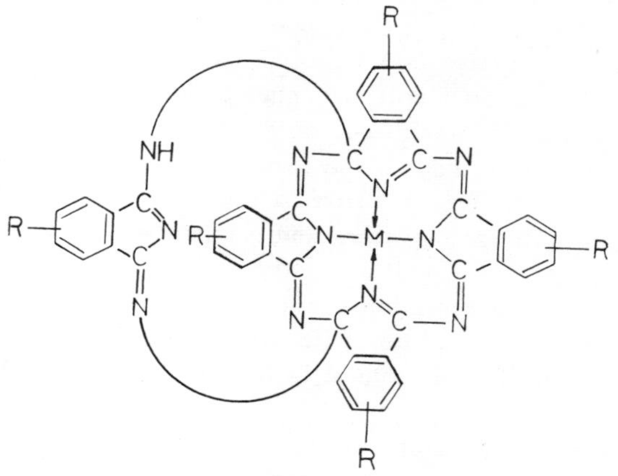

where M = copper or nickel and one of the R's stands for phenyl radical, C_6H_5, and the remaining R's represent hydrogen or phenyl.

The molecular formula for leuco copper pentaphenylphthalocyanine is $Cu(C_6H_5 \cdot C_8H_3N_2) 5 \cdot NH$.

As an example, a mixture of dimethyl formamide and anhydrous cupric chloride is saturated with ammonia gas at room temperature, followed by the addition of methyl glucamine and 4-phenylphthalonitrile. The mixture is heated at 80–85° for 2 hours with passage of air during this time. The reaction mass is filtered hot and is drowned in water. The leuco phthalocyanine precipitate is air dried and is printed on cotton giving '...attractive fast green prints of copper tetra-(4)-phenylphthalocyanine."

Rösch (201) has synthesized leuco sulfuric esters of anthraquinone derivatives of phthalocyanine dyes of the general formula:

$$\left[X—N—SO_2 \right]_n \left[Pc—SO_3H \right]_m$$
$$\quad\ \ \overset{|}{Y}$$

where   Pc = phthalocyanine radical
        X = leuco sulfuric ester of an anthraquinone radical
        Y = methyl or ethyl
        n = integer from 2 to 4
        m = integer from 2 to 0
    n + m = ≤ 4

The leuco sulfuric esters are insolubilized by splitting off the leuco
sulfuric groups such as by treatment with a mixture of sodium nitrite and
sulfuric acid. They may be produced by reacting phthalocyanine sulfonyl
chlorides containing from 2 to 4 sulfonyl chloride groups with leuco sulfonic
esters of anthraquinones which contain an amino group having at least 1
replaceable hydrogen atom, in the presence of a hydrogen chloride acceptor, such as carbonates and organic bases.

For example, the sodium salt of copper phthalocyanine tetra-4-sulfonic
acid is dissolved in chlorosulfonic acid. After stirring for 1 hour at 80-
90°, thionyl chloride is added; the temperature is maintained at 80° for
1–3 hours followed by precipitation on ice. The precipitate is filtered,
washed neutral with cold water, and suspended in water. β-Methyl-
aminoanthraquinone leuco sulfuric ester and barium carbonate are introduced into the suspension cooled to about 10°, followed by stirring for
12 hours at room temperature, filtration, and concentration. The dye
precipitated by addition of ethanol is filtered, washed with ethanol, and
dried.

"The leuco sulfuric ester very readily dissolves in water to give a
green-blue solution from which a clear, greenish blue pigment is precipitated by means of a mixture of sodium nitrite and sulfuric acid. When
applied to textiles by the usual methods for printing the dyestuff yields
bright, greenish blue shades."

CHROME DYES

Hoyer, Bayer, and Nadler (127) developed phthalocyanine chrome dyes
in 1942 by the reaction of phthalocyanine sulfonyl chlorides with aminosalicylic acid to form phthalocyanine o-hydroxy-carboxy-sulfonamides.

For example, a mixture of copper phthalocyanine tetrasulfonyl chloride,
5-amino-2-hydroxybenzoic acid, and sodium acetate in acetone is stirred
at room temperature for several hours. After completion of the reaction,
the solvent is distilled off, and the residue is dissolved in water, salted
out, filtered, and dried, yielding a blue powder soluble in water. This
compound contains at least one aminosalicylic acid group connected to a
sulfonic acid group. The remaining sulfonyl chloride groups are converted
to sulfonic acid groups during the reaction. "This product is capable of
being converted on the fiber into a chromium complex compound. The

dyeings thus produced are characterized by an excellent fastness to washing.''

Bienert, Baumann, and Groll (22) have broadened the series of phthalocyanine chrome dyes to include the reaction products of phthalocyanine sulfonyl chlorides and alkylaminosalicyclic acid, such as, for example, the reaction product of copper phthalocyanine 4-tetrasulfonyl chloride and a compound of the formula:

$$R' \quad R''$$

(structure of benzene ring bearing R', R'' on an N substituent, a COOR group, an OH group, and X)

where X = hydrogen or sulfo group
  R = hydrogen, monovalent metal, alkyl, or aryl group
  R' = hydrogen or alkyl group
  R'' = alkyl group

The resulting dyes "... are characterized by their clear color shade, their very good lightfastness properties and their excellent dyeing properties. They are taken up as chrome dyes. The colors of the finally dyed or printed fabrics are very uniform, very fast to rubbing and are often fast to finishing operations.''

The hydroxybenzyl group of phthalocyanine dyes developed by Jones (140) may be used as chrome dyes "... by the use of salicylic acid as the phenol.''

The o-hydroxy-carboxyphenyl esters of phthalocyanine tetrasulfonic acids are not only water soluble dyes but also may be used as chrome dyes (38).

"Owing to the presence of at least one, and preferably several salicylic acid groups in the dyestuff molecule it is possible to fix the dyestuffs on the fibre in the form of chromium lakes by known methods.

"The new dyestuffs are especially suitable for chrome printing on cotton. The mordant character of the phthalocyanine dyestuffs of the invention increases as the number of salicylic acid groups increases, and this is clearly evident from the increasing improvement in the properties of wet fastness.

"Blue to green dyeings are produced which are in part distinguished by remarkable properties of wet fastness and excellent fastness to light.''

Chrome dyes (21) that show good fastness to washing are made by the reaction at up to 100° of a phthalocyanine sulfonyl chloride, which contains at least one phenylsulfone group per molecule of phthalocyanine and at least one sulfonyl chloride group in one phenylsulfone group, with an aromatic amino-o-hydroxy-carboxylic acid.

Neufang, Rabe, Bienert, and Baumann (171) improve light, moisture, and washfastness in the dyeing and printing of cellulose materials with phthalocyanine dyes in the presence of chromium salts, especially chromium triacetate or chromium trifluoride, in neutral and acid media. For example, dyeing cotton in a solution of a reaction product of phthalocyanine sulfonyl chloride with 5-(2-aminoethyl)-2-hydroxy-3-sulfobenzoic acid or its derivative with addition of chromium triacetate and Glauber's salt, and heating the solution to 95°, gives clear blue dyeings.

PRECURSOR DYES

In a series of patents starting in 1954, Baumann, Bienert, Rösch, Wolf, and Vollmann (14,15,206–210,244) have described techniques for producing phthalocyanine colors in the fiber itself. The first patent (14) consists of 58 pages and contains 92 examples. In general, derivatives of isoindolenine are impregnated in the fiber, followed by chemical and heat treatments that convert the phthalocyanine intermediates to phthalocyanines.

For example, a mixture of amino-imino-isoindolenine, glycol, copper chloride, dimethyl formamide, and water is prepared in which cotton is dyed for 15 minutes at 40–50°. "The material is squeezed off, pre-dried in the air and the copper phthalocyanine is produced by heating at about 120°C. Development may also be performed immediately after dyeing while the dyed goods are still moist. Beautiful, clear shades of excellent fastness properties are obtained."

Chlorine-bearing isoindolenines may also be used as dye intermediates for pigment formation within the fabric (244). The reaction between phthalimide and phosphorous pentachloride gives 1-chloro-3-oxo-isoindolenine and 1,3,3-trichloro-isoindolenine.

Also, isoindolenine nitrates (206) may be prepared for use as phthalocyanine intermediates.

For example, phthalic anhydride is heated with stirring at 150–160° for 20 hours with urea, ammonium nitrate, and ammonium molybdate, forming amino-imino-isoindolenine nitrate which is purified with a water wash.

Other isoindolenine derivatives that have been prepared (207–210) include

where   X = H or from 0 to 4 organic or inorganic radicals, for instance alkyl, alkoxy, aroxy, alkyl mercapto, and aryl
mercapto radicals, heterocyclic radicals, halogen, acyl,
—NO₂, —COOH—SO₃H, —SO₂NH₂, and other groups,
such as one or two cyclic groups condensed to the benzene nucleus of the isoindolenine.

$R_1, R_2,$ and R_3 = hydrogen, organic or inorganic radicals, such as alkyl,
alkylene, aryl, and other polycyclic radicals.

Also, one or more of the carbon atoms of the carbocyclic nucleus may
be replaced by hetero atoms such as nitrogen or sulfur atoms.

For example (207), phthalonitrile is dissolved at 110° in monoethanolamine. After solidification the reaction mass is ground and washed with
ethanol. 1-Oxoethylamino-3-oxoethylimino-isoindolenine is obtained.

As another example (209), phthalimide, urea, sodium naphthalene-1-
sulfonate, and ammonium molybdate are stirred into a solution of sulfuric
acid, heated to 150–160° while distilling off the water, and stirred for
20 hours at this temperature. The cooled reaction mass is mixed with
methanol, precipitating out sodium sulfate and a part of the amino-imino-
isoindolenine naphthalene-1-sulfonate: this part is filtered off and the
sodium sulfate is washed away with water. The filtrate containing
methanol is stirred into ice, the sodium salt of naphthalene-1-sulfonic
acid and glacial acetic acid. The reaction product dissolved in methanol
precipitates as amino-imino-isoindolenine naphthalene-1-sulfonate.

1-Alkoxy-3-imino-isoindolenines (15) have also been prepared. "They
are valuable intermediate products for the production of phthalocyanines
on the fiber as it is described in (14)...."

For example, phthalonitrile is introduced into a solution of sodium in
methanol at room temperature. After stirring for 3 hours at room temperature, the solution is cooled to −10°, sucked off, the precipitated methoxy-
imino-isoindolenine is washed with methanol, and dried at room temperature. "The product consists of brilliant, almost colorless small prisms
which decompose at 132–134°C. with the generation of gas and the formation of a yellow green melt." More than 100 additional examples are
given (207–210).

France (77) in his preparation of phthalocyanine-type compounds from
dinitriles such as dimethylfumaric dinitrile, dimethylmaleic dinitrile,
Δ¹-tetrahydrophthalonitrile, and citraconic dinitrile, stated that the intermediates of these compounds "... can be applied from solution to textile
materials or paper or other substrates and then heated in the presence or
absence of metals to form metal or metal-free tetra-aza-porphin colouring
matters *in situ* on the substrate. By the use of our new intermediates it
is thus possible to obtain the valuable fast colourations characteristic
of the tetra-aza-porphins on a variety of substrates especially textile

materials which could not hitherto be satisfactorily coloured with tetra-aza-porphins.''

France, Haddock, Parkinson, Wood, and Woods (78) have prepared phthalocyanine precursor dyes based on 1-imino-3-alkylmercaptoisoindolenines which can be applied to a substrate and converted to a phthalocyanine *in situ* on the substrate. The intermediates are prepared by treating an iminothiophthalimidine with an alkylating agent, such as dimethyl sulfate and diethyl sulfate, in dilute caustic soda solution. The iminothiophthalimidine is obtained by treating phthalonitrile with sodium sulfide in ethanol. The precursors, of the formula

are applied to textiles by padding or printing and are heated, if desired in the presence of a metal compound, to form a phthalocyanine *in situ*.

Dach (56) dyes cellulose fibers with phthalocyanine intermediates according to German Patent 914,250. A paste is made with diethylene glycol, from which a solution is made with glacial acetic acid. Water is added and cotton fiber penetrated with tannin and tartar emetic or sulfonated chlorophenols is immersed in the solution. The fiber is rinsed, held in boiling water, developed in one-half hour, placed in a bath of hydrochloric acid for 10 minutes at 60–70°, soaped, and treated with sodium carbonate.

Fischer (72) prints precursor phthalocyanine colors on textiles with a paste of phthalodinitrile, sodium sulfide, formamide, piperidine, and methyl cellulose. The printed fabric is dried and heated for 15 minutes at 110°. Then the fabric is led through boiling acetic acid to give a rubfast blue-gray print. Hot methanol changes the color to clear blue of excellent light-, rub-, and washfastness. Treatment with copper sulfate intensifies the color.

Eibl (62) uses the precursor technique for white and colored resists. For example, 3-imino-isoindolenine is dissolved in a solution of tertiary amines, aminoalcohols, and glycols, and diluted with water. The material to be dyed is immersed in the solution and dried. The white or colored resist is printed and redried. After immersion in a 5–10 per cent copper solution and drying, the goods are steamed to develop the color.

A process (71) is described for the production of white and colored discharges on textile materials dyed with phthalocyanines by application to the materials of a discharge paste containing a reducing agent and in the case of colored discharge effects a vat dye and phthalocyanines containing at least one hydrophilic radical such as sulfonic acid, carboxylic acid, hydroxyl or mercapto group, sulfonic acid amide, or carboxylic acid amide group.

For example, a textile fabric dyed with the blue copper phthalocyanine tetra-4-sulfomonoethylamide is locally discharged with a printing paste, for white discharges, consisting of an alkaline reducing agent "Rongalite C", potassium carbonate, anthraquinone paste, sodium hydroxide solution, wheat starch-tragacanth thickening, and zinc oxide in water, and for color discharges with vat dyes, consisting of "Rongalite C", anthraquinone paste, vat dye paste, thickening, potassium carbonate, glycerol, and water. "The discharging pastes are printed in conventional manner on the fabric dyed with the bottoming dyestuff and subsequently steamed in usual manner." The bottom dyeing may be made with a padding liquor that contains copper phthalocyanine tetra-4-sulfomonomethylamide, binder, acetic acid, ammonium nitrate, and water. "The fabric impregnated with the padding liquor is dried and the dyestuff fixed by heating to 140°C. for 5 minutes."

S-TRIAZINE DYES

A new group of water soluble phthalocyanine direct dyes of good wash-fastness are the s-triazine phthalocyanines.

Barker, Heslop, Poole, and Stephen (9) have succeeded to make phthalocyanine dyes containing s-triazine groups such as 2,4-di-(2'-sulfo-4'-methylphenoxy)-6-(2''-sulfo-5''-[4'''-sulfo copper phthalocyanine-4'''-sulfonamido]anilino)-s-triazine; 2,4-di-(6',8'-disulfo-2'-naphthylthio-6-(2''-sulfo-5''-[4'''-sulfo copper phthalocyanine-4'''-sulfonamido]-anilino)-s-triazine; and 2,4-di(4'-chlorophenylthio)-6-(2''-sulfo-5''-[4'''-sulfo copper phthalocyanine-4'''-sulfonamido]-anilino)-s-triazine. These phthalocyanine s-triazine dyes are water soluble and produce bright greenish blue to reddish blue dyeings of good fastness to washing. "... direct dyestuffs as a class do not have very good fastness to severe washing treatments as compared with vat dyestuffs and other temporarily solubilised dyestuffs.

"The basis of the present invention resides in the observation that certain new water-soluble s-triazine compounds have the valuable property that they may be used to colour cellulosic textile materials in shades having an excellent fastness to severe washing treatments approaching, and in most cases equalling, the wash-fastness properties of vat dyestuffs, provided that the colouration process is carried out in conjunction with a treatment with an alkaline substance."

For example, copper phthalocyanine tetra-4-sulfonic acid is heated with chlorosulfonic acid at 115° for 4 hours. The solution is cooled to 20° and is drowned in ice water at below 2° and the suspension is filtered at 0°. The filter cake is suspended in ice water and is washed to neutrality with sodium carbonate. Sodium bicarbonate and a neutral aqueous solution of 2,4-diaminobenzenesulfonic acid are added and the mixture is agitated for 16 hours at 20–25°. The suspension is acidified with concentrated hydrochloric acid, the precipitate is filtered off, washed with 2N hydrochloric acid, and dried, giving copper phthalocyanine 4-N-(3'-amino-4'-sulfophenyl)-sulfonamide-4-sulfonic acid. This substance is dissolved in water and sodium carbonate is added to pH 7. The potassium salt of 2-chloro-4,6-di-(2'-sulfo-4'-methylphenoxy)-s-triazine is added and the mixture is stirred at 80° at pH 7 until the reaction is complete. Sodium chloride is added and the precipitated dye is filtered off, washed with saturated brine, and dried. The product "... gives greenish blue dyeings of good fastness to washing," by padding in an aqueous solution containing caustic soda and sodium chloride. The fabric is steamed for a minute, rinsed in water, boiled in dilute soap solution for 5 minutes, rinsed in water, and dried.

The potassium salt of 2-chloro-4,6-di-(2'-sulfo-4'-methylphenoxy)-s-triazine is obtained by adding a solution of cyanuric chloride in acetone to a solution of the potassium salt of 2-sulfo-4-methylphenol in water at 0–5°. An aqueous solution of potassium hydroxide is added with agitation. The mixture is heated at 25° for 1 hour. Potassium chloride is added and the precipitate is filtered off and dried.

Pütter, Dorlars, and Enders (195) have prepared water soluble direct dyes of the general formula:

$$\left[Pc \!-\! SO_2NH \!-\! C \underset{\underset{N}{\displaystyle N}}{\overset{\displaystyle N}{\diagdown\diagup}} \underset{N}{\overset{C-X}{}} C \!-\! Y \right]_n$$

where X = halogen atom
       Y = halogen atom or hydroxyl group
       n = integer from 1 to 4

The new dyes are prepared by reacting phthalocyanines having at least one and not more than four sulfonamide groups with trihalo-triazines, particularly cyanuric chloride. The sulfonamide group is substituted by the triazine radical with the splitting off of hydrogen halide. In an alkaline medium one of the two remaining halogen atoms is replaced by a hydroxyl group.

"Under suitable conditions the new dyestuffs yield dyeings and prints of excellent fastness to washing on various animal, vegetable and synthetic textile materials.... Presumably, the dyestuffs enter into a chemical bond with reactive groups of the various fibres via the triazine ring with the splitting off of hydrogen halide. The linkage with wool and polyamide fibres probably takes place via amino groups and to cellulose materials via hydroxyl groups."

Clark, Howard, and Wardleworth (52,53) have also prepared compounds of the type

$$\left[Pc \!-\! ZNR \!-\! \underset{\underset{\displaystyle N}{\big\|}}{\overset{\displaystyle X}{\underset{\displaystyle}{C}}} \begin{smallmatrix} N \\ \\ N \end{smallmatrix} C \!-\! Y \right]_n$$

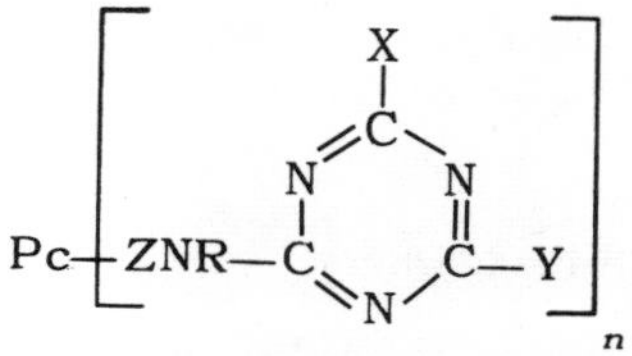

where Z = —SO$_2$—, —CO—, —CH$_2$—, —phenylene—, or at least 21
      other radicals

R = hydrogen, alkyl, aralkyl, or cycloalkyl

X = halogen atom

Y = halogen atom or O—B, where B is a hydrocarbon radical or
      substituted hydrocarbon radical

n = integer

The dyes are stated to have an excellent fastness to washing, are blue to green in color, and may dye both animal and vegetable fibers. They are prepared from phthalocyanine sulfonamides and trihalotriazines such as cyanuric chloride.

Koller prepared compounds of the type (142)

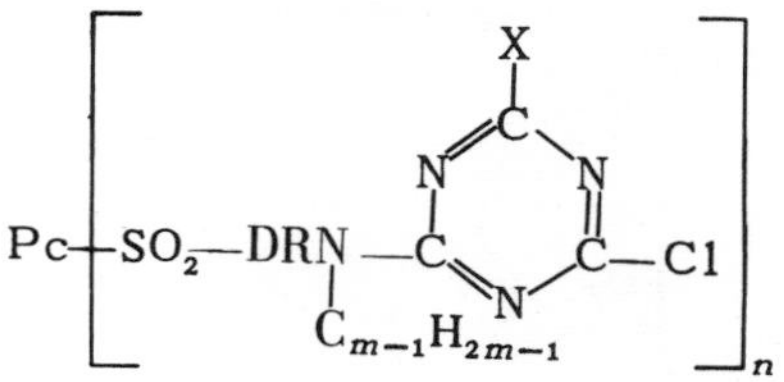

$$\left[Pc \!-\! SO_2 \!-\! DR\underset{\underset{\displaystyle C_{m-1}H_{2m-1}}{\big|}}{N} \!-\! \overset{\displaystyle X}{C} \begin{smallmatrix} N \\ \\ N \end{smallmatrix} C \!-\! Cl \right]_n$$

where D = —O— or azo bridge

R = bivalent organic bridge

X = Cl, ether or amino group

m = an integer

n = number not greater than 4.

They are prepared from trihalotriazines such as cyanuric chloride and phthalocyanine sulfonamides. They are water soluble and are especially useful in coloring polyhydroxy fibers such as regenerated cellulose, viscose, and cotton, as well as synthetic fibers.

Novel phthalocyanine sulfonamides of the formula (135)

have recently been described, where

Y = hydrogen or halogen atom, methyl or alkoxy group
X = hydrogen atom or sulfonic acid group
R_1 = hydrogen atom or alkyl radical
R_2 = hydrogen atom or alkyl radical
R_3 = hydrogen atom or hydroxyalkyl radical

The new dyes impart bright greenish blue colors to cotton, rayon, regenerated cotton, and linen.

New phthalocyanine derivatives (137) of the formula

where R_1 = hydrogen atom or hydrocarbon radical
R_2 = hydrocarbon radical
R_3, R_4 = hydrogen atom, cycloalkyl radical or alkyl radical
Y = bivalent group
X = halogen atom
Z = halogen atom or amino group
a, b, c = 1 or 2; $a + b + c \leq 4$
are useful cellulose dyes in the greenish blue range.

For example, copper phthalocyanine 3-sulfon-*N*-(3′-aminophenyl) amide-sulfon-dimethylamide sulfonic acid is prepared by addition of copper phthalocyanine to chlorosulfonic acid, followed by mixing for 3 hours at 140–145°. The mixture is cooled to 80°; thionyl chloride is added, and the mixture is agitated for 2 hours at 85°, followed by cooling to 20°, pouring on ice, and filtration of the precipitated sulfonyl chloride phthalocyanine, washing in dilute hydrochloric acid, and cooling to 0°. Water, ice, and *m*-amino-acetanilide are added. An aqueous solution of dimethylamine is added to pH 8; the mixture is agitated and heated to 50°. Concentrated hydrochloric acid is added, the mixture is stirred for 4 hours at 90°, cooled to 20°, and the precipitate is filtered, washed with hydrochloric acid, and dried. The copper phthalocyanine 3-sulfon-*N*-(3′-aminophenyl) amide-sulfon-dimethylamide sulfonic acid is slurried in water. Sodium hydroxide solution is added to pH 7. The solution is cooled to 0–5° and a solution of cyanuric chloride in acetone is added. The mixture is stirred for 30 minutes at 0–5° while maintaining the pH between 6.5 and 7.0 by addition of sodium carbonate. Disodium phosphate, monopotassium phosphate, and sodium chloride are added. The precipitate is filtered, mixed with disodium phosphate and monopotassium phosphate, and dried. The dye provides brilliant greenish blue shades possessing excellent washfastness.

REFERENCES

1. Badische Anilin- & Soda-Fabrik A.-G., British Patent 679,808 (Sept. 24, 1952).
2. *Ibid.*, British Patent 681,873 (Oct. 29, 1952).
3. *Ibid.*, British Patent 688,784 (Mar. 11, 1953).
4. *Ibid.*, British Patent 688,786 (Mar. 11, 1953).
5. *Ibid.*, British Patent 694,072 (July 15, 1953).
6. *Ibid.*, British Patent 809,224 (Feb. 18, 1959); German Patent 1,039,163 (Sept. 18, 1958).
7. *Ibid.*, British Patent 827,568 (Feb. 10, 1960).
8. *Ibid.*, British Patent 827,569 (Feb. 10, 1960).
9. Barker, P. W., Heslop, R. N., Poole, V. D., and Stephen, W. E. (to Imperial Chemical Industries Ltd.), U. S. Patent 2,978,289 (Apr. 4, 1961).
10. Barnhart, G., and Skiles, B. F. (to E. I. du Pont de Nemours & Co.), U. S. Patent 2,772,284 (Nov. 27, 1956); British Patent 745,359 (Feb. 22, 1956).
11. Baumann, F., and Bienert, B. (to Farbenfabriken Bayer A.-G.), U. S. Patent 2,613,128 (Oct. 7, 1952); British Patent 704,310 (Feb. 17, 1954).
12. *Ibid.*, U. S. Patent 2,756,119 (July 24, 1956).
13. *Ibid.*, German Patent 839,939 (May 26, 1952); U. S. Patent 2,768,867 (Oct. 30, 1956); British Patent 687,655 (Feb. 18, 1953).
14. Baumann, F., Bienert, B., and Rösch, G. (to Farbenfabriken Bayer A.-G.), U. S. Patent 2,683,643 (July 13, 1954); British Patent 698,039 (Oct. 7, 1953); French Patent 1,023,765 (Mar. 24, 1953); German Patent 888,837 (Sept. 3, 1953).

15. *Ibid.*, U. S. Patent 2,778,819 (Jan. 22, 1957); British Patent 698,070 (Oct. 7, 1953).

16. Baumann, F., Bienert, B., and Vollmann, H. (to Farbenfabriken Bayer A.-G.), German Patent 899,698 (Dec. 14, 1953).

17. Baumann, F., Bienert, B., Vollmann, H., and Rösch, G. (to Farbenfabriken Bayer A.-G.), U. S. Patent 2,897,039 (July 28, 1959); British Patent 759,377 (Oct. 17, 1956).

18. Bienert, B. (to General Aniline Works, Inc.), U. S. Patent 2,133,340 (Oct. 18, 1938); British Patent 481,134 (Mar. 7, 1938); German Patent 737,942 (July 30, 1943).

19. Bienert, B., and Baumann, F. (to Farbenfabriken Bayer A.-G.), U. S. Patent 2,863,875 (Dec. 9, 1958).

20. *Ibid.*, British Patent 784,843 (Oct. 16, 1957); German Patent 1,061,010 (July 9, 1959); German Patent 1,064,661 (Sept. 3, 1959); Swiss Patent 349,728 (Dec. 15, 1960).

21. Bienert, B., Baumann, F., and Burneleit, W. (to Farbenfabriken Bayer A.-G.), British Patent 713,397 (Aug. 11, 1954); German Patent 906,966 (Mar. 18, 1954); Swiss Patent 310,506 (Dec. 16, 1955).

22. Bienert, B., Baumann, F., and Groll, M. (to Farbenfabriken Bayer A.-G.), U. S. Patent 2,843,599 (July 15, 1958); British Patent 785,629 (Oct. 30, 1957); German Patent 1,028,719 (Apr. 24, 1958).

23. Bienert, B., Baumann, F., and Vollmann, H. (to Farbenfabriken Bayer A.-G.), German Patent 935,567 (Nov. 24, 1955).

24. *Ibid.*, U. S. Patent 2,824,109 (Feb. 18, 1958).

25. Bienert, B., Breig, K., and Groll, M. (to Farbenfabriken Bayer A.-G.), U. S. Patent 2,873,280 (Feb. 10, 1959); British Patent 811,221 (Apr. 2, 1959); German Patent 1,066,305 (Oct. 1, 1959).

26. Bienert, B. (deceased—heirs), Breig, K., Groll, M. (to Farbenfabriken Bayer A.-G.), U. S. Patent 3,013,006 (Dec. 12, 1961); Swiss Patent 354,191 (June 30, 1961).

27. Bienert, B., Breig, K., Groll, M., and Gutjahr, H. (to Farbenfabriken Bayer A.-G.), Belgium Patent 566,956 (Oct. 20, 1958); Canadian Patent 628,076 (Sept. 26, 1961); British Patent 844,419 (Aug. 10, 1960); Austrian Patent 204,146 (June 25, 1959).

28. Bienert, B., and Gassner, S. (to General Aniline & Film Corp.), U. S. Patent 2,213,517 (Sept. 3, 1940).

29. *Ibid.*, U. S. Patent 2,280,507 (Apr. 21, 1942).

30. Bienert, B., and Hansen, K. (to Farbenfabriken Bayer A.-G.), German Patent 891,309 (Sept. 28, 1953).

31. Bienert, B., and Holzach, K. (to General Aniline Works, Inc.), U. S. Patent 2,135,633 (Nov. 8, 1938).

32. Bienert, B., and Thielert, H. (to I. G. Farbenindustrie A.-G.), German Patent 698,462 (Nov. 11, 1940); Italian Patent 374, 909 (Sept. 15, 1939).

33. *Ibid.* (to General Aniline & Film Corp.), U. S. Patent 2,266,404 (Dec. 16, 1941).

34. *Ibid.*, U. S. Patent 2,276,918 (Mar. 17, 1942); German Patent 728,931 (Dec. 8, 1942).

35. Bradbrook, E. F., Coffey, S., and Haddock, N. H. (to Imperial Chemical Industries Ltd.), U. S. Patent 2,277,628 (Mar. 24, 1942).

36. Bradbrook, E. F., Heilbron, I. M., Hey, D. H., and Haworth, J. W. (to Imperial Chemical Industries Ltd.), U. S. Patent 2,277,629 (Mar. 24, 1942).

37. Braun, W. (to Badische Anilin- & Soda-Fabrik A.-G.), British Patent 680,511 (Oct. 8, 1952); German Patent 825,866 (Dec. 20, 1951).

38. Brentano, W. (to Durand & Huguenin A.-G.), U. S. Patent 2,706,199 (Apr. 12, 1955); British Patent 768,444 (Feb. 20, 1957)· German Patent 939,827 (Mar. 1, 1956).

39. Brentano, W., Grossmann, H., and Müller, M. (to Durand & Huguenin A.-G.), U. S. Patent 2,776,957 (Jan. 8, 1957); British Patent 763,343 (Dec. 12, 1956); Swiss Patents 307,327 (Aug. 1, 1955), 309,438–52 (Nov. 1, 1955).

40. Brentano, W., (to Durand & Huguenin A.-G.), U. S. Patent 2,776,958 (Jan. (Jan. 31, 1956), 312,914–9 (Apr. 14, 1956), and 314,551–2 (July 31, 1956); French Patent 1,072,608 (Sept. 26, 1960).

41. Brooks, R. A. (to E. L du Pont de Nemours & Co.), U. S. Patent 2,681,348 (June 15, 1954).

42. *Ibid.*, U. S. Patent 2,772,285 (Nov. 27, 1956); British Patent 748,854 (May 9, 1956).

43. *Ibid.*, U. S. Patent 2,782,208 (Feb. 19, 1957).

44. *Ibid.*, U. S. Patent 2,980,691 (Apr. 18, 1961).

45. Bruck, W. (to L G. Farbenindustrie A.-G.), German Patent 696,592 (Sept. 25, 1940).

46. Buc, S. R. (to General Aniline & Film Corp.), U. S. Patent 2,647,908 (Aug. 4, 1953).

47. Bucher, A. (to Ciba Ltd.), U. S. Patent 2,492,732 (Dec. 27, 1949); British Patent 649,652 (Jan. 31, 1951).

48. Carleton, P. W., and Woodward, H. E. (to E. L du Pont de Nemours & Co.), U. S. Patent 2,153,740 (Apr. 11, 1939).

49. Cassella Farbwerke Mainkur A.-G., French Patent 1,237,961 (Aug. 7, 1958); British Patent 884,714 (Dec. 13, 1961); Austrian Patent 212,469 (Dec. 27, 1960).

50. Chechak, J. J., and Allen, C. F. H. (to Eastman Kodak Co.), U. S. Patent 2,600,377 (June 17, 1952); British Patent 665,006 (Jan. 16, 1952).

51. Ciba Ltd., French Patent 1,241,440 (Aug. 8, 1960).

52. Clark, P. F., Howard, H. T., and Wardleworth, J. (to Imperial Chemical Industries Ltd.), British Patent 805,562 (Dec. 10, 1958); Swiss Patent 353,828 (June 15, 1961).

53. *Ibid.*, British Patent 836,647 (June 9, 1960); Belgium Patent 570,101 (Feb. 5, 1959).

54. Clarke, W., Keats, G. H., Thornton, R., and Wood, C. (to Imperial Chemical Industries Ltd.), U. S. Patent 2,768,171 (Oct. 23, 1956).

55. Coffey, S., Haddock, N. H., and Jackson, J. R. F. (to Imperial Chemical Industries Ltd.), U. S. Patent 2,290,906 (July 28, 1942); British Patent 525,237 (Aug. 23, 1940).

56. Dach, B. (to Farbenfabriken Bayer A.-G.), German Patent 1,044,758 (Nov. 27, 1958).

57. Dawson, T. L. (to Imperial Chemical Industries Ltd.), U. S. Patent 2,955,900 (Oct. 11, 1960).

58. Dent, C. E. (to Imperial Chemical Industries Ltd.), U. S. Patent 2,166,240 (July 18, 1939); British Patent 494,738 (Oct. 31, 1938); French Patent 837,402 (Feb. 9, 1959).

59. Dortmann, H. A., and Schmitz, P. (to Farbenfabriken Bayer A.-G.), French Patent 1,256,707 (Feb. 13, 1961).

60. Douglas, G. T., Parkinson, A., and Wakefield, H. (to Imperial Chemical Industries Ltd.), British Patent 603,753 (June 22, 1948).

61. Eckert, W., and Quint, F. (to General Aniline & Film Corp.), U. S. Patent 2,200,689 (May 14, 1940).
62. Eibl, J. (to Farbenfabriken Bayer A.-G.), German Patent 1,007,733 (Oct. 17, 1957).
63. Eisele, J., Federkiel, W., Plankenhorn, E., and Zell, R. (to Badische Anilin- & Soda-Fabrik A.-G.), German Patent 955,858 (Jan. 10, 1957).
64. Eisele, J., Federkiel, W., and Tartter, A. (to Badische Anilin- & Soda-Fabrik A.-G.), German Patent 1,054,059 (Apr. 2, 1959).
65. Eisele, J., Federkiel, W., Tartter, A., Lange, G., Krehbiel, G., and Stein, H. W. (to Badische Anilin- & Soda-Fabrik A.-G.), British Patent 858,737 (Jan. 11, 1961); German Patent 1,069,565 (Nov. 26, 1959).
66. Erbe, F. (to Farbwerke Hoechst A.-G.), German Patent 1,017,720 (Oct. 17, 1957).
67. Farbenfabriken Bayer A.-G., British Patent 687,655 (Feb. 18, 1953).
68. *Ibid.*, British Patent 713,459 (Aug. 11, 1954).
69. *Ibid.*, British Patent 830,920 (Mar. 23, 1960).
70. *Ibid.*, British Patent 877,894 (Sept. 20, 1961).
71. *Ibid.*, British Patent 882,208 (Nov. 15, 1961).
72. Fischer, H. (to Badische Anilin- & Soda-Fabrik A.-G.), German Patent 927,808 (May 16, 1955).
73. Fleischhauer, R. (to Cassella Farbwerke Mainkur A.-G.), British Patent 874,355 (Aug. 2, 1961); German Patent 1,095,429 (Dec. 22, 1960).
74. Fox, A. L. (to E. I. du Pont de Nemours & Co.), U. S. Patent 2,369,666 (Feb. 20, 1945).
75. *Ibid.*, (to General Aniline & Film Corp.), U. S. Patent 2,413,224 (Dec. 24, 1946); British Patent 613,782 (Dec. 2, 1948).
76. *Ibid.*, U. S. Patent 2,459,771 (Jan. 18, 1949); British Patent 614,407 (Dec. 15, 1948).
77. France, H. (to Imperial Chemical Industries Ltd.), British Patent 730,467 (May 25, 1955).
78. France, H., Haddock, N. H., Parkinson, A., Wood, C., and Woods, J. C. (to Imperial Chemical Industries Ltd.), British Patent 731,257 (June 8, 1955).
79. Fukada, N., *Nippon Kagaku Zasshi*, **75**, 378–80 (1954).
80. *Ibid.*, 1141–3.
81. *Ibid.*, **76**, 1378–81 (1955).
82. *Ibid.*, **79**, 396–9 (1958).
83. *Ibid.*, 980–3.
84. Gassner, S., and Bienert, B. (to General Aniline & Film Corp.), U. S. Patent 2,116,196 (May 3, 1938); German Patent 675,964 (May 22, 1939).
85. *Ibid.*, U. S. Patent 2,197,860 (Apr. 23, 1940); French Patent 830,909 (Aug. 12, 1938).
86. Geigy A.-G., French Patent 1,227,999 (Aug. 26, 1960).
87. *Ibid.*, British Patent 876,691 (Sept. 6, 1961); French Patent 1,229,389 (Sept. 6, 1960).
88. General Aniline & Film Corp., British Patent 779,324 (July 17, 1957).
89. Gottlieb, H. B. (to E. I. du Pont de Nemours & Co.), U. S. Patent 2,801,997 (Aug. 6, 1957).
90. Gund, F., *J. Soc. Dyers & Colourists*, **69**, 671–82 (1953).
91. Gutzwiller, E. (to Sandoz Ltd.), U. S. Patent 2,456,274 (Dec. 14, 1948); British Patent 588,231 (May 16, 1947); Swiss Patent 269,707 (Oct. 16, 1950).

92. *Ibid.*, U. S. Patent 2,465,089 (Mar. 22, 1949); British Patent 629,488 (Sept. 21, 1949); Swiss Patents 286,758–67 (Mar. 2, 1953).

93. Haddock, N. H. (to Imperial Chemical Industries Ltd.), British Patent 530,881 (Dec. 24, 1940).

94. *Ibid.*, U. S. Patent 2,280,072 (Apr. 21, 1942).

95. *Ibid.*, U. S. Patent 2,342,662 (Feb. 29, 1944); British Patent 541,146 (Nov. 14, 1941).

96. *Ibid.*, U. S. Patent 2,342,663 (Feb. 29, 1944); British Patent 544,953 (May 5, 1942).

97. *Ibid.*, U. S. Patent 2,349,089 (May 16, 1944).

98. *Ibid.*, U. S. Patent 2,349,090 (May 16, 1944).

99. *Ibid.*, U. S. Patent 2,349,091 (May 16, 1944).

100. *Ibid.*, U. S. Patent 2,351,118 (June 13, 1944).

101. *Ibid.*, U. S. Patent 2,351,119 (June 13, 1944).

102. *Ibid.*, U. S. Patent 2,395,117 (Feb. 19, 1946).

103. Haddock, N. H., Jones, W. O., Page, J. K., and Wilkinson, D. G. (to Imperial Chemical Industries Ltd.), British Patent 633,478 (Dec. 19, 1949).

104. Haddock, N. H., Jones, W. O., Parkinson, A., and Rowe, G. A. (to Imperial Chemical Industries Ltd.), U. S. Patent 2,430,052 (Nov. 4, 1947); British Patent 589,118 (June 11, 1947).

105. *Ibid.*, U. S. Patent 2,479,491 (Aug. 16, 1949).

106. Haddock, N. H., Parkinson, A., and Rowe, G. A. (to Imperial Chemical Industries Ltd.), U. S. Patent 2,414,374 (Jan. 14, 1947); British Patent 569,200 (May 11, 1945).

107. Haddock, N. H., Slinger, F. H., and Wood, C. (to Imperial Chemical Industries Ltd.), British Patent 686,391 (Jan. 21, 1953); German Patent 869,105 (Mar. 2, 1953).

108. Haddock, N. H., and Wood, C. (to Imperial Chemical Industries Ltd.), U. S. Patent 2,416,386 (Feb. 25, 1947); British Patent 566,740 (Jan. 11, 1945).

109. *Ibid.*, U. S. Patent 2,416,387 (Feb. 25, 1947); British Patent 566,741 (Jan. 566,741 (Jan. 11, 1945).

110. *Ibid.*, U. S. Patent 2,435,307 (Feb. 3, 1948); British Patent 586,340 (Mar. 14, 1947).

111. *Ibid.*, U. S. Patent 2,464,806 (Mar. 22, 1949); British Patent 587,636 (May 1, 1947).

112. *Ibid.*, U. S. Patent 2,482,172 (Sept. 20, 1949); British Patent 619,035 (Mar. 2, 1949).

113. *Ibid.*, U. S. Patent 2,542,327 (Feb. 20, 1951).

114. *Ibid.*, U. S. Patent 2,542,328 (Feb. 20, 1951).

115. Harris, J. F., and Marrable, C. D. (to Imperial Chemical Industries Ltd.), British Patent 844,338 (Aug. 10, 1960).

116. Harrison, A. A., and Samuels, H. (to Imperial Chemical Industries Ltd.), U. S. Patent 2,150,741 (Mar. 14, 1939); French Patent 807,052 (Jan. 4, 1937).

117. Hartmann, E., and Moll, F. (to General Aniline Works, Inc.), U. S. Patent 2,187,816 (Jan. 23, 1940).

118. Hashimoto, S., and Isaka, Y., *Dōshisha Kôgaku Kaishi*, **8**, 130–4 (1957).

119. Heslop, R. N., Legg, N., Mawson, J. F., Stephen, W. E., and Wardleworth, J. (to Imperial Chemical Industries Ltd.), U. S. Patent 2,935,506 (May 3, 1960).

120. Heyna, J., and Schumacher, W. (to Farbwerke Hoescht A.-G.), U. S. Patent 2,670,265 (Feb. 23, 1954).

121. Hinokiyama, H. (to Asahi Dye Co.), Japan Patent 2194/54 (Apr. 23, 1954).
122. Hiyama, H., and Manabe, O. (to Asahi Dyestuffs Co.), Japan Patent 8131/59 (Sept. 11, 1959).
123. Holzach, K., and Mühlbauer, F. (to General Aniline Works, Inc.), U. S. Patent 2,124,299 (July 19, 1938); British Patent 469,139 (July 20, 1937); French Patent 817,409 (Sept. 2, 1937).
124. Ibid. (to I. G. Farbenindustrie A.-G.), British Patent 492,177 (Sept. 15, 1938); French Patent Amendment 49,035 (Oct. 14, 1938); German Patent 679,990 (Aug. 18, 1939).
125. Ibid., German Patent 727,947 (Nov. 17, 1942).
126. Howard, H. T., and Marrable, C. D. (to Imperial Chemical Industries Ltd.), British Patent 883,807 (Dec. 6, 1961); French Patent 1,262,186 (Apr. 17, 1961).
127. Hoyer, H., Bayer, O., and Nadler, F. (to General Aniline & Film Corp.), U. S. Patent 2,300,572 (Nov. 3, 1942); French Patent 838,418 (Mar. 6, 1939); German Patent 696,591 (Sept. 25, 1940).
128. Hoyer, H., Schröter, R., and Rinke, H. (to General Aniline & Film Corp.), U. S. Patent 2,242,469 (May 20, 1941); German Patent 878,687 (June 5, 1953); French Patent 838,602 (Mar. 10, 1939).
129. I. G. Farbenindustrie A.-G., British Patent 496,663 (Dec. 5, 1938).
130. Ibid., British Patent 520,199 (Apr. 17, 1940).
131. Ibid., French Patent 976,065 (Mar. 13, 1951).
132. Iino, K., Japan Patent 4869/57 (July 12, 1957).
133. Ibid., Japan Patent 6733/57 (Aug. 26, 1957).
134. Imperial Chemical Industries Ltd., French Patent 995,964 (Dec. 11, 1951).
135. Ibid., French Patent 1,257,598 (Feb. 20, 1961).
136. Ibid., French Patent 1,270,150 (July 17, 1961).
137. Ibid., French Patent 1,270,859 (July 24, 1961).
138. Jaeger, P., Huber, W., and Zollinger, H. (to Ciba Ltd.), U. S. Patent 3,009,920 (Nov. 21, 1961); British Patent 879,244 (Oct. 11, 1961); Canadian Patent 618,739 (Apr. 18, 1961).
139. Jolles, Z. E., Wardleworth, J., and Wood, C. (to Imperial Chemical Industries Ltd.), British Patent 650,850 (Mar. 7, 1951).
140. Jones, W. O. (to Imperial Chemical Industries Ltd.), U. S. Patent 2,604,476 (July 22, 1952); British Patent 691,905 (May 27, 1953).
141. Köberle, K., Bienert, B., and Braun, W. (to I. G. Farbenindustrie A.-G.), German Patent 721,021 (May 22, 1942).
142. Koller, E. (to Ciba Ltd.), Swiss Patent 347,925 (Sept. 15, 1960); Belgium Patent 560,105 (Feb. 17, 1958).
143. Ibid., Canadian Patent 605,962 (Sept. 27, 1960); Belgium Patent 565,997 (Sept. 24, 1958); Swiss Patent 353,479 (May 31, 1961).
144. Lacey, H. T. (to American Cyanamid Co.), U. S. Patent 2,761,868 (Sept. 4, 1956).
145. Lacey, H. T., and Waitkins, G. R. (to American Cyanamid Co.), U. S. Patent 2,823,205 (Feb. 11, 1958).
146. Libby, Jr., J. W. (to E. I. du Pont de Nemours & Co.), U. S. Patent 2,363,537 (Nov. 28, 1944).
147. Libby, Jr., J. W., and Woodward, H. E. (to E. I. du Pont de Nemours & Co.), U. S. Patent 2,363,905 (Nov. 28, 1944).
148. Linch, A. L. (to E. I. du Pont de Nemours & Co.), U. S. Patent 2,414,050 (Jan. 7, 1947).
149. Martin, T. A. (to General Aniline & Film Corp.), U. S. Patent 2,953,574 (Sept. 20, 1960).

150. Martin, T. A., and Randall, D. I. (to General Aniline & Film Corp.), U. S. Patent 2,795,583 (June 11, 1957).

151. *Ibid.*, U. S. Patent 2,795,584 (June 11, 1957).

152. Mayhew, R. L. (to General Aniline & Film Corp.), U. S. Patent 2,459,773 (Jan. 18, 1949); British Patent 613,781 (Dec. 2, 1948).

153. *Ibid.*, U. S. Patent 2,476,991 (July 26, 1949).

154. *Ibid.*, U. S. Patent 2,484,300 (Oct. 11, 1949); British Patent 654,507 (June 20, 1951).

155. *Ibid.*, U. S. Patent 2,493,724 (Jan. 3, 1950).

156. *Ibid.*, U. S. Patent 2,546,130 (Mar. 20, 1951).

157. McCormack, W. B., and Stilmar, F. B. (to E. I. du Pont de Nemours & Co.), U. S. Patent 2,613,129 (Oct. 7, 1952).

158. Montecatini Company, French Patent 848,736 (Nov. 6, 1939).

159. Motokawa, N., Tsutsumi, H., and Nomoto, S. (to Nippon Kayaku Co.), Japan Patent 10,080/56 (Nov. 24, 1956).

160. Mühlbauer, F. (to I. G. Farbenindustrie A.-G.), German Patent 700,225 (Dec. 16, 1940).

161. Mühlbauer, F., U. S. Patent 2,648,672 (Aug. 11, 1953); German Patent 825,112 (Dec. 17, 1951); British Patent 688,790 (Mar. 11, 1953).

162. *Ibid.*, U. S. Patent 2,648,674 (Aug. 11, 1953); British Patent 688,785 (Mar. 11, 1953).

163. *Ibid.* (to Badische Anilin- & Soda-Fabrik A.-G.), British Patent 692,383 (June 3, 1953); German Patent 843,724 (July 10, 1952).

164. *Ibid.*, German Patent 857,791 (Dec. 1, 1952).

165. *Ibid.*, U. S. Patent 2,768,170 (Oct. 23, 1956); British Patent 707,710 (Apr. 21, 1954); German Patent 890,107 (Sept. 17, 1953).

166. Mühlbauer, F., and Pfitzner, H. (to Badische Anilin- & Soda-Fabrik A.-G.), German Patent 903,928 (Feb. 11, 1954).

167. Mühlbauer, F. (to Badische Anilin- & Soda-Fabrik A.-G.), U. S. Patent 2,795,585 (June 11, 1957); British Patent 749,349 (May 23, 1956); German Patent 946,834 (Aug. 9, 1956).

168. Nadler, F., Bayer, O., and Hoyer, H. (to General Aniline & Film Corp.), U. S. Patent 2,288,478 (June 30, 1942).

169. Nadler, F., Hoyer, H., and Bayer, O. (to General Aniline & Film Corp.), U. S. Patent 2,219,330 (Oct. 29, 1940); British Patent 515,637 (Dec. 11, 1939); French Patent 838,935 (Mar. 20, 1939).

170. Nadler, F., Wegler, R., and Bayer, O. (to Leverkusen I. G. Werk), U. S. Patent 2,315,870 (Apr. 6, 1943).

171. Neufang, K., Rabe, P., Bienert, B., and Baumann, F. (to Farbenfabriken Bayer A.-G.), German Patent 1,010,946 (June 27, 1957).

172. Niemann, G. (to I. G. Farbenindustrie A.-G.), British Patent 487,261 (June 17, 1938); German Patent 677,667 (June 30, 1939).

173. Ono, S., and Tsutsumi, H. (to Nippon Kayaku Co.), Japan Patent 5182/55 (July 27, 1955).

174. *Ibid.*, Japan Patent 5183/55 (July 27, 1955).

175. *Ibid.*, Japan Patent 5184/55 (July 27, 1955).

176. *Ibid.*, Japan Patent 5185/55 (July 27, 1955).

177. *Ibid.*, Japan Patent 6645/55 (Sept. 17, 1955).

178. *Ibid.* (to Nippon Chemical Industries Co.), Japan Patent 7393/55 (Oct. 14, 1955).

179. *Ibid.* (to Nippon Kayaku Co.), Japan Patent 9473/56 (Nov. 6, 1956).

180. Ono, S., Tsutsumi, H., and Chiba, T. (to Nippon Kayaku Co.), Japan Patent 9472/56 (Nov. 6, 1956).

181. Ono, S., Tsutsumi, H., Chiba, T., and Nomoto, S. (to Nippon Chemical Drug Co.), Japan Patent 5938/57 (Aug. 6, 1957).

182. Paige, J. (to General Aniline & Film Corp.), U. S. Patent 2,490,704 (Dec. 6, 1949).

183. Pedersen, C. J. (to E. I. du Pont de Nemours & Co.), U. S. Patent 2,741,531 (Apr. 10, 1956).

184. Ibid., U. S. Patent 2,741,534 (Apr. 10, 1956).

185. Ibid., U. S. Patent 2,915,392 (Dec. 1, 1959).

186. Perkins, M. A. (to E. I. du Pont de Nemours & Co.), U. S. Patent 2,795,587 (June 11, 1957).

187. Ibid., U. S. Patent 2,795,588 (June 11, 1957).

188. Perkins, M. A., Oken, A., and Whelen, M. S. (to E. I. du Pont de Nemours & Co.), U. S. Patent 2,957,004 (Oct. 18, 1960).

189. Perkins, M. A., and Whelen, M. S. (to E. I. du Pont de Nemours & Co.), U. S. Patent 2,782,207 (Feb. 19, 1957).

190. Poole, V. D., and Wardleworth, J. (to Imperial Chemical Industries Ltd.), British Patent 826,689 (Jan. 20, 1960); Belgium Patent 563,199 (June 13, 1958); German Patent 1,091,259 (Oct. 20, 1960).

191. Price, R., Reece, C. H., and Wardleworth, J. (to Imperial Chemical Industries Ltd.), British Patent 830,246 (Mar. 16, 1960).

192. Pugin, A. (to Geigy A.-G.), British Patent 676,542 (July 30, 1952); German Patent 825,867 (Dec. 20, 1951).

193. Pugin, A. (to Geigy A.-G.), U. S. Patent 2,647,126 (July 28, 1953); Swiss Patents 278,945 (Feb. 16, 1952), 281,989–90 (Dec. 1, 1952).

194. Pugin, A., and Keller, E. (to Geigy A.-G.), U. S. Patent 2,837,528 (June 3, 1958); British Patent 791,359 (Feb. 26, 1958); Swiss Patent 334,320 (Jan. 15, 1959).

195. Pütter, R., Dorlars, A., and Enders, E. (to Farbenfabriken Bayer A.-G.), U. S. Patent 3,029,123 (Apr. 10, 1962).

196. Randall, D. I., and Martin, T. A. (to General Aniline & Film Corp.), U. S. Patent 2,547,972 (Apr. 10, 1951).

197. Ibid., U. S. Patent 2,859,219 (Nov. 4, 1958).

198. Randall, D. I., and Taras, J. (to General Aniline & Film Corp.), U. S. Patent 2,908,544 (Oct. 13, 1959); Canadian Patent 616,663 (Mar. 21, 1961); British Patent 781,749 (Aug. 21, 1957); Swiss Patent 349,726 (Dec. 15, 1960).

199. Randall, D. I., and Wowk, A. (to General Aniline & Film Corp.), U. S. Patent 2,914,537 (Nov. 24, 1959).

200. Randall, D. I., Wowk, A., and Taras, J. (to General Aniline & Film Corp.), U. S. Patent 2,914,538 (Nov. 24, 1959).

201. Rösch, G. (to Farbenfabriken Bayer A.-G.), U. S. Patent 2,744,914 (May 8, 1956).

202. Rösch, G., and Bayer, O. (to Farbenfabriken Bayer A.-G.), British Patent 717,137 (Oct. 20, 1954); German Patent 852,588 (Oct. 16, 1952).

203. Ibid., British Patent 724,212 (Feb. 16, 1955); German Patent 890,108 (Sept. 17, 1953).

204. Rösch, G., Bayer, O., and Hoyer, H. (to General Aniline & Film Corp.), U. S. Patent 2,285,359 (June 2, 1942); French Patent 846,023 (Sept. 7, 1939); Italian Patent 367,718 (Feb. 1, 1939).

205. Rösch, G., and Gehringer, K. H. (to Farbenfabriken Bayer A.-G.), U. S. Patent 2,882,267 (Apr. 14, 1959); British Patent 858,070 (Jan. 4, 1961); German Patent 1,109,288 (June 22, 1961).

206. Rösch, G., Wolf, W., and Vollmann, H. (to Farbenfabriken Bayer A.-G.), U. S. Patent 2,727,043 (Dec. 13, 1955); British Patent 698,049 (Oct. 7, 1953).

207. *Ibid.*, U. S. Patent 2,739,151 (Mar. 20, 1956); British Patent 698,049 (Oct. 7, 1953).

208. *Ibid.*, U. S. Patent 2,739,154 (Mar. 20, 1956); British Patent 698,049 (Oct. 7, 1953).

209. *Ibid.*, U. S. Patent 2,739,155 (Mar. 20, 1956); British Patent 698,049 (Oct. 7, 1953).

210. *Ibid.*, U. S. Patent 2,752,346 (June 26, 1956); British Patent 698,049 (Oct. 7, 1953).

211. Rossander, S. S., Libby, Jr., J. W., and Woodward, H. E. (to E. I. du Pont de Nemours & Co.), U. S. Patent 2,363,906 (Nov. 28, 1944).

212. Rümens, W., Federkiel, W., Schuster, C., and Maier, K. (to Badische Anilin- & Soda-Fabrik A.-G.), German Patent 1,003,172 (Feb. 28, 1957).

213. Ruppel, W. (to Badische Anilin- & Soda-Fabrik A.-G.), German Patent 897,990 (Nov. 26, 1953).

214. *Ibid.*, German Patent 898,147 (Nov. 26, 1953).

215. Rusznák, L., Marton, E., Sello, L., and Szoke, G., *Magyar Textiltech.*, **1956**, 325-7.

216. Sander, A., German Patent 890,109 (Sept. 17, 1953).

217. Sayler, G. H. (to Parker Pen Co.), U. S. Patent 2,528,390 (Oct. 31, 1950).

218. Schuster, C., Gehm, R., Eisele, J., and Federkiel, W. (to Badische Anilin- & Soda-Fabrik A.-G.), U. S. Patent 2,861,863 (Nov. 25, 1958).

219. Seibert, H., Triebeneck, K., Bienert, B., and Baumann, F. (to Farbenfabriken Bayer A.-G.), U. S. Patent 2,875,211 (Feb. 24, 1959); British Patent 803,525 (Oct. 29, 1958).

220. Spryskov, A. A., and Kobenin, A. L., *Trudy Ivanovsk Khim. Tekhnol. Inst.*, **1956**, No. 5, 196-201.

221. Stefanyak, S., and Borodkin, V. F., *Trudy Ivanovsk. Khim. Tekhnol. Inst.*, **1958**, 8, 107-10.

222. Stevenson, A. C. (to E. I. du Pont de Nemours & Co.), U. S. Patent 2,772,283 (Nov. 27, 1956); British Patent 783,157 (Sept. 18, 1957); Swiss Patent 348,495 (Oct. 14, 1960).

223. Taras, J., and Randall, D. I. (to General Aniline & Film Corp.), U. S. Patent 3,009,919 (Nov. 21, 1961); Canadian Patent 620,934 (May 30, 1961).

224. Tartter, A. (to Badische Anilin- & Soda-Fabrik A.-G.), German Patent 843,725 (July 10, 1952).

225. *Ibid.*, German Patent 843,726 (July 10, 1952).

226. *Ibid.*, German Patent 852,587 (Oct. 16, 1952).

227. *Ibid.*, German Patent 862,817 (Jan. 12, 1953).

228. *Ibid.*, German Patent 866,075 (Feb. 5, 1953).

229. *Ibid.*, U. S. Patent 2,759,950 (Aug. 21, 1956); British Patent 713,865 (Aug. 18, 1954); German Patent 878,686 (June 5, 1953).

230. *Ibid.*, U. S. Patent 2,674,601 (Apr. 6, 1954); British Patent 678,195 (Aug. 27, 1952); German Patent 918,104 (Sept. 20, 1954).

231. *Ibid.*, U. S. Patent 2,759,950 (Aug. 21, 1956).

232. *Ibid.*, British Patent 806,175 (Dec. 23, 1958); German Patent 1,029,956 (May 14, 1958).

233. *Ibid.*, German Patent 1,049,996 (Feb. 5, 1959).

234. *Ibid.*, British Patent 848,782 (Sept. 21, 1960).

235. *Ibid.*, British Patent 853,364 (Nov. 2, 1960).

236. *Ibid.*, U. S. Patent 3,023,218 (Feb. 27, 1962).

237. Tartter, A., Braun, W., and Weissauer, H. (to Badische Anilin- & Soda-Fabrik A.-G.), French Patent 1,270,922 (July 24, 1961).

238. Tartter, A., Dohland, W., Mesch, W., Ludsteck, D., and Federkiel, W. (to Badische Anilin- & Soda-Fabrik A.-G.), French Patent 1,266,094 (May 29, 1961).

239. Tartter, A., Graser, F., Rohland, W., Stöckl, E., Schuster, C., Gehm, R., Eisele, J., and Federkiel, W. (to Badische Anilin- & Soda-Fabrik A.-G.), German Patent 1,066,684 (Oct. 8, 1959); British Patent 868,746 (May 25, 1961).

240. Tartter, A., Hensel, W., and Baumann, H. (to Badische Anilin- & Soda-Fabrik A.-G.), French Patent 1,266,101 (May 29, 1961).

241. Tartter, A., Rohland, W., Ludsteck, D., and Schroedel, R. (to Badische Anilin- & Soda-Fabrik A.-G.), French Patent 1,270,921 (July 24, 1961).

242. Tobel, H. V. (to Sandoz Ltd.), Swiss Patent 341,591 (Nov. 30, 1959).

243. Tsutsumi, H., and Chiba, T. (to Nippon Kayaku Co.), Japan Patent 9474/56 (Nov. 6, 1956).

244. Vollmann, H., Baumann, F., and Bienert, B. (to Farbenfabriken Bayer A.-G.), U. S. Patent 2,701,252 (Feb. 1, 1955).

245. Weinmayr, V. (to E. I. du Pont de Nemours & Co.), U. S. Patent 2,925,423 (Feb. 16, 1960).

246. Whelen, M. S. (to E. I. du Pont de Nemours & Co.), U. S. Patent 2,795,586 (June 11, 1957); Swiss Patent 354,534 (July 15, 1961).

247. Wiest, G., and Niemann, G. (to I. G. Farbenindustrie A.-G.), British Patent 514,857 (Nov. 20, 1939); German Patent 706,950 (June 10, 1941).

248. Wilkinson, D. G. (to Imperial Chemical Industries Ltd.), British Patent 681,929 (Oct. 29, 1952).

249. Woerth, L., and Chabrier, G. (to Compagnie française des matières colorantes), French Patent 1,201,713 (Jan. 5, 1960).

250. Wood, C. (to Imperial Chemical Industries Ltd.), U. S. Patent 2,453,953 (Nov. 16, 1948).

251. *Ibid.*, British Patent 639,487 (June 28, 1950).

252. *Ibid.*, British Patent 681,917 (Oct. 29, 1952).

253. *Ibid.*, British Patent 681,918 (Oct. 29, 1952).

254. Wyler, M. (to Imperial Chemical Industries Ltd.), U. S. Patent 2,213,726 (Sept. 3, 1940).

255. Yagi, H., and Hori, T. (to Sumitomo Chemical Co.), Japan Patent 5634/55 (Aug. 13, 1955).

256. Zemp, R. R. (to E. I. du Pont de Nemours & Co.), U. S. Patent 2,884,326 (Apr. 28, 1959).

257. Zerweck, W., Ritter, H., and Stier, E. (to Cassella Farbwerke Mainkur A.-G.), German Patent 952,657 (Nov. 22, 1956).

258. *Ibid.*, U. S. Patent 2,832,789 (Apr. 29, 1958); British Patents 816,656-7 (July 15, 1959), 792,018 (Mar. 19, 1958), 848,880 (Sept. 21, 1960), 854,579 (Nov. 23, 1960), 761,287 (Nov. 14, 1956), 784,353 (Oct. 9, 1957); German Patents 1,049,993 (Feb. 5, 1959), 947,409 (Aug. 16, 1956).

259. *Ibid.*, German Patent 1,059,133 (June 11, 1959); French Patent 1,195,346 (Aug. 22, 1960).

260. Zickendraht, C., and Koller, E. J. (to Ciba Ltd.), U. S. Patent 2,897,207 (July 28, 1959); German Patent 1,094,898 (Dec. 15, 1960); Belgium Patent 565,782 (Sept. 17, 1958).

CHAPTER 6
COMMERCIAL APPLICATIONS

Although numerous phthalocyanines have been prepared during the first 30 years since elucidation of their structure and initial exploitation, only copper phthalocyanine, copper polychlorophthalocyanine, and their derivatives have found widespread use as colorants in pigment and dye systems. In noncolorant applications, a variety of phthalocyanine compounds have been used. However, it is estimated over 90 per cent of phthalocyanine production has been restricted to copper phthalocyanine and copper polychlorophthalocyanine. This production, which amounted to more than 10,000 pounds in 1940, had increased to two million pounds in 1950, and to about six million pounds in 1960. A useful guide in the study of phthalocyanines as colorants is the list of phthalocyanines presented in the Colour Index. This list of compounds with their Colour Index numbers is reproduced in Appendix 3.

This chapter treats commercial applications of phthalocyanines in two categories: phthalocyanine colorants and noncolorant applications of phthalocyanines. The phthalocyanine colorants category may be resolved into the groups: textile applications, paint applications, printing ink applications, applications in plastic materials, and miscellaneous colorant applications. The noncolorant applications category may be divided into the groups: catalysts, lubricating greases, analytical chemistry, medical applications, electrical applications, and applications in nuclear reactor systems.

It is hoped that with an increasing awareness and appreciation of the phthalocyanine class of compounds, the number of colorant and noncolorant uses will increase.

PHTHALOCYANINE COLORANTS

Although the shade range of the phthalocyanines is rather limited and covers only the blue-green section of the spectrum, their excellent fastness properties, cleanliness, and intensity of color have led to many applications. The insolubility of phthalocyanines makes it necessary to form derivatives prior to application of these products to textile fibers as dyes.

Textile Applications

Phthalocyanine dyestuffs and oil soluble colors are discussed in Chapter 5.

Along with the development of improved resins for textile printing inks, phthalocyanine pigments have found increasing use in this textile application. Gessler and Gans (35) formulated textile inks in such a manner as to avoid crystallizing solvents so that the crystallizing type of copper phthalocyanine could be used without loss of color value. Ferrous phthalocyanine or its sulfonate has been used as a printing assistant for vat dyes to aid in their development on steaming; amounts not exceeding 1.0 per cent of the weight of the vat dye were used (22). Numerous formulations of textile printing inks have used phthalocyanine pigments—usually in the form of an aqueous dispersion, sometimes called a "paste" or a "pulp" containing 10, 20 or more per cent pigment (4,20,28,46,47,51, 53,54,56,72,81,84,85,94,100,110,113,118,126).

Phthalocyanine precursors (see Chapter 5) have been incorporated into textile printing inks (112).

Phthalocyanine pigments in the form of aqueous dispersions have also been used in pad-dyeing with resin emulsions (77,111). A recent review of pigment printing in general included a discussion of phthalocyanine pigments (15).

A process for removing from the surface of textiles phthalocyanine pigments embodied in water insoluble resinous binders comprises immersing the fabrics in an aqueous dispersion containing a quaternary ammonium compound, caustic soda, and an alkali metal hydrosulfite (19).

Another textile application for phthalocyanine pigments is in the field of spin-dyeing. Because of their excellent stability to acids, alkalis and solvents, phthalocyanines are particularly useful. They have been used in coloring polyvinylchloride fibers (6), viscose (64,102,117), cuproammonium cellulose (86), nylon (34,116), "Perlon L," and "Rilsan" (34). They may be used as aqueous dispersions for viscose and in the form of finely ground full-strength colors in the case of nylon, "Perlon L," and "Rilsan."

Paint Applications

Both phthalocyanine blue (copper phthalocyanine) and phthalocyanine green (copper polychlorophthalocyanine containing 14 to 16 atoms of chlorine) have found wide use as paint pigments. Federal Specification TT-P-355 relates to copper phthalocyanine blue pigment and covers full strength pigment and the resinated and benzoate lake types (30).

Phthalocyanine blue and green have had wide application in all types of paints: exterior paints and enamels, lacquers, emulsion paints of various types, automotive finishes, and baking enamels. They have excellent fastness to exterior exposure either full strength or as pastel shades. Noncrystallizing and nonflocculating types have been developed so that the stability of these paint systems meets desired specifications when they are properly formulated. A number of reviews describe some of the properties that make phthalocyanines valuable paint pigments (40,52,76, 87,125).

Mixtures of phthalocyanines and other pigments have found some special use in the paint field. Examples of these are mixtures of copper phthalocyanine with 5 to 75 per cent halogenated isodibenzanthrones to make a redder pigment (106), mixtures of copper phthalocyanine with 33 to 90 per cent of a yellow α-aromatic acylaminoanthraquinone to produce a green (107), and with metallic aluminum (63) or with a chromic hydroxide-ferric hydroxide combination (44) to produce unusual paint effects. Dispersions of phthalocyanines in vehicles suitable for paint and lacquer use have been available for many years (43).

Both phthalocyanine blue and green are valuable colors for preparing so called "universal tinting pastes" (12,60).

An excellent study of the dispersion of phthalocyanine blue in paint systems was reported by J. J. Oates, chairman of a committee of the New York Paint and Varnish Production Club (83).

The committee's object was "To determine, for phthalocyanine blue toner, the principles of dispersion procedure productive of the highest efficiency in terms of

a. economics of operation
b. mechanical ease of handling
c. tinctorial strength
d. stability in admixture with a titanium dioxide tinting base."

The conclusions of the committee regarding the dispersion of phthalocyanine blue in paint systems are:

"(1) There is a practical minimum amount of dispersion work, or investment, which provides the optimum economic return from use of phthalocyanine blue for tinctorial purposes.

"(2) The practical work minimum is not necessarily recognized by gauge measurement of grind fineness, but is best measured by appropriate tint strength evaluation.

"(3) Tint strength evaluation is reliable only if the principles necessary to a broad pigment to vehicle solids to volatile compatibility are recognized and applied.

"(4) In addition to good compatibility practice, it has been established that good mechanical procedure for blending color base and white is essential if the full strength of the dispersion is to be realized and retained.

"(5) Although the equipment for dispersing color pigment is a matter of choice, the evidence obtained indicates a short run in the steel ball mill at high loading is the most economical procedure, and which further offers considerable latitude in ease of handling.

"(6) Much can be gained in developing practical knowledge of the consistency characteristics of both the color base paste and white tinting base. Such information aids design of the best incorporation procedure. Although not extensively explored, this definitely is a primary factor, and may become the subject of a future study.

"(7) Pigmented systems are recognized as complex when the number of pigments exceeds one and the number of liquid components exceeds one. Thus a tint comprising a mixture of two pigments is complex even in a supposedly simple vehicle. The 'simple' vehicle itself, whether it be ordinary linseed oil or a 100 per cent solids alkyd resin is now recognized as a complex mixture of esters, and even the commonly used volatile materials are now seen to be complex mixtures.

"The interplay of these complex vehicle systems in their relationships to pigments which strongly differ by being hydrophilic as opposed to organophilic, insoluble as against soluble, etc., comprises a broad new field of technology where appropriate experimentation and interpretation of basic principles will considerably advance paint science."

The American Society For Testing Materials has established a method for evaluating phthalocyanine blue for stability and other properties in paint systems (2).

Metal phthalocyanines have been used to coat metal surfaces by forming the metal phthalocyanine directly on the metal surfaces. Large metal surfaces can be coated with metal phthalocyanine by dipping them in a solution of phthalonitrile in acetone, drying, and subjecting the metal to temperatures of around 350° in a sealed oven. They may be coated also by subjecting them to vapors of phthalonitrile at 310°. The coating is very adherent; the shade of color depends somewhat upon the metal used but in most cases is a reddish blue (114).

Printing Ink Applications

Present day phthalocyanines are a great improvement over early products which were hard to grind. Toners are available which develop 98 per cent of their full strength with two passes on a three roll mill. Resinated phthalocyanines were the first products to provide a softer ink, better flow, and improved texture; they are still used for some types of inks.

Both the metastable α-type and the stable β-type of copper phthalocyanine are used in the printing ink industry. The metastable α-type is the redder shade and may be used in vehicles containing solvents which do not induce crystallization. It is used in soap-wrapper printing, poster colors, carton inks, and label printing. Both the slightly chlorinated α-type which is noncrystallizing and nonflocculating and the greener noncrystallizing and nonflocculating β-type are used in solvent type inks where the pigment may be in contact with crystallizing solvents. Some forms of β-copper phthalocyanine will flocculate, so it is necessary to determine extent of flocculation in the system being used. β-Copper phthalocyanine, also known as "peacock shade" phthalocyanine, is used in three- or four-color process inks. Flocculation has been eliminated by coprecipitating aluminum benzoate (121) or aluminum p-tertiary butyl benzoate (79,80) with the pigment.

Phthalocyanine green is also used in all types of printing inks. The color is noncrystallizing but may flocculate in some systems. Nonflocculating types have been developed. The shade range of the green has recently been extended toward the yellow.

The phthalocyanines are excellent in soap resistance, detergent resistance, acid resistance, alkali resistance, in insolubility in paraffin and solvents, and in lightfastness. They have twice the strength of Milori Blue, four to seven times the strength of the Erioglycine type of peacock blue, and twenty times the tinting strength of Ultramarine Blue.

The phthalocyanines are also available flushed in litho varnishes, long-oil alkyds, heat-set varnishes, steam-set varnishes, castor oil, mineral oil, flexographic ink vehicles, and gloss varnishes. Phthalocyanines may be flushed into acid resins such as those containing maleic anhydride and acrylic acid (29).

Permut (91) has listed the properties that make phthalocyanines attractive to printing ink formulators.

"Publication Inks: Permanent process blue for four-color printing.

"Metal Lithography: Nonreactive with chemicals, oils, or food acids. Nonbleeding in solvents and greases.

"Flexographic and Gravure Inks: Nonbleeding in alcohols, esters, or ketones. Nonreactive with high acid resins. Permanent in transparent films.

"Steam-set Inks: Nonbleeding in glycols. Nonreactive with fumaric resins.

"Lithography: Permanent process color. Nonreactive with fountain solution.

"Food Wrappers: Nonbleeding in butter fat or other food oils. Nonreactive with lactic and citric acids. Nonbleeding in wax coatings. Nontoxic.

"Soap Wrappers: Nonbleeding in soap; unaffected by soap or alkali. Chemically resistant in pastel shades."

Brouillard reviews the technology of phthalocyanines and their applications, especially in printing inks (13). The printing ink properties of the yellow shade of phthalocyanine green (copper polychlorobromophthalocyanine) have been described (128). The use of phthalocyanines as a raw material for printing inks has also been described (11). A four-color offset printing ink system including copper phthalocyanine as the blue component uses linseed oil as the vehicle in an offset printing ink (65). Plastic films have been printed with phthalocyanine-colored gravure inks of the toluene type containing ethylene oxide or derivatives (41). An improvement in the rub and alkali resistance of phthalocyanine-containing moisture-set printing inks is obtained by incorporating in them solid resinous esters made from polyhydric alcohols containing epoxy groups and an oily fatty acid (7). The National Printing Ink Research Institute at Lehigh University in Bethlehem, Pennsylvania, has published a paper entitled "Transfer and Color Studies with Phthalocyanine Blue Dispersion" (108).

"The transfer and color properties of phthalocyanine blue dispersion were investigated as a function of pigment particle size, vehicle refractive index, pigment loading, paper substrate, and film thickness.

"The transfer behavior of the dispersions during the letterpress printing of solids agreed with previous hypothesis concerning the influence of paper and ink properties: The ink immobilized by the paper during the dwell time increased with increasing paper porosity and with decreasing viscosity of the dispersions. The split of the free film to the paper also decreased with increasing viscosity of the dispersions.

"As pigment concentration in the printed film decreased (due to either film thickness or pigment loading), hue of the prints shifted from red toward green, saturation decreased, and brightness increased. The prints on an uncoated stock were less saturated than those on two coated stocks. Differences due to pigment particle size were marked only in lithographic varnish and not in polybutene or in a hydrocarbon drying oil."

Applications in Plastic Materials

The coloring of plastic materials is receiving more attention with the increasing volume of colored plastics. The greatest problem in coloring plastics involves dispersion of the color. Other problems are involved in the mechanics of incorporating the pigment into the plastic because the extremely fine powders needed to provide good dispersion also cause dusting. The manufacture of pigment-plastic concentrates requires special equipment and supervision and may also be an expensive undertaking (62).

Poor color dispersion is evident when specks or streaks of color are visible in the finished plastic material. One method of improving the dispersion of full strength pigments such as phthalocyanines is by means of additives. Stearic acid has been used to improve the dispersion of phthalocyanines in rubber (21). Another approach to better dispersion, used generally by the floor covering industry as well as some other branches of the plastics industry, uses reduced toners or so called whiting lakes (109). A third method is to disperse the pigment in a plasticizer such as dioctylphthalate by a flushing procedure and then to incorporate the dispersion in the plastic by the usual methods. Similarly, the pigments may be incorporated in a part of the plastic or some other additive or component of the plastic and the color concentrate subsequently is added to the main body of the plastic.

Although ionic copper has a deleterious effect on the aging of rubber, large amounts of copper phthalocyanine or its derivatives may be added to rubber with no effect on the aging properties of the rubber (78,122). Table 6-1 (78) shows that the molecularly bound copper in copper phthalocyanine does not have a detrimental effect on rubber. Sample B referred to in Table 6-1 contains about 1 per cent copper phthalocyanine; since the color contains 11 per cent copper, the amount of copper in B must be about 0.1 per cent, an amount very much greater than that which would normally be considered highly detrimental to aging. Sample A is the unpigmented control.

TABLE 6-1. PROPERTIES OF VULCANIZED RUBBER WITHOUT COPPER PHTHALOCYANINE (A) AND CONTAINING 1% COPPER PHTHALOCYANINE (B) (78)

AGING	Tensile Strength, psi		Elongation at Break, %		Modulus at 500% Elongation, psi	
	A	B	A	B	A	B
Unaged	2790	2830	785	770	620	630
Bomb, 48 hr	2770	2770	740	725	750	805
96 hr	2520	2300	710	690	830	790
Outdoor	2090	2230	680	705	760	710
Oven 10 days	1680	1570	570	545	1075	1140
Oven 15 days	1390	1390	515	490	1240	1275

"It is clear that the changes in properties are not appreciably greater for B than A.

"There is thus no evidence that the copper present in copper phthalocyanine has any appreciable detrimental effect on the aging of vulcanised rubber under the conditions examined. This result, obtained with a mixing containing a relatively enormous amount of copper, demonstrates in striking fashion how the copper can be rendered inert by introducing it into certain types of chemical molecule."

The Japanese industrial standard specifies that the ionic copper in copper phthalocyanine for coloring rubber must be below 0.1 per cent (75).

Copper, magnesium, and copper chlorophthalocyanines act as stabilizers in siloxane rubber, improving the tensile strength and per cent elongation (124). Catalytic quantities of iron, cobalt, tin, or copper phthalocyanine sulfonates may be used in the emulsion polymerization of butadienes (39). Iron phthalocyanine and its chloro or nitro derivatives are effective peptizers, either alone or in conjunction with other peptizers for natural rubber or butadiene styrene polymers (92).

Phthalocyanines have been used to color many types of plastic materials such as rubber (17), styrene polymer foams (18,93), cellulose acetate sheeting (123), polyesters (134), polyurethane foams (3), polyamides (115), vinyl chloride polymers (1,45,129), vinyl aromatic polymers (45), and many other plastic or polymeric materials.

Miscellaneous Colorant Applications

The polysulfonamide derivatives of copper phthalocyanine have been used to formulate improved writing inks. Mayhew used copper sulfonamidopyridinyl phthalocyanines to make bright blue quick-drying writing inks (66). Mayhew also used copper phthalocyanines containing several sulfonamidoalkyl groups (preferably lower members of the alkyl series) (67), unsubstituted sulfonamido groups (68), sulfanilide groups (69), or hydroxyalkyl sulfonamide groups (70), to make blue, quick drying writing inks. The addition of disalicylal ethylenediamine to formulations of writing inks containing copper phthalocyanine sulfonamide derivatives is said to increase the life of the rubber parts of the fountain pen which might be affected by trace amounts of ionic copper (105).

Salts of copper phthalocyanine di-, tri-, or tetrasulfonic acid with a basic dye, namely Victoria Blue BO (Colour Index No. 42595), have found use as colorants for ball point pen inks (73). Similar products from sulfonated phthalocyanines and other dyes such as Malachite Green, Crystal Violet, Rhodamine 6G, and Auramine have been tested in ballpoint pen inks (74). Guanidine salts of sulfonated phthalocyanine containing 2.5 to 3.0 sulfonic acid groups have been used in ball-point pen inks because of their solubility in glycol vehicles (31).

An improved marking ink for fluorinated plastic material has been formulated using copper polychlorophthalocyanine and trifluorochloroethylene polymers (50,127).

Phthalocyanine blue and green have been used to color roofing granules. Phthalocyanine green, however, is more extensively used because of its greater lightfastness under exposure conditions. Several methods of coating roofing granules using phthalocyanine green or blue as one of the colorants have been patented (14,57,58).

Copper phthalocyanine has been used in pigmented casein finishes for leather (61). Metal phthalocyanine complexes may be used to color gasoline and oil (27).

Both copper phthalocyanine sodium sulfonate (55) and leuco copper phthalocyanine (90,133) have been used in photographic processes to produce colored prints.

Copper phthalocyanine has been used as a certified food color in Germany. Sander (101) points out:

"Durch Runderlass des Reichsministers des Innern sind u. a. auch die Kupferphthalocyanine als giftfreie und gesundheitsunshädliche Farbstoffe erklärt und damit zur unbedenklichen Verwendung in der Nahrungsund Genussmittel-industrie sowie für alle der Gesundheitsgesetzgebung unterliegenden Erzeugnisse zugelassen worden."

NONCOLORANT APPLICATIONS OF PHTHALOCYANINES

Catalysts

As shown in Chapter 2, phthalocyanines have many interesting properties not related to their color, including their catalytic properties. A number of patents have disclosed catalytic uses for phthalocyanines.

About 10 to 100 ppm of iron phthalocyanine act as a catalyst in the polymerization of indene, giving a product of twice the viscosity obtained when iron phthalocyanine is omitted (48).

Both iron and cobalt phthalocyanines have also been used to catalyze the polymerization of drying oils (48,49). Hydroperoxides of partly hydrogenated polynuclear aromatic hydrocarbons are more readily formed with improved yields in the presence of metal phthalocyanine (23,42).

Metal phthalocyanines or their sulfonates are catalysts in the air oxidation process for the "sweetening" of petroleum products. Iron phthalocyanine on "Norit" and copper or cobalt phthalocyanine disulfonate are used in particular. The reaction involves the oxidation of mercaptans to products soluble in alkalis (36–38,119,120). Iron, cobalt, tin, and copper phthalocyanines and their derivatives have been used as rubber emulsion catalysts (39,92).

Metal-free phthalocyanine has been used as a metal scavenger in chlorinations where trace amounts of metals might initiate undesired side reactions (26).

A copper oxide catalyst has been made by coating a catalyst support such as pumice with an aqueous dispersion of copper phthalocyanine and then burning off the organic matter in a stream of oxygen (5). The catalyst was used for the oxidation of olefins.

Lubricating Greases

The development of silicone-insulated motors that can operate at high temperatures and the development of guided missiles and jet aircraft have spurred the search for high temperature lubricants and greases. Soap-thickened greases are rapidly oxidized at temperatures much above 100°. Metal phthalocyanines have been successfully used as thickeners for high temperature greases because of their better oxidation and heat stability. These greases consist of liquids such as silicones, polytrifluoromonochloroethylene, or dioctyl sebacate, and crystal-stable partially chlorinated or fully chlorinated copper phthalocyanines (8,32, 33,71).

The report by Fitzsimmons, Merker, and Singleterry (33) concludes:

"1. Phthalocyanine pigments may be used successfully as gelling agents for lubricating greases. The resulting greases are similar to soap-gelled greases in appearance, except that they are all blue or green in color. Smooth, homogeneous, adherent greases have been produced by gelling, with properly prepared phthalocyanine pigments, such types of lubricating liquids as petroleum hydrocarbons, diesters, "Ucons," silicones, and halocarbon fluids.

"2. Phthalocyanine greases are much more stable to heat and oxidation than are corresponding greases made with conventional soaps. The limiting factor in the use of these greases at high temperatures is the chemical instability and volatility of the lubricating fluid rather than the gelling agent.

"3. Phthalocyanine greases thicken as the temperature is increased. That shearing at room temperature restores the original consistency is a valuable property for lubricating applications.

"4. Phthalocyanine greases exhibit low bleeding and evaporation rates and no dropping point below 350°.

"5. Phthalocyanine greases function successfully as lubricants in ball bearings running at speeds of 1800 to 10,000 rpm and at all temperatures up to 225°, the maximum for which suitable ball bearings are available."

A grease with twice the useful life of a grease containing 25 per cent of a noncrystallizing copper phthalocyanine is claimed for one containing 7.5 per cent noncrystallizing copper phthalocyanine, 7.5 per cent sodium myristate, 1.0 per cent diphenyl-p-phenylene diamine, 3 per cent tricresylphosphate, 76.9 per cent synthetic ester liquid and 4.1 per cent mineral oil. The synthetic ester liquid was obtained by reacting sebacic acid, 2-ethylhexane-1,3-diol and 2-ethylhexanol in about a 2:1:2 ratio (25). A study of the factors responsible for gel formation in nonsoap lubricating greases discusses copper phthalocyanine greases made with synthetic diesters, silicones, disiloxanes, and three types of petroleum base oils (132).

Applications in Analytical Chemistry

A solution of copper phthalocyanine in concentrated sulfuric acid has been used as a test for oxidizing agents: NO_2^-, NO_3^-, ClO_3^-, BrO_3^-, IO_3^-, $Cr_2O_7^{2-}$, and MnO_4^- (16). Copper phthalocyanine tetrasulfonic acid is used (1) as an oxidation-reduction indicator in the cerimetric determination of iron (II) and ferrocyanine (95); (2) in the cerimetric determination of uranium (IV), molybdenum (V), and arsenic (III) (96); (3) in the titration of hydroquinone and "Metol" with ceric sulfate solution (103); (4) in the titration of iron (II), ferrocyanide, and uranium (IV) with permanganate (104); and (5) in the titration of iron (II), uranium (IV), and molybdenum (V) with sodium vanadate (97).

Medical Applications of Phthalocyanines

Copper phthalocyanine trisulfonic acid barium and sodium salts ("Monosol Blue" 2G and 2GS) have been used to color various tissues *in vivo.* They are practically nontoxic to various species of protozoa, crustaceans, nematodes and fish upon prolonged contact. They are nontoxic to rabbits, rats, and guinea pigs when given daily for long periods (82).

Phthalocyanine dyes have been used to stain virulent germs (24) and they specifically stain lipids which contain choline (89). They may be used to stain phospholipids and may be applied in the determination of lipidoses (88).

Cobalt phthalocyanine has been used as an antagonist to inactivate hydrogen peroxide and/or isonicotinoyl hydrazide (INH) so that tubercle bacteria from the sputum of patients being treated with INH may be cultured (9). Cobalt phthalocyanine also inactivates thenyl-2-hydrazide and furfuroyl-2-hydrazide, agents against *mycobacterium bovis* (10).

Tetrasulfonated copper phthalocyanine prepared from metallic copper produced focal uptake of X-rays in the experimentally produced brain injuries of mice. Doses of sulfonated phthalocyanine of up to 100 mg/kg were given to rabbits, mice, guinea pigs, cats, and dogs with apparent impunity. Although the biological half-life exceeds the 12.8 hour physical half-life of the Cu^{64}, after two days only 6 per cent of the injected radioactivity remained to injure tissues. The biliary system was the major route of excretion (130).

Copper polychlorophthalocyanine has been used as a component of an ointment used both as a camouflage and for protection against mustard gas (59).

Applications of Phthalocyanines in the Electrical Industry

Insulating coatings of metal phthalocyanine have been applied to electrical conductors as wires or in multilayered coils by subjecting the cleaned metal conductors to the vapors of phthalonitrile or phthalimide at a temperature between 200° and 500° for a few minutes. The vapors may be diluted with an inert gas such as nitrogen but oxidizing and reducing gases should be absent (98). Electrical condensers can be similarly insulated at the edges with the vapors of phthalonitrile while other dielectric material is used between the flat surfaces of the foils. This construction minimizes the tendency for breakdown at the edges of the foil (99).

Application of Phthalocyanines to Nuclear Reactors

The addition of 0.1 to 10 per cent of phthalocyanine to polyphenyl coolants for nuclear reactors improves their resistance to deterioration induced by exposure to neutron irradiation at high temperatures (131).

REFERENCES

1. Adekawa, M., Japan Patent 9889 (Nov. 7, 1959).
2. American Society for Testing Materials, Standards, 8, 72 (1958).
3. Anderson, N. L., and McGinn, C. E. (to Allied Chemical Corp.), U. S. Patent 2,986,536 (May 30, 1961).
4. Auer, L., U. S. Patent 2,637, 621 (May 5, 1953).
5. Baldwin, M. M. (to Mathieson Chemical Corp.), U. S. Patent 2,688,603 (Sept. 7, 1954).
6. Baron, A. (to Compagnie française des matières colorantes), French Patent 1,136,965 (May 22, 1957).
7. Bernardi, D. J., Tringali, A. M., Roth, H. T., Engle, L. S. (to Interchemical Corp.), U. S. Patent 3,017,374 (Jan. 16, 1962).
8. Boner, C. J., "Manufacturing and Application of Lubricating Greases," p. 690, New York, Reinhold Publishing Corp., 1954.
9. Bönicke, R., Z. Hyg. Infektions-krankh., 142, 339 (1956).
10. Bönicke, R., Z. Hyg. Infektions-krankh., 145, 263 (1958).
11. Bowles, R. F., ed., "Printing Ink Manual," pp. 256, 276, 413, and 467, Cambridge, W. Heffer & Sons Ltd., 1961.
12. Bram, L. S., and Vecchio, L. F. (to Benjamin Moore & Co.), U. S. Patent 2,942,997 (June 28, 1960).
13. Brouillard, R. E., Am. Ink Maker, 32, (1), 32, 65 (1954).
14. Buzzell, M. E., and Swenson, G. W. (to Minnesota Mining & Manufacturing Co.), U. S. Patent 2,417,058 (Mar. 11, 1947).
15. Cassel, N. S., Am. Dyestuff Reptr., 49, (6), 35 (Mar. 21, 1960).
16. Černý, P., Chem zvesti., 9, 94 (1955).
17. Ciba Ltd., British Patent 685,582 (Jan. 7, 1953); Swiss Patent 279,293 (Mar. 1, 1952).
18. Colwell, R. E., and Platzer, N. (to Monsanto Chemical Co.), U. S. Patent 2,857,341 (Oct. 21, 1958).
19. Cook, A. A., and Sapers, I. (to Arkansas Co.), U. S. Patent 2,587,597 (Mar. 4, 1952).
20. Craemer, K., and Hölscher, F. (to Badische Anilin-& Soda-Fabrik A.-G.), U. S. Patent 2,719,831 (Oct. 4, 1955); German Patent 937,343 (Jan. 5, 1956).

21. Dahlen, M. A., and Detrick, S. R. (to E. I. du Pont de Nemours & Co.), U. S. Patent 2,291,452 (July 28, 1942).

22. Davidson, A., Chapman, E., McQueen, S. T., and Payman, J. (to Imperial Chemical Industries Ltd.), U. S. Patent 2,327,405 (Aug. 24, 1943).

23. Dehydag Deutsche Hydrierwerke G.m.b.H., British Patent 777,501 (June 26, 1957).

24. Desbordes, J., Fournier, E., and Gautier, M., Ann. inst. Pasteur, 91, 584 (1956).

25. Dilworth, J. P., and Roach, J. R. (to The Texas Co.), U. S. Patent 2,836,563 (May 27, 1958).

26. Eckert, W., and Quint, F., (to Farbwerke Hoechst A.-G), German Patent 855,105 (Nov. 10, 1952).

27. Erbe, F. (to Farbwerke Hoechst A.-G.), German Patent 1,017,720 (Oct. 17, 1957).

28. Farbenfabriken Bayer A.-G., British Patent 798,437 (July 23, 1958).

29. Farbwerke Hoechst A.-G., British Patent 801,522 (Sept. 17, 1958).

30. Federal Specification TT-P-355 (Feb. 26, 1959), U. S. Government Printing Office.

31. Fiess, N. W. (to American Cyanamid Co.), U. S. Patent 3,010,970 (Nov. 28, 1961).

32. Fitzsimmons, V. G., Merker, R. L., and Singleterry, C. R., Ind. Eng. Chem., 44, 556 (1952).

33. Fitzsimmons, V. G., Merker, R. L., and Singleterry, C. R., Naval Research Laboratory Report 3672, May 25, 1950.

34. Geiger, G. (to Sandoz Ltd.), U. S. Patent 3,006,922 (Oct. 31, 1961).

35. Gessler, A. E., and Gans, D. M. (to Interchemical Corp.), U. S. Patent 2,317,371 (Apr. 27, 1943).

36. Gleim, W. K. T., and Urban, Jr., P., (to Universal Oil Products Co.), U. S. Patent 2,882,224 (Apr. 14, 1959).

37. Gleim, W. K. T. (to Universal Oil Products Co.), U. S. Patent 2,966,452 (Dec. 27, 1960).

38. Gleim, W. K. T., and Urban, P. (to Universal Oil Products Co.), U. S. Patent 2,853,432 (Sept. 23, 1958).

39. Gumlich, W., and Dennstedt, I. (to Jasco Inc.), U. S. Patent 2,234,076 (Mar. 4, 1941).

40. Herrmann, E., Farbe und Lacke, 64, 130 (1958).

41. Hochuli, E., Werdenberg, H., and Fisch, W. (to Ciba Ltd.), Swiss Patent 330,094 (July 15, 1958).

42. Hock, H., and Kropf, H. (to Ruhrchemie A.-G.), U. S. Patent 2,954,405 (Sept. 27, 1960).

43. I. G. Farbenindustrie A.-G., Italian Patent 372,603 (July 4, 1939).

44. Jackson, J. (to E. I. du Pont de Nemours & Co.), U. S. Patent 2,879,246 (Mar. 24, 1959).

45. Jefts, A. W., and Rotherham, H. G. (to American Cyanamid Co.), U. S. Patent 2,986,547 (May 30, 1961).

46. Johnson, J. L., Booth, A., and Messmer, E. (to Interchemical Corp.), U. S. Patent 2,865,871 (Dec. 23, 1958).

47. Jones, G. F. (to Imperial Paper & Color Corp.), U. S. Patent 2,616,861 (Nov. 4, 1952).

48. Kaufmann, H. P. (to Svenska Oljeslageriaktiebolaget), Sweden Patent 148,757 (Feb. 8, 1955); German Patent 920,666 (Nov. 29, 1954).

49. Kaufmann, H. P., German Patent 1,074,176 (Jan. 28, 1960).

50. Kaufman, H. S., and West, F. W. (to Minnesota Mining & Mfg. Co.), U. S. Patent 3,019,115 (Jan. 30, 1962).

51. Kienle, R. H., and Peiker, A. L. (to American Cyanamid Co.), U. S. Patent 2,601,661 (June 24, 1952).

52. Killian, D. B., *Paint, Oil, Chem. Rev.*, **115**, (8), 14, 18 (1952).

53. Kine, B. B., and Nuessle, A. C. (to Rohm & Haas Co.), U. S. Patent 2,886,474 (May 12, 1959).

54. Kleiner, H., and Lehmann, W. (to Farbenfabriken Bayer A.-G.), U. S. Patent 2,800,417 (July 23, 1957); German Patent 915,329 (July 11, 1957).

55. Kodak-Pathé, French Patent 974,715 (Feb. 26, 1951).

56. Kuhn, J. M. (to Sherwin-Williams Co.), U. S. Patent 3,017,377 (Jan. 16, 1962).

57. Langseth, A. O. (to Minnesota Mining & Mfg. Co.), U. S. Patent 2,943,002 (June 28, 1960).

58. Larssen, P. A. (to Central Commercial Co.), U. S. Patent 2,986,476 (May 30, 1961).

59. Lazier, W. A., Peppel, W. J., and Salzberg, P. L. (to the United States of America, as represented by the Secy. of War), U. S. Patent 2,725,335 (Nov. 29, 1955).

60. Leipen, F. (to W. A. Cleary Corp.), U. S. Patent 2,963,380 (Dec. 6, 1960).

61. Liss, Z., *Kožařství*, **5**, 65 (1955).

62. Lowe, P., *Brit. Plastics*, **27**, 304 (1954).

63. McAdow, W. R. (to American-Marietta Co.), U. S. Patent 2,941,894 (June 21, 1960).

64. McLellan, K. M. (to Industrial Rayon Corp.), U. S. Patent 2,875,077 (Feb. 24, 1959).

65. Malova, T. N., Sbornik Nauch. Rabot Vsesoyuz. Nauch.-Issledovatel. Inst. Poligraf. Prom. i Tekh., **6**, 27 (1953); Referat. Zhur. Khim., **1956**, Abstr. No. 17672.

66. Mayhew, R. L., (to General Aniline & Film Corp.), U. S. Patent 2,476,991 (July 26, 1949).

67. Mayhew, R. L., (to General Aniline & Film Corp.), U. S. Patent 2,493,724 (Jan. 3, 1950).

68. Mayhew, R. L. (to General Aniline & Film Corp.), U. S. Patent 2,545,823 (Mar. 20, 1951).

69. Mayhew, R. L. (to General Aniline & Film Corp.), U. S. Patent 2,546,130 (Mar. 20, 1951).

70. Mayhew, R. L. (to General Aniline & Film Corp.), U. S. Patent 2,560,881 (July 17, 1951).

71. Merker, R. L., and Singleterry, C. R., U. S. Patent 2,597,018 (May 20, 1952).

72. Meunier, P. L., and Summerill, R. J. (to E. I. du Pont de Nemours & Co.), U. S. Patent 2,641,554 (June 9, 1953).

73. Miller, C. Q., and Ranson, W. W. (to E. I. du Pont de Nemours & Co.), U. S. Patent 2,950,285 (Aug. 23, 1960).

74. Miller, C. Q., and Ranson, W. W. (to E. I. du Pont de Nemours & Co.), U. S. Patent 2,950,286 (Aug. 23, 1960).

75. Minatoya, S., Aoe, I., and Ishiyama, H., *J. Soc. Rubber Ind. Japan*, **26**, 76 (1953).

76. Moll, I. S., *Paint Manuf.*, **21**, 402, 418 (1951).

77. Moncrieff, Robert W., "Man Made Fibers," 3rd ed., New York, John Wiley & Sons, 1957.

78. Morley, J. F., *J. Rubber Research*, 16, 31 (1947).
79. Moser, F. H. (to Standard Ultramarine & Color Co.), U. S. Patent 2,965,511 (Dec. 20, 1960).
80. Moser, F. H. (to Standard Ultramarine & Color Co.), U. S. Patent 2,965,662 (Dec. 20, 1960).
81. Müller, R. (to Concentra G. m. b. H. Gebr. Hartmann), German Patent 1,076,715 (Mar. 3, 1960).
82. Neuzil, E., and Bailenger, J., *Compt. rend. soc. biol.*, 146, 1108 (1952); *J. méd. Bordeaux*, 129, 343 (1952).
83. New York Paint and Varnish Production Club, *Offic. Dig., Federation Paint & Varnish Production Clubs* 29, 1113 (1957).
84. Oda, R., Tajima, S., and Matsumoto, K. (to Sumitomo Chemical Co.), Japan Patent 2086 (1959).
85. Oda, C., Tajima, S., and Matsumoto, K. (to Sumitomo Chemical Co.), Japan 3936 (Apr. 19, 1960).
86. Odaira, S., Japan Patent 5893 (July 4, 1959).
87. Payne, H. F., "Organic Coating Technology," pp. 896–905, New York, John Wiley & Sons, 1961.
88. Pearse, A. G. E., "Chemistry of Copper Phthalocyanin Staining for Phospholipids and Its Application to the Lipidoses," in J. N. Cumings and A. Lowenthal, "Cerebral Lipidoses Symposium, Antwerp, 1955," pp. 98–106, Charles C. Thomas, 1957.
89. Pearse, A. G. E., *J. Pathol. Bacteriol.*, 70, 554 (1955).
90. Pedersen, C. J. (to E. I. du Pont de Nemours & Co.), U. S. Patent 2,915,392 (Dec. 1, 1959).
91. Permut, A., *Am. Ink Maker*, 31 (9), 40, 69 (1953).
92. Pikl, J. (to E. I. du Pont de Nemours & Co.), U. S. Patent 2,860,116 (Nov. 11, 1958).
93. Platzer, N. (to Monsanto Chemical Co.), U. S. Patent 2,857,342 (Oct. 21, 1958).
94. Radley, J. A. (to Imperial Chemical Industries Ltd.), U. S. Patent 2,506,892 (May 9, 1950).
95. Rao, G. G., and Sastri, T. P., *Z. anal. Chem.*, 160, 109 (1958).
96. Rao, G. G., and Sastri, T. P., *Z. anal. Chem.*, 163, 1 (1958).
97. Rao, G. G., and Sastri, T. P., *Z. anal. Chem.*, 167, 1 (1959).
98. Robinson, P., and Reid, C. C., (to Sprague Electric Co.), U. S. Patent 2,585,037 (Feb. 12, 1952).
99. Robinson, P., and Reid, C. C., (to Sprague Electric Co.), U. S. Patent 2,590,650 (Mar. 25, 1952).
100. Saiki, K., *et al.*, (to Sanyo Pigment Co.), Japan Patent 1195 (Mar. 4, 1954).
101. Sander, A., *Die Chemie*, 55, 255 (1942).
102. Saposnikov, G. V., *Chem. prúmysl*, 8, 438 (1958).
103. Sastri, T. P., and Rao, G. G., *Z. anal. Chem.*, 163, 263 (1958).
104. Sastri, T. P., and Rao, G. G., *Z. anal. Chem.*, 163, 266 (1958).
105. Sayler, G. H. (to The Parker Pen Co.), U. S. Patent 2,528,390 (Oct. 31, 1950).
106. Scalera, M., and Brouillard, R. E. (to American Cyanamid Co.), U. S. Patent 2,439,222 (Apr. 6, 1948).
107. Scalera, M., and Brouillard, R. E. (to American Cyanamid Co.), U. S. Patent 2,505,744 (Apr. 25, 1950).
108. Schaeffer, W. D., Hammel, J. J., Fetsko, J. M., and Zettlemoyer, A. C., in

Banks, ed., "Printing Inks and Color," p. 33, London, Pergamon Press, 1961.

109. Stepp, J. D. (to Standard Ultramarine & Color Co.), U. S. Patent 3,013,889 (Dec. 19, 1961).

110. Sulzer, G., Guertler, P., Fatzer, W., and Maeder, A. (to Ciba Ltd.), U. S. Patent 2,888,420 (May 26, 1959).

111. Sulzer, G., Guertler, P., Fatzer, W., and Maeder, A., U. S. Patent 2,898,239 (Aug. 4, 1959).

112. Summerill, R. J. (to E. I. du Pont de Nemours & Co.), U. S. Patent 2,980,487 (Apr. 18, 1961).

113. Takeshita, M., and Miya, T., Japan Patent 2886 (May 26, 1954).

114. Tanner, H. G. (to E. I. du Pont de Nemours & Co.), U. S. Patent 2,163,768 (June 27, 1939).

115. Taul, H., and Indest, H. (Vereinigte Glanzstoff-Fabriken A.G.), U. S. Patent 2,997,450 (Aug. 22, 1961).

116. Twitchett, H. J., and Wild, A. S. (to Imperial Chemical Industries Ltd.), British Patent 820,975 (Sept. 30, 1959).

117. Uarova, S. P., and Aleksandrova, E. M., Trudy Moskov. Khim.-Tekhnol. Inst. im D. I. Mendeleeva, 25, 11 (1957).

118. Ubuaki, K., Japan Patent 2885 (May 26, 1954).

119. Urban, Jr., P., and Gleim, W. K. T. (to Universal Oil Products Co.), U. S. Patent 2,921,020 (Jan. 12, 1960).

120. Urban, Jr., P., and Brown, K. M. (to Universal Oil Products Co.), U. S. Patent 2,921,021 (Jan. 12, 1960).

121. Vesce, V. C., and Stalzer, F. M. (to Harmon Color Works, Inc.), U. S. Patent 2,327,472 (Aug. 24, 1943).

122. Villain, H., Rev. gen. caoutchouc, 26, 740 (1949); Rubber Chem. & Technol., 23, 352 (1950).

123. Walker, E. E., Shaw, M. P., and Fisher, V. W. F. (to British Celanese Ltd.), U. S. Patent 2,825,656 (Mar. 4, 1958).

124. Warrick, E. L. (to Dow-Corning Corp.), U. S. Patent 2,723,964 (Nov. 15, 1955); British Patent 731,166 (June 1, 1955).

125. Weinmann, J. G., By Gum!, 17, (5), 10 (1947).

126. Weisz, H., and Costner, D. (to Rock Hill Printing & Finishing Co.), U. S. Patent 2,691,602 (Oct. 12, 1954).

127. West, F. W. (to Minnesota Mining & Mfg. Co.), U. S. Patent 2,915,416 (Dec. 1, 1959).

128. Wich, E. A., Am. Ink Maker, 37, (8), 26, 63 (1959).

129. Wormald, G., and Spengeman, W. F., Ind. Eng. Chem., 44, 1104 (1952).

130. Wrenn, Jr., F. R., Good, M. L., and Handler, P., Science, 113, 525 (1951).

131. Wright, J. R., and Bolt, R. O. (to U. S. Atomic Energy Commission), U. S. Patent 2,915,567 (Dec. 1, 1959).

132. Young, G. J., and Chessick, J. J., J. Colloid Sci., 13, 358 (1958).

133. Zemp, R. R. (to E. I. du Pont de Nemours & Co.), U. S. Patent 2,884,326 (Apr. 28, 1959).

134. Zoetbrood, G. J. (to N. V. Onderzoekingsinstituut Research), U. S. Patent 3,002,942 (Oct. 3, 1961).

CHAPTER 7

PHTHALOCYANINE-TYPE COMPOUNDS

Phthalocyanine-type compounds are defined here as porphin derivatives with one, two, three, or four aza groups joining the pyrrole nuclei, with one or more inorganic-organic groups replacing the β-hydrogen atoms, and with any suitable metal replacing the two hydrogen atoms in the center of the molecule. From 1 to 8 of the β-hydrogen atoms may be replaced. Phthalocyanine-type compounds, like the phthalocyanines, are pigments, being insoluble in aqueous solutions and the common organic solvents. Unlike the phthalocyanines, substitutions on the β-carbon atoms of the pyrrole nuclei may be unsymmetrical.

Thus, consideration of the fact of at least 40 different central metal atoms, replacement of one to three aza links with methine links, and an array of substitutions of various inorganic-organic groupings in the eight available positions along the periphery of the porphin molecule, it would appear possible to synthesize several hundred thousand phthalocyanine-type compounds.

One of the first phthalocyanine-type molecules to be synthesized was naphthalocyanine. 1,2-Naphthalocyanine (tetra-3,4-benzophthalocyanine) (I) and 2,3-naphthalocyanine (II) were synthesized by Linstead and co-workers from 1,2- and 2,3-dicyanonaphthalene (1,14). Naphthalocyanines were also made by I. G. Farbenindustrie in the same period (45).

I   II

The properties of the naphthalocyanines are similar to the properties of the phthalocyanines. The compounds are dark green with a blue-to-purple luster; they do not sublime readily; and they may be purified by crystallization from high-boiling solvents. At least two crystal isomers of 1,2-naphthalocyanine and magnesium 1,2-naphthalocyanine have been isolated; zinc and copper naphthalocyanines are stable in concentrated sulfuric acid, whereas lead and magnesium 1,2-naphthalocyanines are decomposed with the formation of 1,2-naphthalocyanine. The 1,2-naphthalocyanines are more stable to heat and are more inert chemically than the phthalocyanines; however, the stability of the metals in concentrated sulfuric acid is similar (14).

Borodkin and Smirnov (13) have also reported the synthesis of analogs of naphthalocyanine.

Tetra-4-β-naphthylphthalocyanines (III) may be prepared from 4-β-naphthylphthalimide (23).

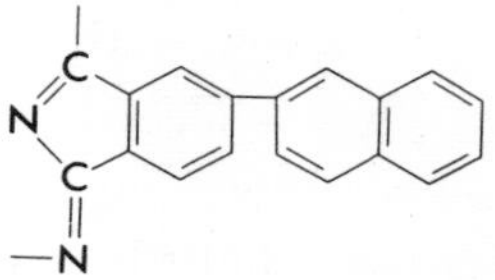

III

4-β-Naphthylphthalimide is synthesized by catalytic hydrogenation and dehydration of 4-phthalimido-α-naphthoquinone.

Hexadecahydrophthalocyanine (IV) and several metal derivatives have been prepared from 3,4,5,6-tetrahydrophthalonitrile and from 3,4,5,6-tetrahydrophthalic anhydride (24,27,29).

3,4,5,6-Tetrahydrophthalonitrile and magnesium in an alcoholic slurry react to give magnesium hexadecahydrophthalocyanine (24). "The product crystallised from chlorobenzene as blue needles, much less green than phthalocyanine...." Magnesium hexadecahydrophthalocyanine becomes hexadecahydrophthalocyanine in boiling acetic acid. Metal-bearing compounds can then be prepared from hexadecahydrophthalocyanine. Hexadecahydrophthalocyanine may also be prepared from cis-hexahydrophthalimidine (25) upon refluxing the imidine, o-dichlorobenzene and nitrobenzene.

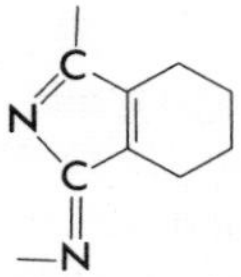

IV

"The compounds of the above formula wherein the metal is nickel are especially valuable for use as pigments, for example nickel hexadecahydrophthalocyanine... is an especially valuable blue-violet pigment of good fastness properties and high tinctorial strength" (27).

Tetramethyltetraazaporphins and their magnesium, copper, and nickel derivatives have been prepared from citracononitrile. The pigments form purple crystals (73).

Octamethyltetraazaporphins (V) and their cobalt, nickel, copper, zinc, and magnesium derivatives have also been prepared in an attempt to obtain pigments with a redder shade than the corresponding phthalocyanines (3,6,28,29,65,76).

$$
\begin{array}{c}
\text{C—C—CH}_3 \\
\text{N} \quad \| \\
\text{C—C—CH}_3 \\
\text{—N}
\end{array}
$$

V

"For example dimethyl maleic dinitrile (melting point 48°C) and dimethyl fumaric dinitrile (melting point 81°C)... both give pigments when heated with nickel or cobalt compounds" (29). Octaethyltetraazaporphin may also be prepared from diethylmaleic anhydride or diethylmaleonitrile. Other lower alkyl bearing maleic- or fumaric-nitriles may be used as well as mixtures, such as methylethylmaleic and methylethylfumaric dinitrile. Also, mixtures of 3,4,5,6-tetrahydrophthalonitrile, dimethylmaleonitrile, and diethylmaleonitrile can be made to react to yield a variety of tetraazaporphins containing one or more benzene, cyclohexeno, methyl, and ethyl substituents (27,29,68).

The alkyl derivatives of tetraazaporphin may be hydrogenated to give tetrahydro derivatives and tetracyclohexenotetraazaporphin may be dehydrogenated (26). Tetrahydrotetramethyltetraazaporphin is a dark purple solid.

$$
\begin{array}{c}
\text{C—C—C}_6\text{H}_5 \\
\text{N} \quad \| \\
\text{C—C—C}_6\text{H}_5 \\
\text{—N}
\end{array}
$$

VI

Octaphenyltetraazaporphin (VI) and its metal derivatives have been prepared from diphenylmaleonitrile (1,19,54,76).

"Octaphenylporphyrazine and its metal derivatives are green bodies which have properties similar to the phthalocyanines except that they are quite soluble in organic solvents, and are much more resistant to degradation by oxidation" (19).

Tetrabenzomonoazaporphin (VII), tetrabenzodiazaporphin (VIII), tetrabenzotriazaporphin (IX), and metal complexes of these compounds have been synthesized (4,5,20,40,41,42,61,69). Although not defined here as phthalocyanine-type compound, it is of interest that tetrabenzoporphin has been synthesized also.

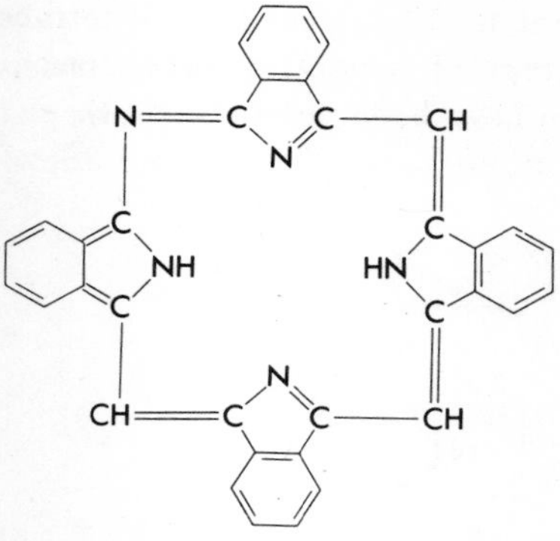

VII

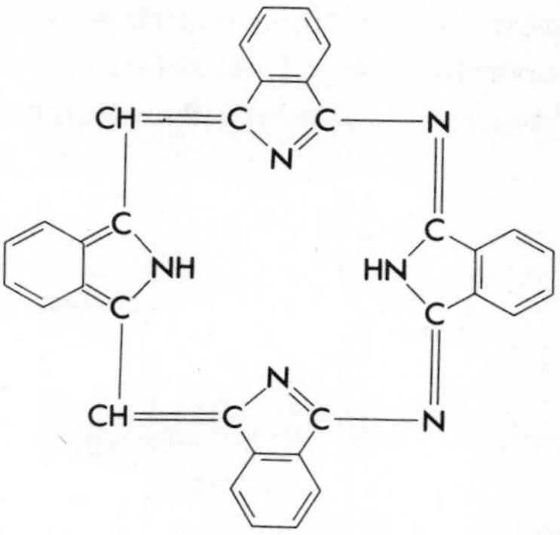

VIII

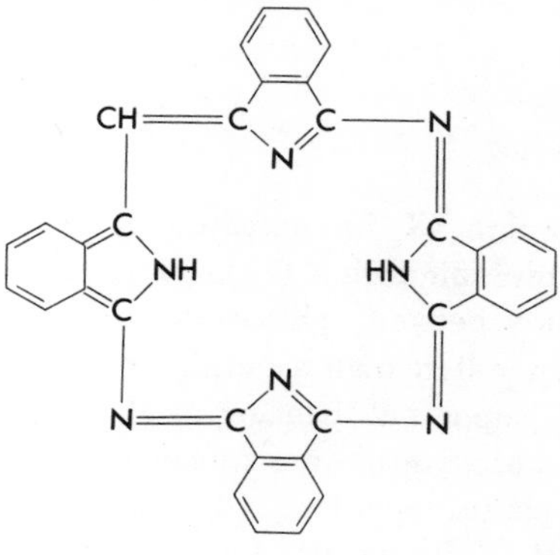

IX

Octaphenyltetraazaporphin, and compounds (VII), (VIII), and (IX) are reported to be dull, greenish blue pigments. However, their corresponding dyes may be bright. "The salts, e.g., alkali metal salts, of these tetra-benz-triaza-porphin-sulphonic acids are soluble in water and their aqueous solutions dye cotton, wool, and acetate rayon in bright green shades" (20). Copper tetrabenzotriazaporphin can be made by reacting phthalodinitrile and methylenephthalimide with cupric chloride at 250°. The purified product may be crystallized from boiling chloronaphthalene to give purple needles having a "coppery" luster (20). It is stated the reaction of o-cyanoacetophenone with cuprous chloride in quinoline at 200 to 220° yields a pigment the properties and analysis of which indicate it to be the copper salt of tetrabenzomonoazaporphin. If

1 mole of *o*-cyanoacetophenone is reacted with 0.5 mole phthalodinitrile in the presence of 1 mole cuprous chloride, the copper salt of tetra-benzodiazaporphin is obtained; if the reactants are brought together in the ratio $1:1:1$, the resulting pigment is the copper salt of tetrabenzo-triazaporphin (42). Absorption spectra of several tetrabenzomonoaza-porphins and tetrabenzotriazaporphins have been determined (4).

X

Tribenzotetraazaporphin (X) is prepared by the condensation of suc-cinimidine with diiminoisoindoline (22). Tribenzotetraazaporphin is in-termediate in properties between phthalocyanine and tetraazaporphin. It crystallizes in small needles with a purple reflex; it decomposes without melting at about $400°$; upon sublimation at $350°$ and 15 mm Hg pressure, phthalonitrile and phthalocyanine are formed. Tribenzotetraazaporphin is more soluble than phthalocyanine. Benzene, pyridine, anisole, and morpholine dissolve it in the amount 1 to 10 mg/l (22).

Synthesis of monobenzotetraazaporphin (XI) is indicated (67,68), "where Me is cobalt, iron, tin or vanadium, which may carry one or more hydroxy or acid groups, the aromatic ring may be substituted, R_1 and R_2 each represent hydrogen or a substituted or unsubstituted alkyl, cycloalkyl, aryl or aralkyl group or R_1 and R_2 may be joined together to form an alicyclic ring and R_3, R_4, R_5 and R_6 each represent hydrogen or a sub-stituted or unsubstituted alkyl, cycloalkyl, aryl or aralkyl group or where either or both of the pairs of groups R_3 and R_4, R_5 and R_6 which is not readily vatted with alkaline hydrosulphite, is mixed with a vattable metal tetraazaporphin...." The tetraazaporphin compound may be made "by heating with a substance consisting of or containing a metal, a mixture of phthalonitrile with tetrahydrophthalonitrile, maleic dinitrile, or the ap-propriate substituted maleic dinitrile or fumaric dinitrile" (68).

Tetraazaporphin and magnesium, copper, and nickel tetraazaporphins

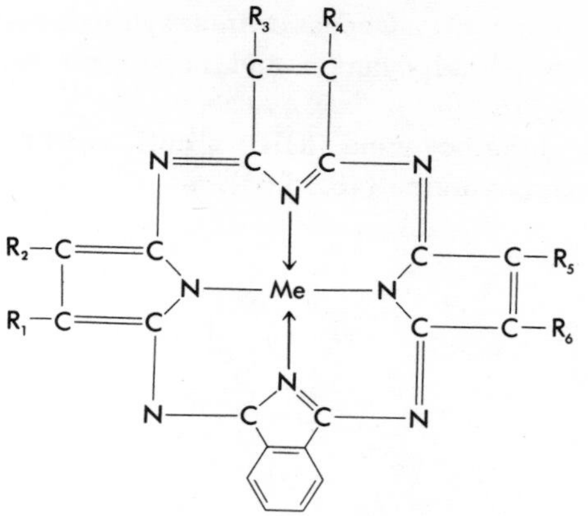

XI

have been prepared (64). Magnesium tetraazaporphin can be obtained by reacting maleic dinitrile with magnesium *n*-propoxide in *n*-propyl alcohol. Tetraazaporphin is made by treating magnesium tetraazaporphin with glacial acetic acid. Copper and nickel tetraazaporphins are obtained by treating tetraazaporphin with copper-bronze and anhydrous nickel chloride in boiling *o*-dichlorobenzene. Tetraazaporphin is violet-blue in color; magnesium and copper tetraazaporphins are blue; and nickel tetraazaporphin is purple-violet.

Copper phthalocyanine is less green and superior in pigment properties to copper tetraazaporphin and copper hexadecahydrophthalocyanine (24, 64).

In addition to phenyl and alkyl derivatives of phthalocyanine, and hexeno and naphthyl derivatives of tetraazaporphin, there are phthalocyanine pigments in which the substituents on the four benzene groups contain atoms other than carbon and hydrogen alone, or the benzene ring may be replaced by heterocyclic rings.

Copper tetraazaphthalocyanine (XII), (or tetrapyridinoporphyrazine or tetrapyridinotetraazaporphin)

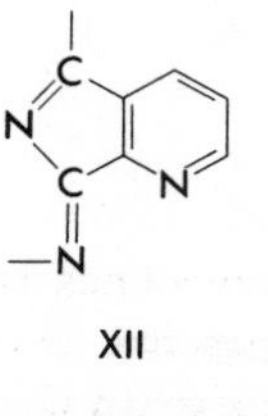

XII

is made by the reaction of quinolinic acid with urea and copper salts (9, 57,63). Tetraazaphthalocyanine and magnesium tetraazaphthalocyanine have also been prepared. Copper tetraazaphthalocyanine is redder in shade than copper phthalocyanine and is similar in lightfastness and other properties (9,57).

Copper octaazaphthalocyanine (XIII), a dull, red-blue pigment, or copper tetrapyrazinoporphyrazine (48,58,63)

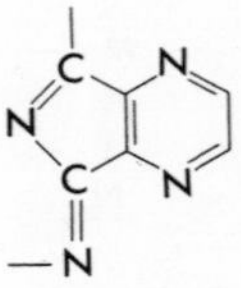

XIII

has been made from the reaction of diaminomaleic acid nitrile, glyoxal, and cuprous cyanide. The tetraaza- and octaazaphthalocyanines, and octamethyl- and octaethyltetraazaporphins may be the reddest shade phthalocyanine-type compounds yet prepared.

Substituted octaazaphthalocyanines have been made also, such as tetra-4,5-dimethyloctaazaphthalocyanine (XIV), tetra-4,5-diphenyloctaazaphthalocyanine (XV), tetra-peri-naphthylene-4,5-octaazaphthalocyanine (XVI), 4,5-thionaphthene-octaazaphthalocyanine (XVII), and tetra-4-phenyloctaazaphthalocyanine (XVIII) (48).

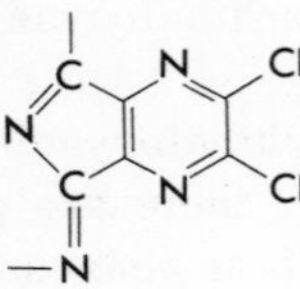

XIV 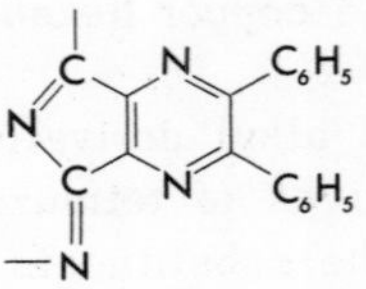   XV 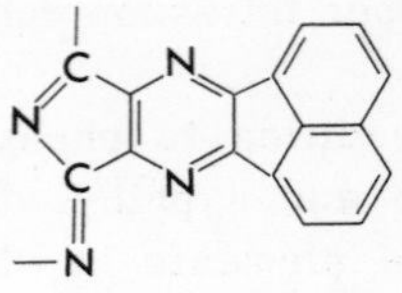   XVI

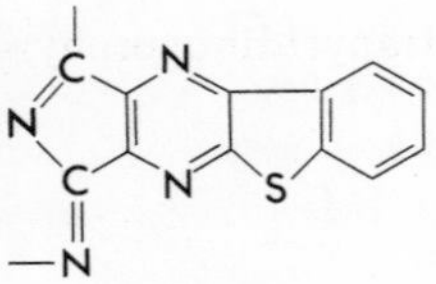

XVII 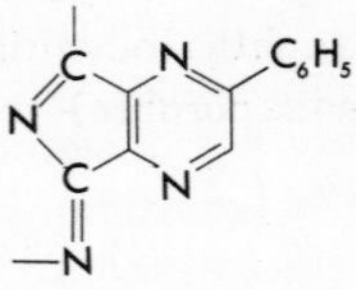   XVIII

Other phthalocyanine-type compounds in which structural changes have been made in the phenylene rings are tetrathiophenotetraazaporphin (XIX) and tetrathionaphthenotetraazaporphin (XX) (1,63).

Copper tetrathiophenotetraazaporphin or copper tetra-2,3-thiophenoporphyrazine is prepared from thiophene, which is oxidized directly to thio-

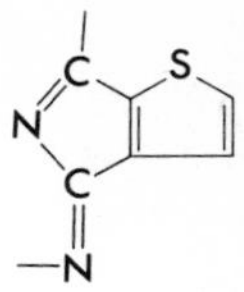

XIX 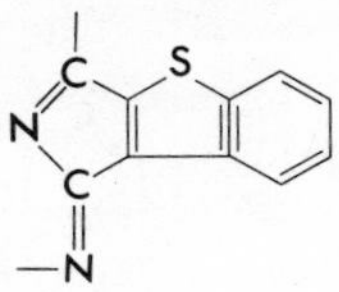   XX

pheno-2,3-dicarboxylic acid, which is reacted with ammonia to give 2,3-dicyanothiophene. 2,3-Dicyanothiophene is heated at 230 to 250° with cuprous chloride; the product is extracted with boiling alcohol, acid pasted in concentrated sulfuric acid, precipitated on ice, and crystallized from chloronaphthalene. The compound (XIX) is a green-blue powder with a purple luster and is greener than phthalocyanine (63).

Copper tetrathionaphthenotetraazaporphin or copper tetra-2,3-thionaphthenoporphyrazine is prepared from a mixture of 2,3-dicyanothionaphthene and cuprous chloride heated at 240 to 250° for 30 minutes. The product is cooled, powdered, extracted with alcohol, acid pasted, precipitated on ice, and crystallized from chloronaphthalene. The compound (XX) is dull green with a faint purple luster (63).

Copper tetrapyridylphthalocyanine (XXI) can be synthesized from the reaction of pyridylphthalonitrile with copper salts or by the reaction of pyridine with diazotized copper tetraaminophthalocyanine (15,16,35,38).

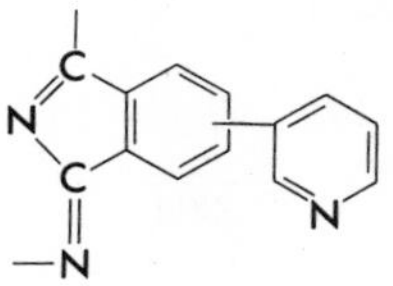

XXI

Copper tetra-4-pyridylphthalocyanine is a green pigment. "The products obtained are, as indicated, tetrapyridylphthalocyanines. They are, however, most probably not chemical individuals, but mixtures of isomerides as the situation or relation one to another of the original four amino groups that are diazotised to give the tetradiazo compounds used as starting materials is unknown.

"Hence it follows that the situation or relation one to another, or, in other words, the orientation of the pyridyl radicals, is unknown, except that they are in either the 3- or the 6-, or in the 4-, or the 5-position according as the parent phthalic derivatives are numbered. Furthermore, the pyridyl radical may become attached so as to constitute an α, β or γ-pyridyl radical, or a mixture of such derivatives may be produced" (35).

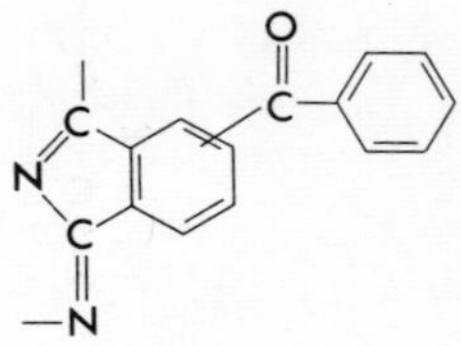

XXII

"In the substituted tetraphenylphthalocyanines and the tetrapyridyl-phthalocyanines described in this communication, the phthalocyanine structure may be attached to the substituted phenyl or pyridyl group at any one of three positions, and, further, the four groups may be all of the same kind or different. Such substituted tetraphenyl- and tetrapyridyl-phthalocyanines probably exist therefore in a relatively large number of different isomeric forms" (38).

A green shade phthalocyanine is made from incorporation of acyl groups such as benzoyl (XXII) to the phenylene nuclei of phthalocyanine by the Friedel-Crafts reaction between phthalocyanines and acyl chlorides (56,66) or by the condensation of aroylphthalonitriles to phthalocyanines (30,46).

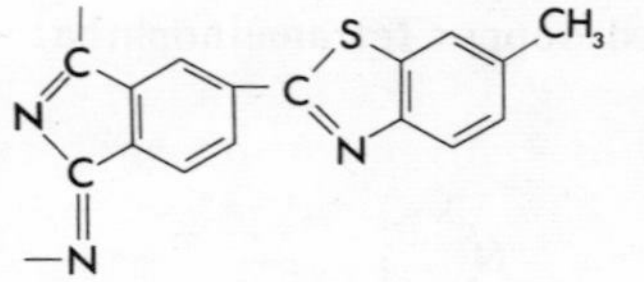

XXIII

Acylamino groups may be introduced also (51). Nickel tetra-4-acetyl-aminophthalocyanine is prepared from 4-acetylaminophthalonitrile and nickelous chloride in quinoline. A green phthalocyanine pigment, made from dehydro-para-toluidine, is copper tetra-(6-methyl-benzothiazolyl)-phthalocyanine (XXIII) (32,55).

Alkyl phthalocyanines such as tetramethylphthalocyanine (XXIV) may be synthesized (55).

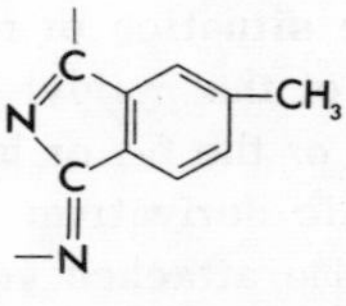

XXIV

Tetramethylphthalocyanine is prepared from *m*-aminotoluene, which is successively converted to *m*-cyanotoluene, *m*-cyano-*p*-nitrotoluene, *m*-cyano-*p*-aminotoluene, 3,4-cyanotoluene, and finally tetramethylphthalocyanine. This pigment is a trace greener than phthalocyanine, but otherwise apparently equivalent in pigment properties.

Arylphthalocyanines such as tetraphenylphthalocyanine (XXV) may be prepared (11,38,43,47) from ortho-dinitriles of the phenyl series such as 4-phenylphthalonitrile with appropriate metal salts.

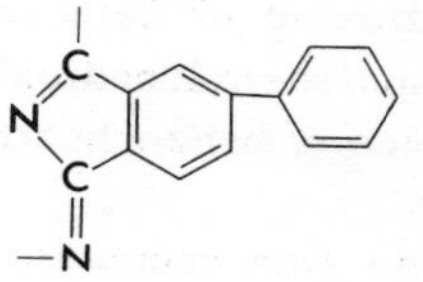

XXV

Copper tetraphenylphthalocyanine is somewhat greener than copper phthalocyanine.

A copper phthalocyanine mixture containing an average of two phenyl groups per phthalocyanine molecule has also been prepared by the reaction of a mixture of phthalonitrile, 3,4-dicyanodiphenyl, and copper salts at 180 to 185° (10).

Alkoxy (XXVI), aryloxy (XXVII), alkylmercapto (XXVIII), and arylmercapto (XXIX) phthalocyanines can be prepared by reacting halogen-containing phthalocyanines with aliphatic and aromatic alcohols or hydroxy compounds and mercaptans (31,44,52,59,60).

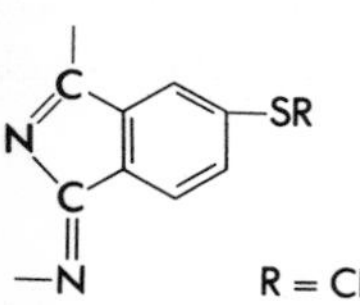

R = CH₃, C₂H₅ ...

XXVI

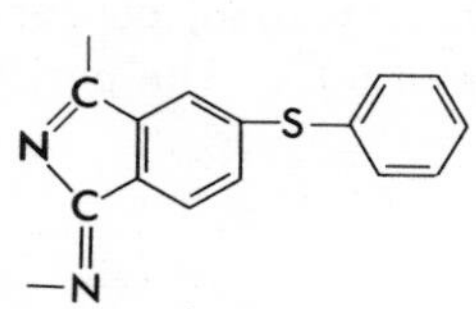

XXVII

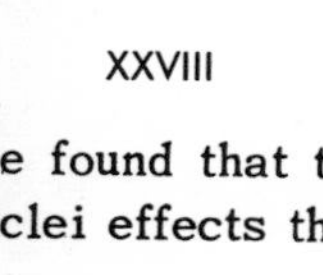

R = CH₃, C₂H₅ ...

XXVIII

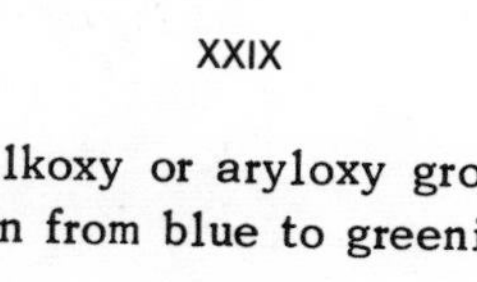

XXIX

"We have found that the presence of alkoxy or aryloxy groups in the benzene nuclei effects that the shades turn from blue to greenish-blue or green'' (31). Di-alkoxy or aryloxy groups may be introduced also, such as in tetra-4,5-diphenylenedioxide phthalocyanine (XXX).

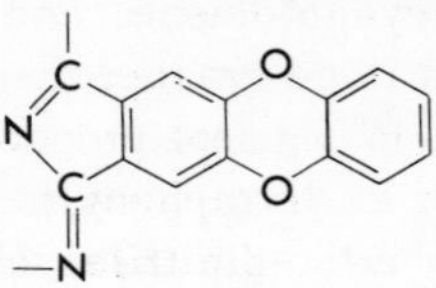

XXX

Copper 4,5-diphenylenedioxide phthalocyanine is prepared by heating the mixture of 2,3-dicyanodiphenylenedioxide with cuprous chloride 2 hours at 180° in the presence of benzophenone and pyridine. The product is dull olive in shade (31).

A phthalocyanine pigment from monothiophthalimide is reported (70), with a structure which may be as shown (XXXI). The structure remains to be determined, however. Copper sulfur phthalocyanine pigment is a blue powder, greener and duller than copper phthalocyanine.

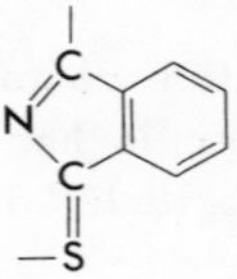

XXXI

Phthalocyanine pigments having enhanced resistance to crystallization and flocculation are claimed to be made by treating phthalocyanines with hydroxymethylimides of the formula

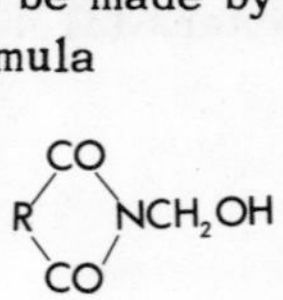

from which imidomethylphthalocyanine may be prepared. Copper phthal-imidomethylphthalocyanine (XXXII) is prepared from the mixture of copper phthalocyanine, concentrated sulfuric acid, paraformaldehyde, and phthalimide at 50°. The purified product is bright blue in color (62).

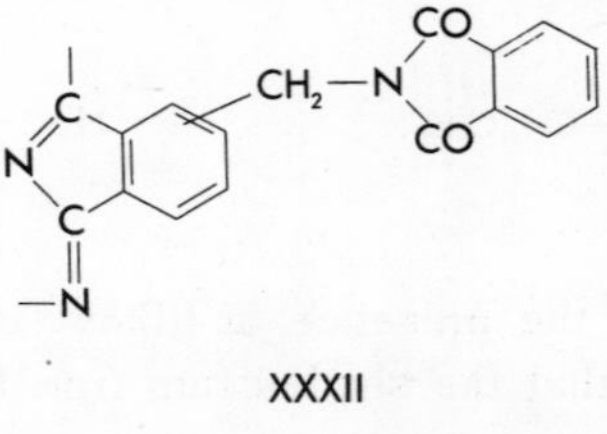

XXXII

Trifluoromethylphthalocyanines such as copper tetra-4-trifluoromethylphthalocyanine (XXXIII) is prepared

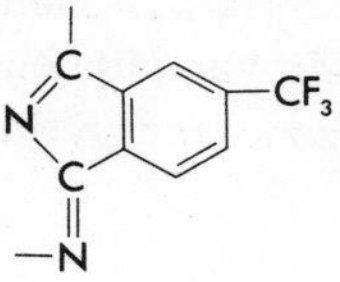

XXXIII

from the reaction of 4,5-dichloro-1,3-bis-trifluoromethylbenzene with cuprous cyanide in the presence of quinoline and cuprous bromide at 230 to 235° for from 6 to 8 hours (17). After purification, the pigment forms violet-blue crystals.

Pigments with similar properties are obtained from 3,4-dichloro-1-trifluoromethylmercaptobenzene, giving tetra-4-trifluoromethylmercaptophthalocyanines (XXXIV) (17).

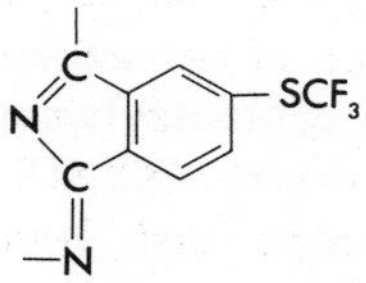

XXXIV

Acylaminophthalocyanine pigments have been synthesized. They are greener in shade than the corresponding phthalocyanines (8). Starting materials are o-dinitriles of the benzene series with an amino group substituent in which a hydrogen atom is substituted by the radical of an aliphatic or aromatic acid such as acetyl, butyryl, propionyl, benzoyl, methylbenzoyl, and methoxybenzoyl. Nickel tetra-4-acetylaminophthalocyanine (XXXV) is prepared from 4-acetylaminophthalonitrile and anhydrous nickel chloride heated together in quinoline at 180°.

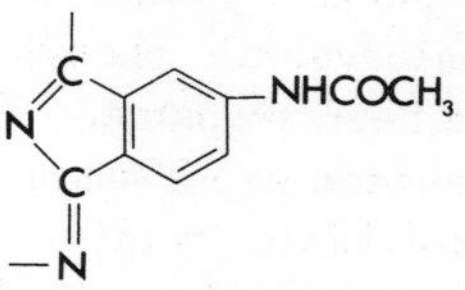

XXXV

Tetraphenylphthalocyanines in which the phenyl groups are connected to the phenylene groups by an oxygen (XXXVI), sulfur (XXXVII), or carbonyl group (XXXVIII) are prepared from 2,3-dicyanodiphenyleneoxide, 2,3-dicyanodiphenylenesulfide, and 2,3-dicyanofluorenone respectively (12). For example, copper tetra-2,3-phenyleneoxide phthalocyanine is prepared from a mixture of 2,3-dicyanodiphenyleneoxide and copper chloride in the presence of benzophenone and pyridine heated at 180 to 190° for 2 hours.

XXXVI   XXXVII   XXXVIII

Dialkylamino-, diaralkylamino-, and dicycloalkylaminophthalocyanines may be prepared by the reaction of halogenated phthalocyanine compounds with dialkyl-, diaralkyl-, or dicycloalkylamines (53). For example, tetra-p-methylphenylaminophthalocyanine (XXXIX) is made by the reaction of copper tetrachlorophthalocyanine and 1-amino-4-methylbenzene heated at 240 to 300° for several hours.

XXXIX

Copper tetra-4-nitrophthalocyanine is prepared by the reaction of 4-nitrophthalonitrile with copper bronze (39). It is dull and green in shade.

Yellow-green to green phthalocyanine pigments containing an azo bridge between the phthalocyanine phenylene groups and phenyl or naphthyl substituents have been prepared. For example, heating at 180 to 185°, 3,4-dicarboxybenzene-azo-2'-aminonaphthalene, urea, cupric chloride, and ammonium molybdate in nitrobenzene, gives copper tetra-naphthotriazolylphthalocyanine (33,71), (XL). Copper tetranaphthotri-azolylphthalocyanine is a yellow-green pigment with good lightfastness.

Tetradiazophthalocyanines may be prepared directly from tetranitrophthalocyanines by reduction with reducing agents such as alkali sulfides, sulfites, and hydrosulfites, and tin or zinc and acid, or stannous

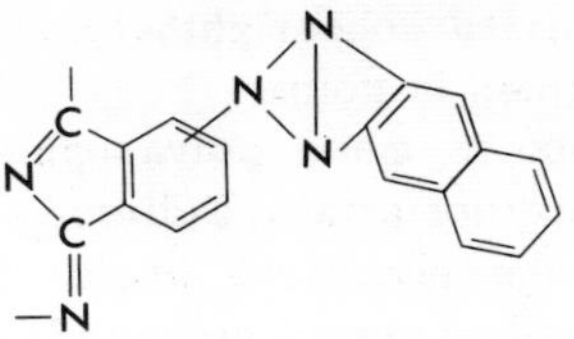

XL

chloride, to tetraaminophthalocyanines, followed by diazotization (34). For example, tetra-4-aminophthalocyanine can be prepared from tetra-4-nitrophthalocyanine by mixing copper tetra-4-nitrophthalocyanine in water and concentrated hydrochloric acid. The suspension is cooled to 5° and stannous chloride is added. After dilution with water, the product is filtered. The filter cake is mixed with sodium hydroxide solution and the mixture is boiled and filtered to free the copper tetra-4-aminophthalocyanine product from tin. The product is washed with water and dried. The dry material is green. Copper tetra-4-aminophthalocyanine can be diazotized by mixing it with cold water and sodium nitrite. Concentrated hydrochloric acid is added to this mixture at below 10°, forming the tetradiazo compound.

Di-, tri-, or tetradiazophthalocyanines "...may be converted into valuable pigments by coupling the same to coupling components which are devoid of water-solubilizing groups.

"Among the various coupling components suitable for the above purpose may be mentioned alpha- and beta-naphthol, acetoacetanilide, aceto-acet-o-toluidide, aceto-acet-o-chloro-anilide, 2-hydroxy-carbazole-3-carboxylic-p-chloro-anilide, and the various arylamides of 2,3-hydroxynaphthoic acid and 1-aryl-3-methyl-5-pyrazolones which are devoid of sulfo and carboxy groups, either in the form of the free acid or in the form of their salts.... The resulting polyazo compounds are generally intensely coloured bodies and have other properties making them very suitable for use as pigments. They are insoluble in water and also in high boiling organic solvents" (36).

Alkyl-, aralkyl-, and cycloalkylaminophthalocyanines have been prepared (49). These compounds are greener than the corresponding unsubstituted phthalocyanines. Copper phthalocyanine piperidine (XLI) is prepared by heating a mixture of piperidine, potassium hydroxide, copper,

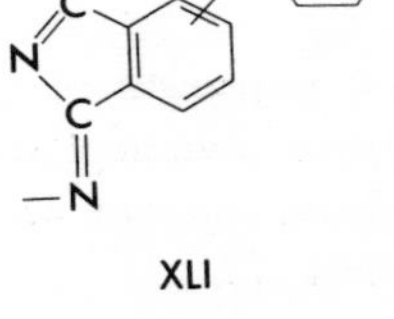

XLI

naphthalene, and chlorinated copper phthalocyanine at 350° for several hours. The product is green in color.

The possibility exists to make polyazophthalocyanine pigments in which the azo groups are not attached directly to the phenylene nuclei but are removed from the phenylene nuclei by oxygen, carbonyl, or sulfonyl bridges connected to phenyl groups (37). Such an azo intermediate is copper tetra-4-p-aminobenzoylphthalocyanine (XLII).

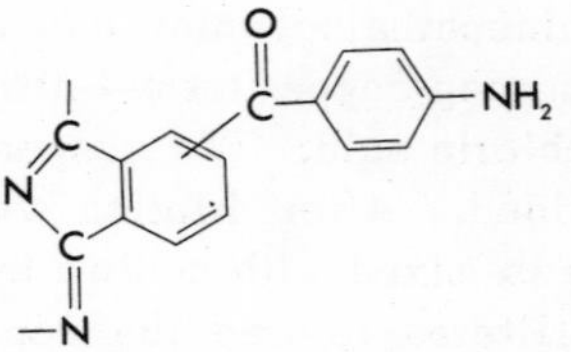

XLII

"It may be dried to form a greenish blue solid, but is conveniently kept in the form of an aqueous paste for the purpose of diasotization and coupling with azo coupling components."

Phthalocyanines substituted by phenyl groups and containing carboxylic groups in the phenylene rings of phthalocyanine that are converted into salts by alkaline earth metals have been prepared (50). They are green in shade. For example, 1-phenylbenzene-3,4,6-tricarboxylic acid, urea, and cuprous chloride, ammonium molybdate, and boric acid are heated at 200° several hours. Upon purification in alkaline, acid, and water media, the green copper tetraphenylphthalocyanine tetracarboxylic acid is obtained which is soluble in alkaline solution.

Copper tetraphenylphthalocyanine tetrabarium or tetracalcium carboxylate (XLIII) is prepared when the acid is treated with barium or calcium salts.

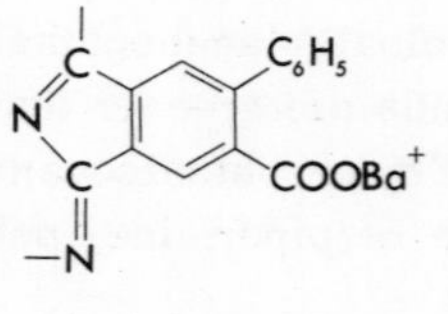

XLIII

Similar alkaline earth salt pigments of phthalocyanines may be prepared from mellitic, pyromellitic, hemimellitic, and trimellitic acids (75) as well as from other polyhydroxybenzene derivatives presumably such as prehnitic and mellophanic acids (7).

Halomethylphthalocyanines are prepared at elevated temperatures from mixtures of phthalocyanines, aldehydes, and halogen bearing acids and aldehydes (2). Copper tetrachloromethylphthalocyanine (XLIV) can be produced from a mixture of paraformaldehyde or trioxane, copper phthalocyanine, chlorosulfonic acid, and sulfuric acid.

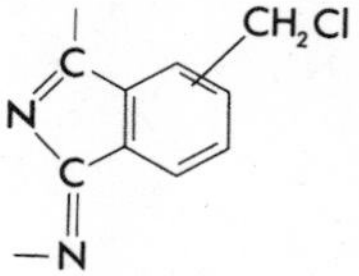

XLIV

Compounds similar to phthalocyanine-type compounds which vary from yellow to orange to brown in color have recently been synthesized (18). These compounds are outside the blue-green range of the phthalocyanine class, and they apparently do not possess as good heat stability as copper phthalocyanine. For example, a hemiporphyrazine of the formula (XLV), which forms greenish yellow crystals, decomposes at 380 to 385°.

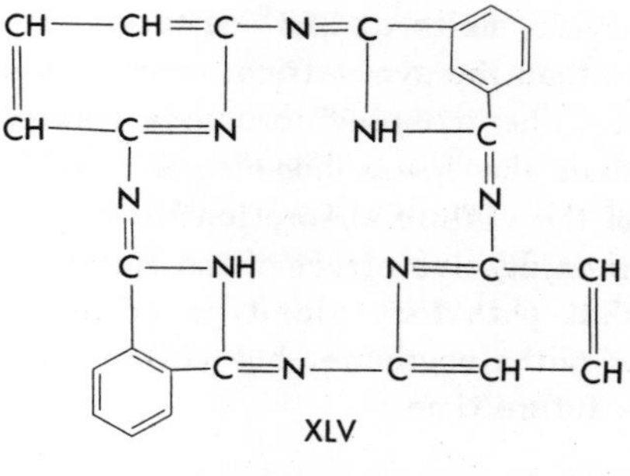

XLV

It may be prepared by heating the mixture of o-phthalonitrile, and 2,6-diaminopyridine in ethylene glycol at 197 to 198° for 1 hour.

Although not phthalocyanine-type compounds by definition, a series of unsymmetrical compounds such as (XLVI), similar to the phthalocyanine-type compounds, have recently been prepared, which vary from yellow to orange to brown in color (74).

Compound (XLVI) is prepared from a mixture of 4,4'-diaminophenyl-amine, phthalodinitrile, and sodium methylate solution at 40 to 50°. The product is orange-brown and has no melting point. It is heated in nitro-benzene at 200 to 205° several minutes from which methanol and ammonia evolve. The product (XLVI) crystallizes in long needles with a black reflex.

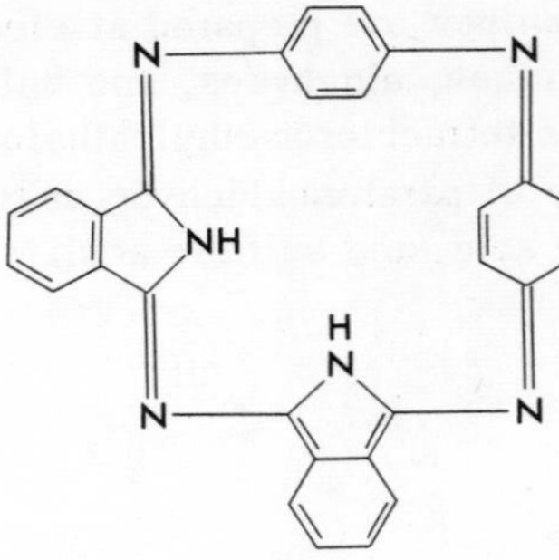

XLVI

Also, new red macrocycles, related to phthalocyanine-type compounds, have been made (21). "The new triisoindole macrocycles (XLVII) and (XLVIII) are cross-conjugated and bear an interesting structural relation to the fully conjugated tribenzotetrazaporphin and phthalocyanine on the one hand and the cross-conjugated benzene macrocycle (XLIX) on the other...

"The triisoindole-benzene macrocycle (XLVII) is obtained as felted burgundy-red needles, best by rapid crystallisation from nitrobenzene. Although the macrocycle melts at 353° with decomposition, it is much less stable thermally than the symmetrical cross-conjugated macrocycles, such as (XLIX).... The triisoindoletoluene macrocycle (XLVIII) is a shade darker red than the lower homologue (XLVII) as a result of a bathochromic shift of the visible absorption band to 5420 Å. This may be attributed to a hyperconjugative effect of the methyl substituent."

It may well be that phthalocyanine-type compounds, possessing the properties of copper phthalocyanine, but yellow to red in color will be synthesized at some future time.

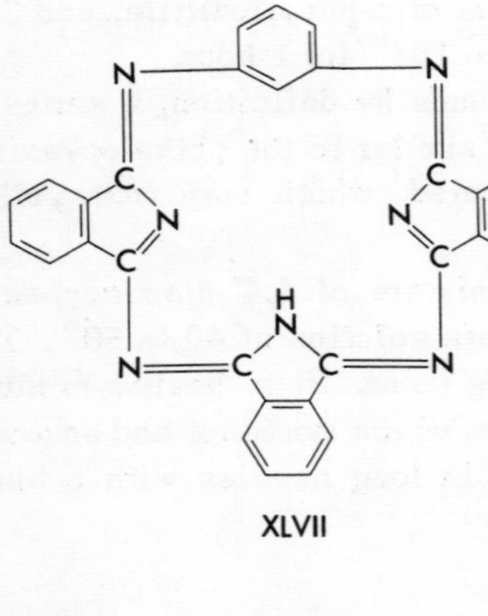

XLVII

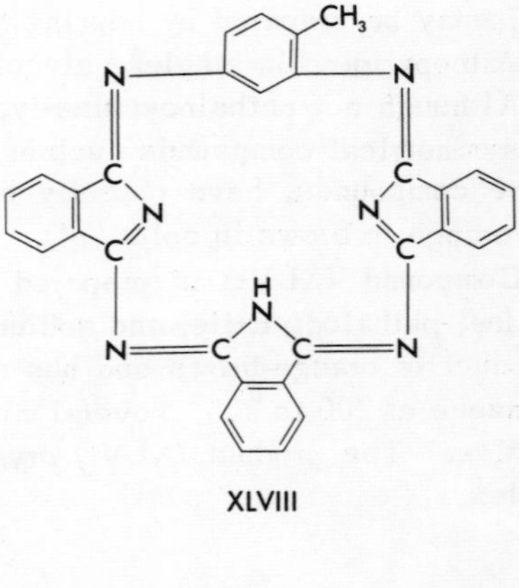

XLVIII

XLIX

REFERENCES

1. Anderson, J. S., Bradbrook, E. F., Cook, A. H., and Linstead, R. P., *J. Chem. Soc.*, 1938, 1151.

2. Badische Anilin-& Soda-Fabrik (I. G. Farbenindustrie A.-G. "In Auflösung"), British Patent 689,153 (Mar. 18, 1953).

3. Baguley, M. E., France, H., Linstead, R. P., and Whalley, M., *J. Chem. Soc.*, 1955, 3521.

4. Barrett, P. A., Linstead, R. P., Rundall, F. G., and Tuey, G. A. P., *J. Chem. Soc.*, 1940, 1079.

5. Barrett, P. A., Linstead, R. P., and Tuey, G. A. P., *J. Chem. Soc.*, 1939, 1809.

6. Beech, W. F., France, H., Haddock, N. H., Howard, H. T., Parkinson, A., and Woods, J. C. (to Imperial Chemical Industries Ltd.), British Patent 750,240 (June 13, 1954).

7. Bergwerksverband zur Verwertung von Schutzrechten der Kohlentechnik G. m. b. H., British Patent 801,488 (Sept. 17, 1958).

8. Bienert, B. (to General Aniline & Film Corp.), U. S. Patent 2,133,340 (Oct. 18, 1938).

9. Bienert, B. (to I. G. Farbenindustrie A.-G.), German Patent 696,590 (Sept. 25, 1940).

10. Bienert, B. (to I. G. Farbenindustrie A.-G.), German Patent 710,235 (Sept. 8, 1941).

11. Bienert, B., and Gassner, S. (to General Aniline & Film Corp.), U. S. Patent 2,213,517 (Sept. 3, 1940).

12. Bienert, B., and Gassner, S. (to I. G. Farbenindustrie A.-G.), German Patent 742,392 (Dec. 14, 1943).

13. Borodkin, V. F., and Smirnov, R. P., Izvest. Vysshikh Ucheb. Zavedeniĭ, *Khim. i Khim. Tekhnol.*, 3, (4), 718 (1960).

14. Bradbrook, E. F., and Linstead, R. P., *J. Chem. Soc.* 1936, 1744.

15. Bradbrook, E. F., Heilbron, I. M., Hey, D. H., and Haworth, J. W., U. S. Patent 2,277,629 (March 24, 1942).

16. Bradbrook, E. F., Coffey, S., and Haddock, N. H., U. S. Patent 2,277,628 (March 24, 1942); (to Imperial Chemical Industries Ltd.), British Patent 522,293 (June 13, 1940).

17. Braun, W., and Koeberle, K. (to General Aniline & Film Corp.), U. S. Patent 2,225,441 (Dec. 17, 1940).

18. Campbell, J. B. (to E. I. du Pont de Nemours & Co.), U. S. Patent 2,765,308
    (Oct. 2, 1956).
19. Cook, A. H., and Linstead, R. P., *J. Chem. Soc.*, 1937, 929.
20. Dent, C. E. (to Imperial Chemical Industries Ltd.), U. S. Patent 2,166,240
    (July 18, 1939); *J. Chem. Soc.*, 1938, 1.
21. Elvidge, J. A., and Golden, J. H., *J. Chem. Soc.*, 1957, 700.
22. Elvidge, J. A., and Linstead, R. P., *J. Chem. Soc.*, 1955, 3536.
23. Farbenfabriken Bayer A.-G., British Patent 735,048 (Aug. 10, 1955).
24. Ficken, G. E., and Linstead, R. P., *J. Chem. Soc.* 1952, 4846.
25. Ficken, G. E., and Linstead, R. P., *J. Chem. Soc.*, 1955, 3525.
26. Ficken, G. E., Linstead, R. P., Stephen, E., and Whalley, M., *J. Chem. Soc.*,
    1958, 3879.
27. France, H. (to Imperial Chemical Industries Ltd.), British Patent 686,395
    (Jan. 21, 1953); U. S. Patent 2,681,344 (June 15, 1954).
28. France, H. (to Imperial Chemical Industries Ltd.), U. S. Patent 2,744,913
    (May 8, 1956).
29. France, H., and Jones, W. O. (to Imperial Chemical Industries Ltd.), British
    Patents 689,387, 8 and 9 (March 25, 1953); U. S. Patent 2,681,345 (June
    15, 1954).
30. Gassner, S., and Bienert, B. (to General Aniline & Film Corp.), U. S. Patent
    2,116,196 (May 3, 1938).
31. Gassner, S., and Bienert, B. (to General Aniline & Film Corp.), U. S. Patent
    2,122,137 (June 28, 1938); I. G. Farbenindustrie A.-G., British Patent
    470,703 (Aug. 16, 1937).
32. Gassner, S., and Bienert, B. (to General Aniline & Film Corp.), U. S. Patent
    2,197,860 (Apr. 23, 1940); I. G. Farbenindustrie A.-G., British Patent
    488,201 (July 1, 1938).
33. Geigy A.-G., French Patent 1,146,075 (Nov. 6, 1957).
34. Haddock, N. H. (to Imperial Chemical Industries Ltd.), British Patent 529,847
    (Nov. 29, 1940).
35. Haddock, N. H., U. S. Patent 2,277,588 (March 24, 1942).
36. Haddock, N. H., (to Imperial Chemical Industries Ltd.), U. S. Patent 2,351,119
    (June 13, 1944).
37. Haddock, N. H., Parkinson, A., and Rowe, G. A. (to Imperial Chemical In-
    dustries Ltd.), U. S. Patent 2,414,374 (Jan. 14, 1947).
38. Haworth, J. W., Heilbron, I. M., Hey, D. H., Wilkinson, R., and Bradbrook,
    E. F., *J. Chem. Soc.*, 1945, 409.
39. Heilbron, I. M., Irving, F., and Linstead, R. P., U. S. Patent 2,286,679
    (June 16, 1942).
40. Helberger, J. H., *Ann.*, 529, 205 (1937).
41. Helberger, J. H. (to I. G. Farbenindustrie A.-G.), German Patent 704,927
    (Apr. 10, 1941).
42. Helberger, J. H., and von Rebay, A., *Ann.*, 531, 279 (1937).
43. Higashiura, K., *Technol. Repts. Kansai Univ.*, 35, 139 (1960).
44. Holzach, K., and Mühlbauer, F. (to General Aniline & Film Corp.), U. S.
    Patent 2,124,299 (July 19, 1938).
45. I. G. Farbenindustrie A.-G., British Patent 457,526 (Nov. 30, 1936); French
    Patent 805,879 (Dec. 2, 1936); U. S. Patent 2,212,924 (Aug. 27, 1940).
46. *Ibid.*, British Patent 468,043 (June 28, 1937).
47. *Ibid.*, British Patent 470,542 (Aug. 17, 1937).
48. *Ibid.*, British Patent 471,418 (Aug. 30, 1937).

49. *Ibid.*, British Patent 471,435 (Sept. 6, 1937).
50. *Ibid.*, British Patent 496,819 (Dec. 7, 1938).
51. *Ibid.*, French Patent 809,785 (Mar. 10, 1937).
52. *Ibid.*, French Patent 816,859 (Aug. 19, 1937).
53. *Ibid.*, French Patent 817,167 (Aug. 27, 1937).
54. *Ibid.*, German Patent 663,552 (Aug. 9, 1938).
55. I. G. Farbenindustrie, FIAT 1313, PB 85172, Vol. III, p. 323.
56. *Ibid.*, p. 325.
57. *Ibid.*, p. 334.
58. *Ibid.*, pp. 336–7.
59. I. G. Farbenindustrie, PB 70339, frames 11352–11353 and 11488.
60. *Ibid.*, PB 70340, frame 12468.
61. Imperial Chemical Industries Ltd., Italian Patent 361,978 (Aug. 9, 1938).
62. Lacey, H. T. (to American Cyanamid Co.), U. S. Patent 2,761,868 (Sept. 4, 1956); British Patent 695,523 (Aug. 12, 1953).
63. Linstead, R. P., Noble, E. G., and Wright, J. M., *J. Chem. Soc.*, 1937, 911.
64. Linstead, R. P., and Whalley, M., *J. Chem. Soc.*, 1952, 4839.
65. Linstead, R. P., Whalley, M., and Ficken, G. E., British Patent 713,208 (Aug. 4, 1954).
66. Mühlbauer, F. (to I. G. Farbenindustrie A.-G.), German Patent 686,054 (Jan. 2, 1940).
67. Parkinson, A. (to Imperial Chemical Industries Ltd.), British Patent 762,778 (Dec. 5, 1956).
68. Parkinson, A. (to Imperial Chemical Industries Ltd.), British Patent 763,084 (Dec. 5, 1956).
69. PB 70337, frames 8662-7.
70. Porter, J. C., Robinson, R., and Wyler, M., *J. Chem. Soc.*, 1941, 620.
71. Pugin, A., and Keller, E. (to Geigy A.-G.), U. S. Patent 2,837,528 (June 3, 1958).
72. Shigemitsu, M., *Bull. Chem. Soc., Japan*, 32, 541 (1959).
73. Whalley, M., Brown, P. M., and Spiers, D. B., *J. Chem. Soc.*, 1957, 2882.
74. Wolf, W. (to Farbenfabriken Bayer A.-G.), German Patent 945,782 (July 19, 1956).
75. Wyler, M. (to Imperial Chemical Industries Ltd.), British Patent 464,673 (Apr. 22, 1937).
76. Yagi, H. (to Sumitomo Chemical Co.), Japan Patent 633 (Feb. 12, 1959).

CHAPTER 8
POLYMERS

INTRODUCTION

In general, there are three types of phthalocyanine polymers: (1) phthalocyanines in which the phenylene rings of adjacent monomers are connected in the manner of a diphenyl bond (Figure 8-1), (2) phthalocyanines in which the monomers are joined together by substituents attached to the phenylene rings (Figure 8-2 and Figure 8-3), and (3) phthalocyanines which share phenylene rings in common (Figure 8-4 and Figure 8-5).

Copper phthalocyanine polymers may have first been prepared in the 1940's. In 1949 Ciba reported a black pigment from the reaction of 4,4'-dicyanobenzophenone-3,3'-dicarboxylic acid with cupric chloride and ammonium molybdate catalyst. The reported solubility of the powders obtained is characteristic of properties reported for phthalocyanine sheet polymers prepared under similar conditions from pyromellitic acid and 3,4,3',4'-tetracyanodiphenyl (11). In the words of the patent, "Es wurde gefunden, dass ein wertvoller Farbstoff der Phthalocyaninreihe hergestellt werden kann,wenn man 4,4'-Dicyanbenzophenon-3,3'-dicarbonsäure mit Harnstoff und einem kupferabgebenden Mittel zusammen kondensiert" (2). Also, in a Japanese patent of 1954, copper tetra-4-aminophthalocyanine was treated in a series of reactions, which included a potassium dichromate oxidation, forming a black pigment, presumably polymeric copper phthalocyanine (20).

The potential of phthalocyanine polymers in colorant and noncolorant applications remains to be determined (4). Present difficulties in determining chain types and lengths as well as limitations in chain size to perhaps no more than six repeating units may well be surmounted; and a systematic and thorough exploration of this polymer field, so well begun by the pioneers mentioned in this chapter, may yield a valuable increase in knowledge useful to the market place and to pure science.

TYPE I POLYMERS

The first apparent deliberate attempts to synthesize phthalocyanine polymers were made at Sprague Electric Company (12–17) and at American Cyanamid Company (5). At Sprague Electric Company, the object was to make polymeric copper phthalocyanine for use as a high temperature dielectric film coating on copper wire, condenser surfaces, and spacers for transformers (12). Phthalonitrile vapor reacts with copper wire to form a thin insulating film of copper phthalocyanine on the copper surface. However, copper phthalocyanine monomer was not a suitable dielectric because of its crystallinity, despite its low dielectric constant of 4.85 in the form of air-packed powder (18).

It was believed that 3,4,3′,4′-tetracyanodiphenyl would be a suitable monomer, leading to copper phthalocyanine polymer upon reaction with copper.

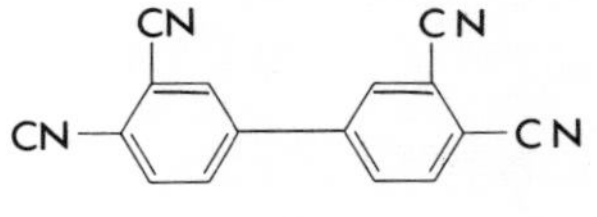

3,4,3′,4′-tetracyanodiphenyl

The expected polymer from condensation of 3,4,3′,4′-tetracyanodiphenyl with copper would be as shown in Figure 8-1 (13):

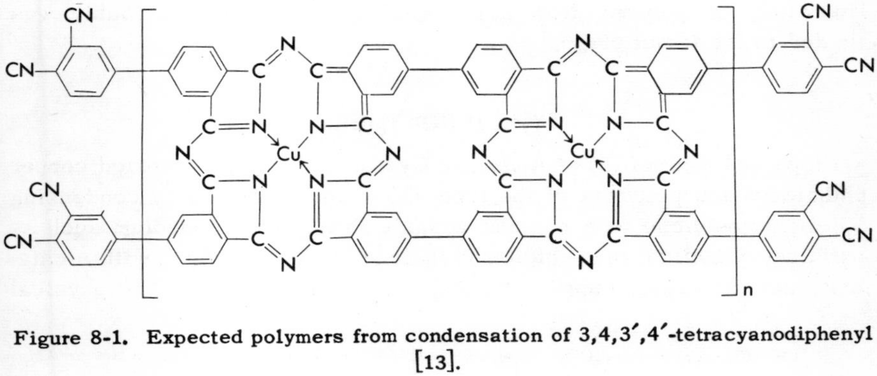

Figure 8-1. Expected polymers from condensation of 3,4,3′,4′-tetracyanodiphenyl [13].

The 3,4,3′,4′-tetracyanodiphenyl was synthesized by reacting 4,4′-dicyanodiphenyl-3,3′-disulfonate with anhydrous potassium ferrocyanide at 350 to 390° (16,17). Disodium 4,4′-diaminodiphenyl-3,3′-disulfonate (I) was tetraazotized by nitrous acid and reacted under conditions of the Sandmeyer reaction with potassium cyanide and copper sulfate or cuprous cyanide to yield disodium 4,4′-dicyanodiphenyl-3,3′-disulfonate (II). The dicyanodisulfonate was reacted at 380 to 450° with anhydrous potassium ferrocyanide in a Pyrex tube in a stream of carbon dioxide to give the tetranitrile (III) in about 5 per cent yield. After sublimation, the tetra-nitrile was characterized by a melting point of 205 to 210°. The structure was confirmed by chemical analysis and its ultraviolet absorption spectrum.

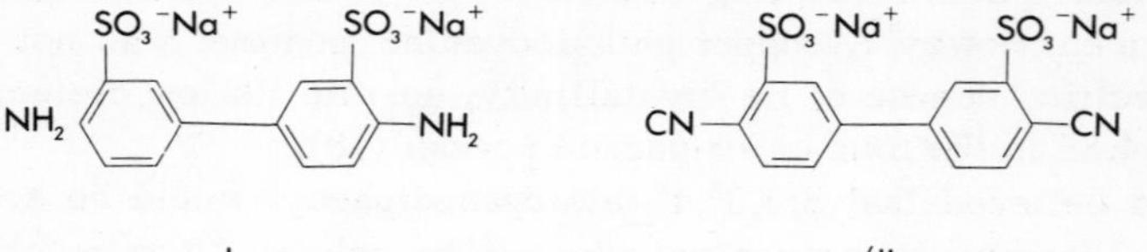

The Sprague Electric Company chemists also synthesized a polymeric copper phthalocyanine-type compound using 3,4,3′,4′-tetracyanodiphenyl starting from another route, namely, from diphenyl-3,4,3′,4′-tetracarboxylic acid, urea, cuprous chloride, and ammonium vanadate. The 3,4,3′,4′-tetracarboxylic acid was prepared from dimethyl-4-iodophthalate (14). Formation of polymer from 3,4,3′,4′-tetracyanodiphenyl probably was limited to the trimer stage.

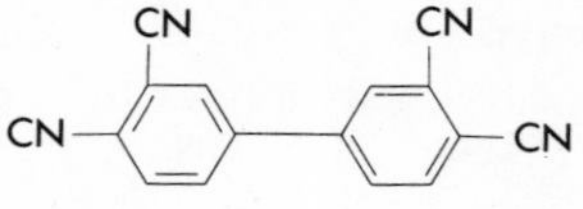

TYPE II POLYMERS

Kropa and Roemer (5) at American Cyanamid Company prepared copper phthalocyanine polymers of the type shown in Figure 8-2 by condensing 3,4-dichlorostyrene with cuprous cyanide in an organic medium such as pyridine, quinoline, or *o*-chloronaphthalene, at 200 to 260°, with a catalyst such as iodine, cupric chloride, or cuprous bromide. The physical

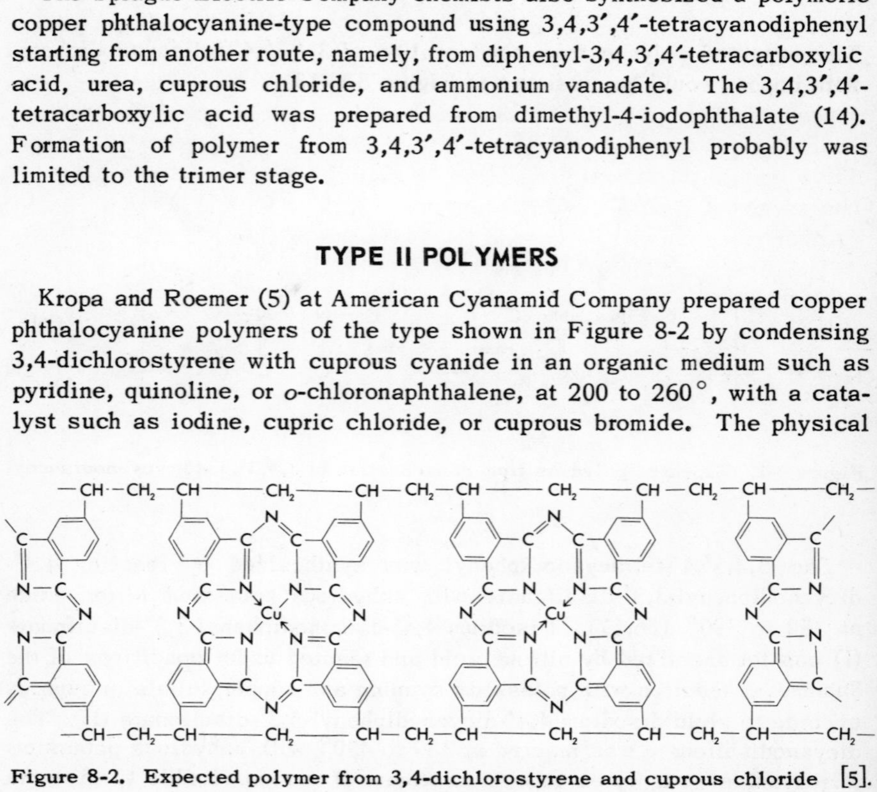

Figure 8-2. Expected polymer from 3,4-dichlorostyrene and cuprous chloride [5].

properties of the polymer were not stated; however, the polymer probably was a short chain with n not exceeding two or three. "52 parts of ortho-dichlorostyrene, 65 parts of cuprous cyanide, and 30 parts of pyridine were heated at 210° C for about 21 hours and the temperature then raised to 250°C for three hours. A greenish-brown pigment was obtained which, on acid pasting with concentrated sulfuric acid showed only partial solubility and is, therefore, considered to contain a large portion of polymerized product" (5).

Marvel, Rassweiler, and Martin have prepared low molecular weight copper phthalocyanine polymers from mixtures of 3,4,3',4'-tetracarboxy-diphenylether, phthalic anhydride, and urea with molybdenum catalyst (8–11). The polymer product was a greenish black powder. "It is

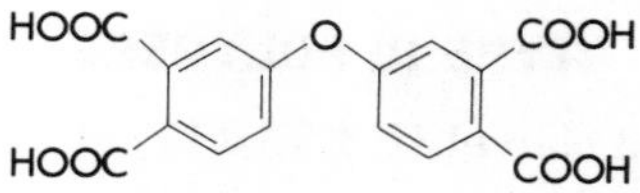

3,4,3',4'-tetracarboxydiphenylether

impossible to assign definite molecular structures or molecular weight ranges to these polymers at the present time. They are quite stable to heat, but are decomposed slowly in the air at temperatures above 350°. They burn with difficulty and this is partly the cause of erratic carbon analyses, but part of the difficulty is the lack of uniformity of polymers. Further research will be needed to clarify these points" (10).

The recurring units of the polymer are shown in Figure 8-3.

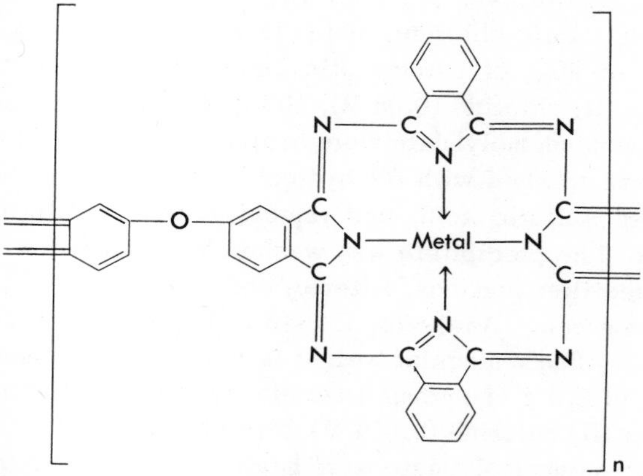

Figure 8-3. Presumed polymer from 3,3'-tetracarboxydiphenylether, phthalic anhydride, and urea [10].

Polymers of copper phthalocyanine from 3,4,3',4'-tetracyanodiphenylether, phthalonitrile, and copper-bronze were also made (9). The polymers were of low molecular weight, presumably dimers or trimers. Evidence for formation of these polymers came from elemental analysis, infrared spectra, and viscosities in sulfuric acid solution. Infrared absorption bands of monomer and polymer were only slightly different.

These authors also prepared polymers by the condensation of 3,4,3',4'-tetracyanodiphenylether without phthalonitrile. After eleven hours at 275°, "a phthalocyanine was formed which was insoluble in concentrated sulfuric acid, indicating that a high molecular weight, crosslinked polymer had been formed. This is the first sulfuric acid-insoluble polymer reported and probably represents the first instance of the formation of a high molecular weight polymeric phthalocyanine" (9).

TYPE III POLYMERS

Professors Bailar and Marvel (1,3,9,10,11) at the University of Illinois have undertaken to synthesize copper phthalocyanine polymers having the repetitive form shown in Figure 8-4.

The polymer in Figure 8-4 is linear. Polymerization presumably can take place in two dimensions, however, producing a sheet-like polymer as indicated in Figure 8-5.

In 1951 at the Plastics Laboratory at Princeton University, Willoch, Zawadski, and Vasileff (19) reported an attempt to make a Type III phthalocyanine polymer from pyromellitic anhydride, urea, cupric chloride, and boric acid catalyst. The authors' chemical analysis did not permit them to conclude that their dark green pigment product was a polyphthalocyanine.

Bailar and Drinkard have prepared Type III polymers from pyromellitic anhydride, urea, cupric chloride, and catalyst at 180° (1,3).

"A mixture of 20 g of pyromellitic dianhydride (0.092 M), 8 g of anhydrous copper (II) chloride (0.06 M), 108 g of urea (1.8 M), and catalytic amounts of ammonium molybdate were heated at 160°C for thirty minutes. The product was washed with 6N hydrochloric acid, dissolved in 200 ml of concentrated sulfuric acid, and reprecipitated by dilution with three liters of water. The precipitate was washed by decantation with 24 liters of water in three liter portions, filtered, and dried at 110°C. The product was light blue-green. Analysis, C:54.01, H:1.60, N:14.25, C/N:4.6, equiv. wt.:133. The molecular weight is believed to be near 1,500.

"A mixture of 5.0 g of pyromellitic dianhydride (0.023 M), 2.0 g of anhydrous copper (II) chloride (0.014 M), 26 g of urea (0.43 M), and catalytic amounts of ammonium molybdate were heated at 180°C for thirty minutes. The product was reprecipitated as described previously.... A mixture of 2.0 g of polymeric copper phthalocyanine, 0.1 g of anhydrous copper

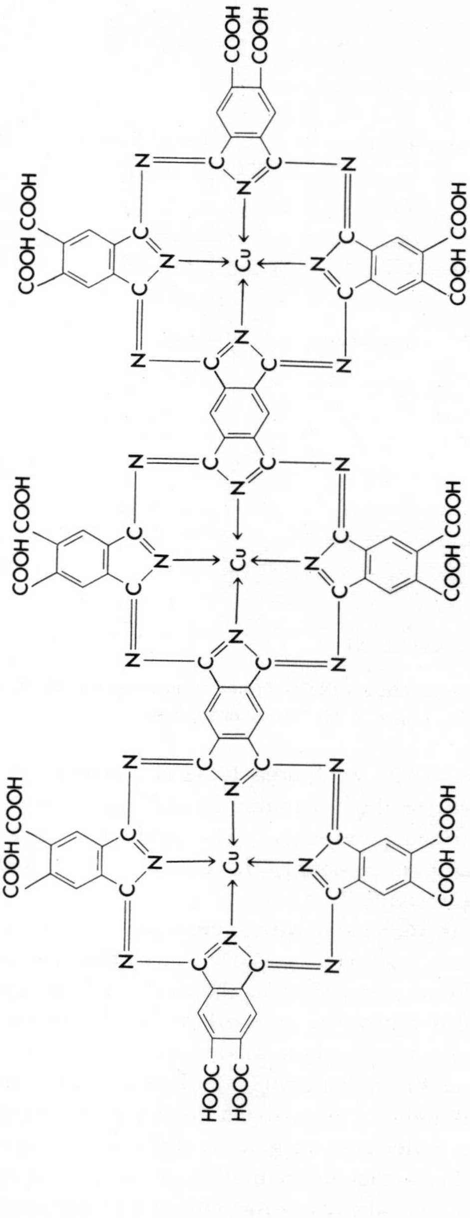

Figure 8-4. Trimer from reaction of pyromellitic dianhydride, cuprous chloride, urea, and catalyst [1,3].

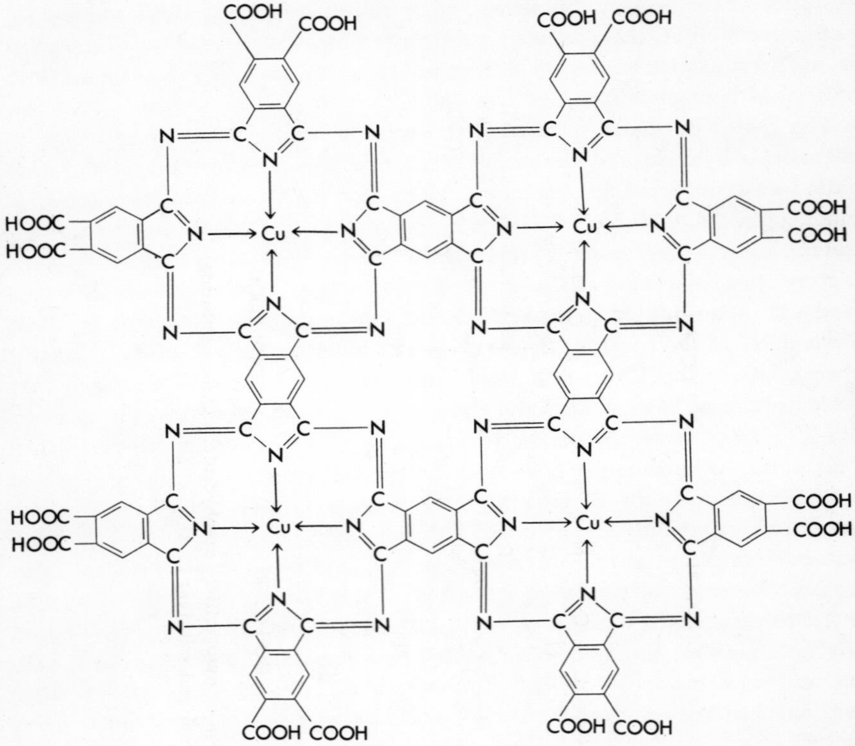

Figure 8-5. Hypothetical sheet-like polymer from reaction of pyromellitic dianhydride, cuprous chloride, urea, and catalyst [3].

(II) chloride (0.0008 M), 26 g of urea (0.43 M), and 0.1 g of ammonium
molybdate was heated for thirty minutes at 180°C. The product was reprecipitated as described previously. The product is dark grey (black).
The molecular weight is probably in excess of 20,000. Analysis:
C : 52.23, N : 20.67, C/N : 2.9."

The polymer size is increased with increasing reaction time. Heating
above 210° decreases polymer yield. Since the elemental analysis
changes with growth of the polymer, the molecular weight can be determined by elemental analysis, as well as by end-group titration. A
rapid method for molecular weight analysis is given by X-ray powder
diffraction patterns of the polymers (1,3). Powder patterns show a variation in relative peak heights as nitrogen analysis and end-group analysis
indicate a change in molecular weight. A difficulty in assigning a definite molecular weight is the determination of copper content (1). Analyzed copper content was always below calculated copper content. Heat

stability of the polymer increases with molecular weight. With increasing molecular weight, there is less sublimation and the residue may be heated in an inert atmosphere with a Bunsen flame or in air to a red heat with only slow decomposition.

The linear polymers were also presumably formed when three moles of phthalic anhydride and one mole of pyromellitic acid were heated under phthalocyanine-forming conditions. The polymers are dark blue-green to black powders, soluble in dimethyl formamide, and show visible and infrared absorption bands characteristic of the phthalocyanines. Satisfactory analyses were difficult to obtain. "The best evidence that the products were really polymeric phthalocyanines was obtained by their absorption in the visible spectrum in the 6000 to 7000 Å range, by their absorption in the 12 to 14 μ range in the infrared, and by the fact that their solutions in dimethylformamide were more viscous than the solvent itself" (10). However, it is impossible to assign "definite molecular weight ranges to these polymers at the present time."

Different catalysts do not appear to affect polymer size. For example, ammonium molybdate and zirconyl chloride exert equal effects (3). "The molecular weights of the polymers reported here are deceptive as to chain length. Because of the large weight of a single unit, a molecular weight of 4,000 represents a chain of only six units. From the data reported, it may be seen that maximum size seems to be reached at six units. At reaction temperatures below 180°, shorter units may be produced. Longer heating, heating at a higher temperature, or a combination of both, does not increase molecular weight. It is possible that solubility factors within the melt play a large part in fixing the maximum size of the polymer" (3).

Studies of phthalocyanine polymers may yield conclusions relating to the properties of phthalocyanine monomers. Lawton (6) has described Type III polymers such as the type of Figure 8–4. It was observed that copper phthalocyanine could be heated to 900° under vacuum with no apparent change in properties. Therefore, a mixture of Type III polymers was prepared from a mixture of phthalic anhydride, pyromellitic anhydride, urea, and cupric chloride. "The copper phthalocyanine was removed easily from the mixture by sublimation in high vacuum below 530°. Further increasing the temperature slowly to 696° gave no additional sublimate but led to total decomposition of the sample." Lawton concluded, "that the stability displayed by copper phthalocyanine at 800° and higher is due to a very slow rate, i.e., high activation energy, of decomposition and is not a measure of the intrinsic thermal stability of this compound."

In addition to interest in phthalocyanine polymers as colorants and dielectric materials, Lawton, Allen, and Cosgrove at the Battelle Memorial Institute (7) have described the use of phthalocyanine and Type III phthalocyanine sheet polymers as lubricants over a wide range of temperature. "What is claimed is: (1) A method of minimizing friction between metal-containing bearing surfaces comprising applying metal-free phthalocyanine to one of said metal-containing surfaces and moving said bearing surfaces in rubbing relationship to each other, while maintaining said bearing surfaces at a temperature in the range of from about 600°F to about 1500°F thereby forming a layer of metal phthalocyanine *in situ* on said surface, and thereby permitting the bearing surfaces to be moved in rubbing relationship to each other while being maintained at a temperature in the range of from about −90°F to about 1500°F. (2) The method of claim 1 wherein the metal-free phthalocyanine is polymeric."

REFERENCES

1. Bailar, Jr., J. C., Drinkard, Jr., W. C., and Judd, M. L., WADC Technical Report 57-391, ASTIA Document No. AD 131100, PB 131517, September, 1957.
2. Ciba Ltd., Swiss Patent 263,655 (Dec. 1, 1949).
3. Drinkard, Jr., W. C., and Bailar, Jr., J. C., *J. Am. Chem. Soc.*, **81**, 4795 (1959).
4. Helberger, P., *Paint & Varnish Prod.*, **50**, 54, January, 1960.
5. Kropa, E. L., and Roemer, J. J. (to American Cyanamid Co.), U. S. Patent 2,513,098 (June 27, 1950).
6. Lawton, E. A., *J. Phys. Chem.*, **62**, 384 (1958).
7. Lawton, E. A., Allen, C. M., and Cosgrove, S. (to Battelle Memorial Institute), U. S. Patent 3,023,164 (Feb. 27, 1962).
8. Martin, M. M., Thesis, Doctor of Philosophy, University of Illinois, 1958.
9. Marvel, C. S., and Martin, M. M., *J. Am. Chem. Soc.*, **80**, 6600 (1958).
10. Marvel, C. S., and Rassweiler, J. H., *J. Am. Chem. Soc.*, **80**, 1197 (1958).
11. Rassweiler, J. H., Thesis, Doctor of Philosophy, University of Illinois, 1957.
12. Robinson, P., and Reid, C. C. (to Sprague Electric Co.), U. S. Patent 2,590,650 (Mar. 25, 1952).
13. Sprague Electric Company, "High Temperature Dielectric Film," Fifth Progress Report, Contract No. Da-36-039-sc-87, U. S. Army Signal Corps Project 32-2005-33, PB 114092, August, 1951.
14. *Ibid.*, Sixth Progress Report, PB 114093, November, 1951.
15. *Ibid.*, Seventh Progress Report, PB 114094, February, 1952.
16. *Ibid.*, Eighth Progress Report, PB 114095, May, 1952.
17. Sprague Electric Company, PB 114096, Final Report, Contract No. Da-36-039-sc-87, U. S. Army Signal Corps Project: 32-2005-33, 1952.
18. Voet, A., and Suriani, L. R., *J. Colloid Sci.*, **7**, 1 (1952).
19. Willoch, J., Zawadski, T., and Vasileff, N., PB 108915, June, 1951.
20. Yagi, H., and Kuwabara, Y., Japan Patent 1996 (Apr. 14, 1954).

APPENDIX I
REFERENCES

1. Beretta, A., *Atti Xth congr. intern. chim.*, **4**, 823 (1939).
2. Beretta, A., *Chim. e ind.* (*Milan*), **21**, 273 (1939).
3. Bigelow, N. M., and Perkins, M. A., in Lubs, ed., "The Chemistry of Synthetic Dyes and Pigments," pp. 577–606, New York, Reinhold Publishing Corp., 1955.
4. Bradley, W., *Roy. Inst. Chem.* (*London*), *Lectures, Monographs, Repts.*, **5**, 39 (1958).
5. Brouillard, R. E., *Am. Ink Maker*, **32**, No. 2, 30, 65, 67 (1954).
6. Brouillard, R. E., and Katz, L., *Paint Manuf.*, **25**, 143 (1955).
7. Brouillard, R. E., *Am. Ink Maker*, **35**, No. 3, 36, 73 (1957).
8. Cronshaw, C. T. J., *Endeavour*, **1**, No. 2, 79 (1942).
9. Dahlen, M. A., *Ind. Eng. Chem.* **31**, 839 (1939).
10. Fierz-David, H. E., and Blangey, L., "Dye Chemistry," pp. 338–40, New York, Interscience Publishers, Inc., 1949.
11. Gerstner, H., "Die Chemie der Application von Komplexfarbstoffen," pp. 187–95, Berlin, Akademie Verlag, 1959.
12. Ghisolfi, G., *Ind. vernice* (*Milan*), **8**, 219 (1954).
13. Gordon, P. L., *Am. Paint J.*, **29**, No. 40, 62, 64, 66, 68, 72 (1945).
14. Haddock, N. H., *J. Soc. Dyers and Colourists*, **61**, 68 (1945).
15. Haddock, N. H., and Linstead, R. P., in "Thorpe's Dictionary of Applied Chemistry," M. A. Whitely, ed., Vol. 9, pp. 617–20, London, Longmans, Green & Co., 1949.
16. Jakobson, I., *Przemysl. Chem.* **37**, 137 (1958).
17. Johnson, K. C., "Phthalocyanines," Kirk-Othmer, ed., in "Encyclopedia of Chemical Technology," New York, Interscience Publishers, Inc., **10**, 607 (1953).
18. Kappelmeier, C. P. A., *Verfkroniek*, **9**, 39 (1936).
19. Kittel, H., ed., "Pigmente," pp. 462–3, Stuttgart, Wissenschaftliche Verlagsgesellschaft m.b.H., 1960.
20. Linstead, R. P., *Ber.*, **72**, 93 (1939).
21. Marcellaz, R., *Tiba*, **18**, 95 (1940).
22. Moll, I. S., *Paint Manuf.*, **21**, 402, 418 (1951).
23. Mühlbauer, F., *Paintindia*, **4**, No. 11, 27 (1955).
24. Payne, H. F., "Organic Coating Technology," pp. 896–905, New York, John Wiley & Sons, Inc., 1961.
25. PB 85172 (FIAT 1313), Vol. 3, pp. 273–347.
26. Permut, A., *Chem. Week*, 31, 46 (Nov. 29, 1952).
27. *Ibid.*, *Am. Ink Maker*, **31**, No. 9, 35–37, 63, 65, 67, 69 (1953).

28. "Phthalocyanine Pigments: Explosion of Color Paints a Bright Future," *Oil, Paint, and Drug Reptr.*, (Nov. 2, 1959).
29. Pratt, L. S., "Organic Pigments," pp. 8, 68, 214–24, 278, 283–4, 309, New York, John Wiley & Sons, Inc., 1947.
30. Sander, A., *Die Chemie*, **55**, 255 (1942).
31. Scully, S. A., *Interchem. Rev.*, **3**, 39 (1944).
32. Shugam, E. A., *Uspekhi Khim.*, **23**, 622 (1954).
33. Struve, W. S., in Lubs, ed., "The Chemistry of Synthetic Dyes and Pigments," pp. 607–24, New York, Reinhold Publishing Corp., 1955.
34. Ueda, U., *Chem. Rev. (Japan)*, **6**, 457 (1940).
35. Urban, G. J., *Mendel Bull.*, **13**, 102 (1941).
36. Varley, D. M., *Paint Manuf.*, **31**, 373 (1961).
37. Venkataraman, K., "The Chemistry of Synthetic Dyes," pp. 1118–42, New York, Academic Press, Inc., 1952.
38. Wahl, H., in Grignard, Dupont, Locquin, and Baud, ed., "Traité de Chimie Organique," Paris, Masson et Cie, **22**, 408 (1953).
39. Wahl, H., *Teintex*, **19**, 589 (1954).
40. Woodhead, A. H., *Paint Manuf.*, **15**, 192 (1945).
41. *Ibid.*, **17**, 369 (1947).

Comprehensive reviews of the phthalocyanine field are the excellent articles by Bigelow and Perkins [3], Struve [33], and Venkataraman [37].

References Relating to Phthalocyanine Dyes

1. Baumann, F., Bienert, B., Rösch, G., Vollmann, H., and Wolf, W., *Angew. Chem.*, **68**, 133 (1956).
2. Bowker, E. E., *Dyer*, **117**, 355 (1957).
3. Christ, W., *Tidsskr. Textiltek.*, **11**, 53 (1953).
4. Clarke, W., *Can. Textile J.*, **72**, 57 (1955).
5. Eibl, J., *Melliand Textilber.*, **39**, 522 (1958).
6. Gund, F., *ibid.*, **38**, 440 (1957).
7. Krolik, L. G., *Khim. Nauka i Prom.*, **3**, 212 (1958).
8. Struve, W. S., in Lubs, ed., "The Chemistry of Synthetic Dyes and Pigments," pp. 607–24, New York, Reinhold Publishing Corp., 1955.
9. Thaler, H., *Melliand Textilber.*, **38**, 1038 (1957).
10. Wittenberger, W., *ibid.*, **32**, 454 (1951).
11. Yoshita, Z., *Yûki Gôsei Kagaku Kyôkai Shi*, **16**, 240 (1958).

APPENDIX II

TEST PROCEDURES

A. Crystallization Tests

1. Xylene Test (2).

One g of pigment is added to 10 cc of xylene in a test tube. The slurry is agitated to ensure thorough wetting and the test tube is immersed in a beaker of boiling water for 15 min. A few drops of the slurry are spread on a microscope slide and the particles are viewed through a compound microscope at a magnification of approximately 200 diameters. As a control, some of the original dry pigment is mixed with xylene on a slide and compared with the above immediately.

2. Xylene Test (9).

Add 0.5 g copper phthalocyanine to 10 cc xylene in a test tube, shake until the color is well moistened, place the test tube in a beaker of boiling water and boil for 15 minutes. After filtration and drying, compare with the starting material by checking color intensity by normal rub-up procedures (1 : 10 with titanium dioxide). If the copper phthalocyanine is very unstable, needles can also be seen clearly under a microscope.

3. Alkyd Enamel Test (2).

"The enamel (10/90 color/'Ti-Pure' R-610) is diluted (50 cc enamel/20 cc xylene) to spraying viscosity and a portion sprayed to record 'initial color.' The remainder of the reduced enamel is aged at 140 °F. for three days and panels again sprayed. Strength loss of the enamels on aging is a measure of the extent of crystallization."

4. Zinc Yellow Test (9).

Grind in a mortar 50 mg copper phthalocyanine, 10 g zinc yellow, and 3 drops of mineral oil. To 1 g of the mixture in a test tube add 10 cc xylene. Place the test tube in a beaker of boiling water for 2 hr and compare it with a freshly prepared sample of the same composition. A shift in hue from green toward yellow will indicate the degree of crystallization.

5. Urea-Formaldehyde Resin Lacquer Test (9).

Grind a mixture of 0.5 g copper phthalocyanine, 5 g rutile titanium dioxide, 35 g 60 per cent urea-formaldehyde resin in xylene-butanol solution of low viscosity and 65 g glycerol-phthalate-alkyd resin or a dehydrated castor oil-modified alkyd base, in a ball mill, dilute with xylene to 150 g; spray a panel with this lacquer and heat it for 1 hour at 105 °; prepare another panel in a similar manner when the lacquer has aged for 5 days, 1 month, 2 months and compare each sprayed panel with the original panel. If the lacquer shows loss of color value as it is aged, the copper phthalocyanine is crystallizing.

6. Lacquer Test (9).

A lacquer tinted with 1 part copper phthalocyanine to 10 parts titanium dioxide is reduced to spraying consistency by adding 20 parts of xylene to 50 parts of lacquer. It is sprayed on a test panel at once. The remaining dilute lacquer is held at 60 ° for three days in an oven and a second test panel is prepared. The difference in color intensity between the 2 panels is a measure of the crystal stability of the copper phthalocyanine.

B. Flocculation Tests

1. Enamel Test (9).

Grind 1.3 g copper phthalocyanine, 31 g rutile titanium dioxide, and 88 g oil-modified phthalate resin in a ball mill for 48 hr. Dilute it with toluene to 150 g and add 0.9 cc 16 per cent lead drier and 0.25 cc 6 per cent cobalt drier. Spray the enamel on a panel, and after 10 min place a drop on the panel and allow it to run. If the drop is less intense in color, the pigment is not resistant to flocculation. If it is the same shade or darker, it is flocculation resistant.

2. ASTM Tentative Specifications for Copper Phthalocyanine
   Blue (D 963-58T) (1). Used by permission of ASTM. Method is reviewed
   periodically by ASTM.
   Scope

1. These specifications cover copper phthalocyanine blue pigment to be purchased in dry powder form for use in paints, printing ink, and related products. Several types are available, intended for different end uses. The specific end use will determine which of the tests in Section 4 are applicable.

Composition and Properties

2. (a) Pigment—The pigment shall consist of the product known commercially as copper phthalocyanine blue, with or without other ingredients incorporated during manufacture to improve or alter the working properties of the pigment, but free of any other coloring matter, either organic or inorganic. The pigment shall conform to the following requirements:

Moisture and other volatile matter, max, per cent..... 3.0
Other coloring matter............................. None
(b) Mass Color and Character of Tint—The mass color and character of the tint formed by mixture with a white pigment shall be the same as, and the strength not less than, that of a reference sample mutually agreed upon by the purchaser and the seller.
(c) Oil Absorption—The oil absorption shall be between 90 and 110

per cent of that of a reference sample mutually agreed upon by the purchaser and the seller.

(d) Reaction in Identification Tests—The pigment shall show the same reaction in identification tests (Section 4(d) to (h)) as a reference sample mutually agreed upon by the purchaser and the seller.

(e) End Product Dispersion Stability—When specified, end product dispersion stability, determined as described in Section 4 (i) or by using a mutually agreed upon system, shall be the same as or better than that of a reference pigment sample also mutually agreed upon by the purchaser and the seller.

End product dispersion stability of a phthalocyanine pigment is frequently referred to as flocculation-resistance. It is judged as the difference in depth of tint between a sprayed and a poured or brushed coating. The behavior of the pigment can be markedly affected by the formulation used, the type of vehicle, thinner, etc. It is important that the buyer and seller define the type of composition to be used in carrying out the test if the one described in Section 4 (i) is not acceptable.

(f) End Product Storage Stability—When specified, end product storage stability, determined as described in Section 4 (j), shall be the same as or better than that of a reference pigment sample mutually agreed upon by the purchaser and the seller.

Storage stability of a phthalocyanine is frequently referred to as crystal stability, since it may be a measure of the tendency of the phthalocyanine to grow in particle size, that is, to grow crystals and thus lose strength. It is also related to a change in dispersion stability as defined in (e).

Sampling.

3. Two samples shall be taken at random from different packages from each lot, batch, day's pack, or other unit or production in a shipment. When no markings distinguishing between units of production appear, samples shall be taken from different packages in the ratio of two samples for each 1000 lb, except that for shipments of less than 1000 lb, two samples shall be taken. At the option of the purchaser, each sample may be tested or samples from the same production may be blended in equal quantities to form a composite sample.

Methods of Testing

4. Tests shall be conducted in accordance with the following methods of the American Society for Testing Materials. Test procedures not covered by ASTM methods shall be mutually agreed upon by the purchaser and the seller.

(a) Moisture and other Volatile Matter—Method A of the Method of Test for Hygroscopic Moisture (and Other Matter Volatile Under the Test Conditions) in Pigments (ASTM Designation: D 280).

(b) Mass Color and Tinting Strength—Method of Test for Mass Color and Tinting Strength of Color Pigments (ASTM Designation: D 387).

(c) Oil Absorption—Method of Test for Oil Absorption of Pigments by Spatula Rub Out (ASTM Designation: D 281).

(d) Identification—Section 19 of the Methods for Chemical Analysis of Blue Pigments (ASTM Designation: D 1135).

(e) Basic Dye Derivatives—Section 21 of Methods D 1135.

(f) Other Organic Coloring Matter—Section 22 of Methods D 1135.

(g) Ultramarine Blue—Section 23 of Methods D 1135.

TABLE I

Ingredient	Amount	Specification
Porcelain balls, 1/2 in. diam..........	1350 g	...
Toluene (industrial grade)	380 cc	D 362[a]
Titanium dioxide (rutile type)	750 g	D 476[b]
Soya-modified phthalic alkyd solution,[c] 50 per cent solids	275 g	...

[a]Specification for Industrial Grade Toluene for Use in Paint, Varnish, Lacquer, and Related Products (ASTM Designation: D 362)

[b]Specifications for Titanium Dioxide Pigments (ASTM Designation: D 476)

[c]Glyptal Resin, ZA-262, available from General Electric Co., Chemical Materials Dept., 1052 West 6th St., Los Angeles, Calif. has been found satisfactory for this purpose.

(h) Iron Blue—Section 24 of Methods D 1135.

(i) End Product Dispersion Stability—The dispersion stability shall be determined with a paint, enamel, or lacquer agreed upon, using the pigment sample under test and a reference pigment sample. Unless the buyer and seller agree otherwise, the following procedure shall be used. It has the advantage of combining the dispersion stability and storage stability (Paragraph (i)) tests.

(1) Tinting White—Charge a 1-gal porcelain ball mill with the ingredients given in Table I. Rotate the mill at 70 to 75 rpm for 24 hr; then add 1900 g of alkyd resin solution, 90 cc of toluene, and 15 g of liquid drier containing lead and cobalt and conforming to the Specifications for Liquid Paint Driers (ASTM Designation: D600). Rotate the mill for 1 hr and pour the mixture through a paint strainer and store in tightly closed containers.

(2) Mill Base—In an 8-oz flat cream jar, charge 315 g of 1/8-in. diam steel shot, 63 cc of toluene, 31.0 g of alkyd resin solution, and 12.5 g of copper phthalocyanine blue. Rotate for 24 hr, at 60 to 80 rpm. Add 100 g of alkyd resin and 10 cc of toluene, and rotate for 30 min. Pour the mixture through a paint strainer and store in a tightly closed container until used.

(3) Tint—Mix 32 g of mill base (Item (2)), 93 g of tinting white (Item (1)), and 40 cc of toluene. Shake vigorously for 30 min. Spray at once to good covering on glazed cardboard or primed metal panels.

(4) Procedure—Allow the freshly sprayed panel to dry until the film becomes tacky (15 to 30 min); then with the finger gently rub a streak on the panel. This streak will usually show an increase in tint depth over the sprayed portion (Figure 1). Allow the remaining sample of tint to stand for 30 min, then hand-mix or shake it briefly and pour over a part of the previously sprayed panel. Air dry the panels for 2 hr at room temperature and bake for 1 hr at 105°. The poured portion of the film is generally equal to or lighter in tint than the sprayed portion (see Figure

1). The difference between the strength of the sprayed portion and that of the rubbed and poured areas shall be no more than that of a previously agreed upon standard sample.

(j) End Product Storage Stability—Unless the purchaser and the seller have agreed otherwise, the following procedure shall be used. Tint a portion of the mill base prepared as described in Item (2) of Paragraph (i), and spray the panel at once. Store the remainder at 50 to 60° for a period of six weeks in a tightly closed container (Caution—Prolonged storage at elevated temperatures will cause some alkyds to gel.). Then cool to room temperature, shake well, and prepare a tint as before. Any tendency toward crystallization or flocculation will result in a loss of tinting strength. The behavior of a given sample shall be compared to that of a previously agreed upon standard sample.

C. Identification Tests (4).

1. Add a saturated solution of trichloroacetic acid in water to about 0.01 g pigment. With copper phthalocyanine no color change takes place, but when a few drops of concentrated nitric acid are added to the mixture an intense violet is produced. Copper polychlorophthalocyanine does not undergo any color change (4).

2. N.P.I.R.I. Standard Test Methods for Pigment Identification (6).

This test method includes a procedure for establishing the presence of phthalocyanine and/or ultramarine blues, a confirming test for ultramarine blue, and an identifying test for copper phthalocyanine. The first of these is based on the resistance of both pigments to caustic. Potassium hydroxide is employed to remove all other blue pigments which might be present. The print is then subjected to dilute hydrochloric acid and if the blue coloration disappears, phthalocyanine is absent and ultramarine is present. If the blue color persists, phthalocyanine is present and ultramarine may or may not be present.

The confirming test for ultramarine blue involves a reaction of this pigment with potassium or ammonium alum to liberate hydrogen sulfide. The latter is detected on filter paper moistened with lead acetate which darkens on contact with hydrogen sulfide vapors as lead sulfide is formed.

The test for copper phthalocyanine is essentially a flame test for copper. A bright bluish-green colored flame indicates the presence of phthalocyanine. Since other copper containing pigments are not used in printing inks, the method is considered specific to copper phthalocyanine. Phthalocyanine green also contains copper, but the color of its flame is whitish, due to the chlorine present, and the difference is readily distinguished.

Results of the checking program indicated that the confirming tests must be used if the results are to be reliable. While two operators identified both the phthalocyanine and ultramarine pigments correctly in every print which contained either or both, a third operator failed to detect the pigments in four different instances. The third operator, however, on repeating the determinations (but without knowledge of previous errors), made correct identification on all but one print. This experience indicated that familiarity with this method is important for the correct interpretation of results. Such familiarity could be obtained by running prints of known composition and concentration along with those being tested.

3. Identification of Paint (8).

Paints containing organic pigments such as copper phthalocyanine, Hansa Yellow and Permanent Red R, are identified by capillary analysis with a solvent composed of hydrochloric acid, ethanol, butanol, benzyl alcohol, and acetone in the ratio of 1 : 25 : 5 : 5 : 30.

D. Quantitative Determinations

1. Use of Ceric Sulfate (3).

A known weight (about 0.3 g) of the finely divided compound is triturated with a little dilute sulfuric acid, and a known excess of exactly N/10-ceric sulfate solution added. The bulk of the pigment rapidly disappears. To ensure the completion of the reaction, the solution is kept at 60° until clear, any lumps being crushed. N/10-Ferrous ammonium sulfate equivalent to the original amount of ceric sulfate is then added, and the excess of ferrous salt titrated with N/10-ceric sulfate, Xylene Cyanole FF being used as indicator. The color changes from greenish yellow to brown in the presence of excess of the ceric salt; the endpoint is sharp and can be approached from either side. The final ceric sulfate titer is equivalent to the amount originally employed to oxidize the phthalocyanine.

2. Vanadametric Determination of Phthalocyanines (7).

About 60 mg of the pigments are accurately weighed and triturated with 10 cc of syrupy phosphoric acid (this step can be omitted in the case of the sulfonic acid phthalocyanine derivatives). Then the finely dispersed pigment is treated with 20 cc of about 0.05 N sodium vanadate solution (10–20 cc for the sulfonic acid) and enough 20 N sulfuric acid to make the desired normality, such as 10 N, 6 N, and 2 N for metal-free phthalocyanine, copper phthalocyanine and copper phthalocyanine sulfonic acid, respectively. The volume is made up to 60 cc and the mixture is heated on a boiling water bath for 60 min, 30 min and 5–10 min, respectively. After cooling the unreacted vanadate is determined by titration with a standard solution of Mohr's salt. A blank is carried out under identical conditions, but omitting the pigment. The difference in the two titer values corresponds to the amount of pigment taken.

3. Copper Determination (5).

Weigh about 1 g copper phthalocyanine into a 35 cc porcelain crucible and decompose it with nitric acid (d 1.465), introduced slowly to avoid violent decomposition. Heat the crucible slowly and carefully to complete the decomposition. The decomposition products are washed from the crucible sides with nitric acid (d 1.5). Carefully evaporate the nitric acid and avoid ignition of the contents of the crucible. Finally, calcine the product in an oven at red heat. Cool and weigh the product as copper oxide (CuO).

REFERENCES

1. American Society for Testing Materials, *Standards*, 8, 41–44 (1961).
2. Botti, E. C., Offic. Dig. Federation Paint and Varnish Production Clubs, 305, 408–17 (1950).
3. Dent, C. E., Linstead, R. P., and Lowe, A. R., *J. Chem. Soc.*, 1934, 1033.
4. Hepworth, R. L. P. R., *Chem. and Industry*, 1952, 272.
5. Kanyaev, N. P., and Spryskov, A. A., *Zhur. Priklad. Khim.*, 25, 1220–1 (1952).
6. Moore, C. E., *Paint Manuf.*, 27, 377–80 (1957).
7. Rao, G. G., and Sastri, T. P., *Z. Anal. Chem.*, 169, 11–16 (1959) (in English).
8. Tsujimoto, Y., and Nagahama, S., *Kagaku Keisatsu Kenkyusho Hokoku*, 13, 57–60 (1960).
9. Turk, M. J. H., *Verfkroniek*, 32, 494 (1959).

APPENDIX III
COLOUR INDEX NUMBERS AND MANUFACTURERS

The information in this appendix is from the COLOUR INDEX, Second Edition, 1956-, compiled, edited, and published by the Society of Dyers and Colourists, Bradford, Yorkshire, England, and the American Association of Textile Chemists and Colorists, Wm. D. Appel, Editor, Chevy Chase, Maryland.

Colour Index Number	Manufacturer	Trade Name
C. I. 74100	General Dyestuff Company	Heliogen Blue G
(Pigment Blue 16; phthalocyanine.)	Imperial Chemical Industries, Ltd.	Monastral Fast Blue G
	Imperial Chemical Industries, Ltd.	Vulcafor Fast Blue G
	Imperial Chemical Industries, Ltd.	Vynamon Blue G
C. I. 74160	American Cyanamid Co.	Cyan Blue Toner GT 55-3300
(Pigment Blue 15; copper phthalocyanine.)	Ansbacher Siegle Corp.	Fastolux Blue
	Aziende Colori Nazionali Affini A.C.N.A.	Segnale Light Turquoise NB
	Badische Anilin- & Soda-Fabrik A. G.	Heliogen Blue B, BR, BG
	Ciba Ltd.	Oralith Blue BLL Conc.
	CIECH, Jasna 12, Warsaw, Poland	Pigment Fast Blue B
	Clayton Aniline Co. Ltd.	Oralith Blue BLL Conc.
	Du Pont Co.	Monastral Fast Blue BC, BFP, BNC, BWD
	Du Pont Co.	Ramapo Blue
	Du Pont Co.	Rubber Blue PCD
	Federal Color Laboratories	Duratint Blue 1001
	Geigy Ltd.	Irgalite Fast Brilliant Blue BL
	General Dyestuff Company	Ceres Blue BHR
	General Dyestuff Company	Fenalac Blue B Disp.

Colour Index Number	Manufacturer	Trade Name
C. I. 74160, cont.	General Dyestuff Company	Heliogen Blue BA-CF, BH, BKA-CF, BNC, BV, BWS, BWSN
	General Dyestuff Company	Rubber Blue BKA
	Harmon Color Company	Congo Blue B-4
	Harmon Color Company	Palomar Blue B-4773
	Harmon Color Company	Phthalocyanine Blue WDB-4675
	Harmon Color Company	Resamine Blue B-4703
	Harmon Color Company	Skyline Blue B-4712
	Holland Color Company	Permanent Blue BT-398
	Imperial Chemical Industries, Ltd.	Monastral Fast Blue B, BV, Lb
	Imperial Chemical Industries, Ltd.	Vulcafor Fast Blue B
	Imperial Chemical Industries, Ltd.	Vynamon Blue B
	Industria Piemontese dei Colori di Anilina, S.p.A.	Turquoise Blue Base G
	National Aniline Div. Allied Chemical & Dye Corp.	Solastral Blue B, WP
	Reichhold Chemicals Inc.	Phthalocyanine Blue Toner 4515
	Reichhold Chemicals Inc.	Reduced Phthalocyanine Blue 4580
	Sandoz Ltd.	Graphtol Fast Blue BL
	Siegle G. m. b. H.	Siegle Fast Blue BS, BSN
	Sherwin-Williams Co.	Solfast Sky Blue
	Standard Ultramarine & Color Co.	Bahama Blue BC, BNC, WD
	Standard Ultramarine & Color Co.	Bahama Blue Lake NCNF
	Standard Ultramarine & Color Co.	Bermuda Blue
C. I. 74180 (Direct Blue 86; copper phthalocyanine sodium 3-disulfonate.)	American Cyanamid Co.	Calcodur Turquoise GL
	Aziende Colori Nazionali Affini A.C.N.A.	Eliamina Light Turquoise G, GL
	Badische Anilin- & Soda-Fabrik A. G.	Lurantin Supra Turquoise Blue GL
	Belle Chemical Co. Inc.	Belamine Fast Turquoise LGL
	Ciba Ltd.	Chlorantine Fast Turquoise VLL

Colour Index Number	Manufacturer	Trade Name
	Ciba Ltd.	Chlorantine Fast Turquoise Blue GLL
	CIECH, Jasna 12, Warsaw, Poland	Helion Turquoise Blue GL
	Clayton Aniline Co. Ltd.	Chlorantine Fast Turquoise Blue GLL
	Compagnie Française des Matières Colorantes	Diazol Light Turquoise JL
	Du Pont Co.	Pontamine Fast Turquoise 8GL
	Geigy Ltd.	Solophenyl Turquoise Blue GL
	General Dyestuff Company	Fastusol Turquoise Blue LGA
	General Dyestuff Company	Fenaluz Turquoise G
	General Dyestuff Company	Helion Blue SBLA
	Imperial Chemical Industries, Ltd.	Durazol Blue 8G
	Industria Piemontese dei Colori di Anilina, S.p.A.	Diaphtamine Light Turquoise G
	Interchemical Corp.	Interchem Direct Fast Turquoise GLN
	National Aniline Div. Allied Chemical & Dye Corp.	Solantine Turquoise G
	Raritan Dyestuff Corp.	Direct Light Turquoise Blue 8GL
	Sandoz Ltd.	Cuprofix Blue Green B, FB
	Sandoz Ltd.	Solar Turquoise Blue FGLL, GLL
	Toyo Ink Co. Ltd.	Toyo Cupro Cyanine Blue GL
C. I. 74200 (Pigment Blue 17; barium lake of copper phthalocyanine 3,3′,3″-trisulfonic acid.)	General Dyestuff Company	Fenalac Blue S Disp.
	Imperial Chemical Industries, Ltd.	Monosol Fast Blue 2G, 2GP
	Imperial Chemical Industries, Ltd.	Durazol Paper Blue 10G
C. I. 74200 + 76603 (Pigment Green 13; barium lake of copper phthalocyanine 3,3′,3″-trisulfonic acid + lead chromate.)	British Paints Ltd.	Brilliant Green BS, GS, 2GS
	Cornbrook Chemical Co. Ltd.	Kromon Vivid Green BS, YS, 2YS
	Dainichi Gosei Co. Ltd.	Dainichi Brilliant Green D
	Imperial Chemical Industries, Ltd.	Chromastral Green M
C. I. 74260 (Pigment Green 7; copper	Ansbacher Siegle Corp.	Fastolux Green
	Badische Anilin- & Soda-	Heliogen Green G,

Colour Index Number	Manufacturer	Trade Name

polychloro-phthalocy-
anine containing 15 or
16 Cl atoms in the
molecule.)
	Fabrik A.G.
	CIECH, Jasna 12, Warsaw,
	   Poland
	Du Pont Co.
		GN
		Pigment Fast Green
		   G
		Monastral Fast Green
		   G, GF, GFP, GWD

	Federal Color Laboratories
	   Inc.
	Geigy Ltd.
		Duratint Green 1001
		
		Irgalite Fast Brilliant
		   Green GL

	General Dyestuff Company General Dyestuff Company	Ceres Green 3B Fenalac Green G, G Disp.
	General Dyestuff Company	Heliogen Green GA, GTA, GV, GWS
	Harmon Color Company	Non-flocculating Green G-25
	Harmon Color Company Harmon Color Company	Opaline Green G-1 Phthalocyanine Green WDG-47

	Harmon Color Company	Resinated Phthalo-
		   cyanine Green G-
		   5025

	Holland Color Company	Permanent Green Toner GT-376

	Imperial Chemical Industries,
	   Ltd.
	Reichhold Chemicals Inc.
		Monastral Fast Green
		   G
		Reduced Phthalocya-
		   nine Green 3580

	Siegle G. m. b. H.
	Standard Ultramarine & Color
	   Co.
	Standard Ultramarine & Color
	   Co.
		Siegle Fast Green G
		Granada Green Lake
		   GL
		Phthalocyanine
		   Green

C. I. 74350
(Solvent Blue 25; convert
   copper phthalocyanine
   to its tetrasulfonyl
   chloride with chlorosul-
   fonic acid, then treat
   with isohexylamine; see
   reference 130 Chapter 5.)
	Badische Anilin- & Soda-
	   Fabrik A.G.
	Imperial Chemical Industries,
	   Ltd.
		Zapon Fast Blue
		   HFL
		Methasol Fast Blue
		   2G

C. I. 74380
(Solvent Blue 24; treat
   highly sulfonated copper
   phthalocyanine first with
   dimethylamine and then
   with palmitic acid; see
   reference 225 Chapter 5.)
	General Dyestuff Company	Azosol Fast Blue
		   HLGG

AUTHOR INDEX

SUBJECT INDEX

Absorption spectra, 29–38
Aluminum phthalocyanine, 105, 143
  applications, 158, 167
  preparation, 104, 122–4
  properties, 123–4
    absorption spectra, 32
    catalytic, 62
    valency, 45
  structure, 42
Aluminum polychlorophthalocyanine,
  124
Antimony phthalocyanine, 105
  preparation, 129
  properties, 43, 129
  structure, 43, 129
Azo dyes, 248–56

Barium phthalocyanine, 105, 109
  applications, 167
  preparation, 122
  properties, 42, 122
  structure, 42
Beryllium phthalocyanine, 105, 109
  applications, 107
  preparation, 118
  properties, 18, 118
    catalytic, 62
  structure, 41

Cadmium hexadecachlorophthalocyanine, 122
Cadmium phthalocyanine, 105, 109
  preparation, 122
  properties, 42, 122
  structure, 42
Calcium phthalocyanine, 27, 105, 109
  applications, 145, 152
  manufacture, 119
  preparation, 106, 118–9
  properties, 42
  structure, 42
Catalysts, 61–67
Central metal atom-ligand bonding,
  38–45
Cerium phthalocyanine, 62
Chlorophyll, 6, 46, 76–9, 82–7, 95
Chrome dyes, 272–4

Chromium phthalocyanine, 105
  preparation, 104, 130–2
  properties, 44, 130–2
    absorption spectra, 34
    catalytic, 62–3
    magnetic moment, 46
    valency, 45
    vatting, 61
  structure, 44
Cobalt chlorophthalocyanine, 136, 171
Cobalt phthalocyanine, 105
  applications, 167, 299, 300
  preparation, 104, 106, 135–6
  properties, 18, 47, 82, 136
    absorption spectra, 33–6
    catalytic, 63–6
    magnetic moment, 44, 46
    neutron irradiation, 90
    oxidation, 56
    paramagnetic resonance, 48
    photoconductivity, 73–4
    polymorphism, 35
    semiconductivity, 68
    solubility, 94
    solubility constant, 44
    valency, 45
    vatting, 60–1
  structure, 41–2
Colour Index information and numbers,
  346–9
Commercial applications, 292–303
  phthalocyanines as colorants, 293–
    300
    leather, 300
    paints, 293–5
    photography, 300
    plastics, 297–9
    printing inks, 295–7
    roofing granules, 299
    rubber, 298
    textiles, 293
    writing inks, 299
  other phthalocyanine applications,
    300–3
    analytical systems, 302
    catalyst, 300
    electrical, 302
    lubricating grease, 301